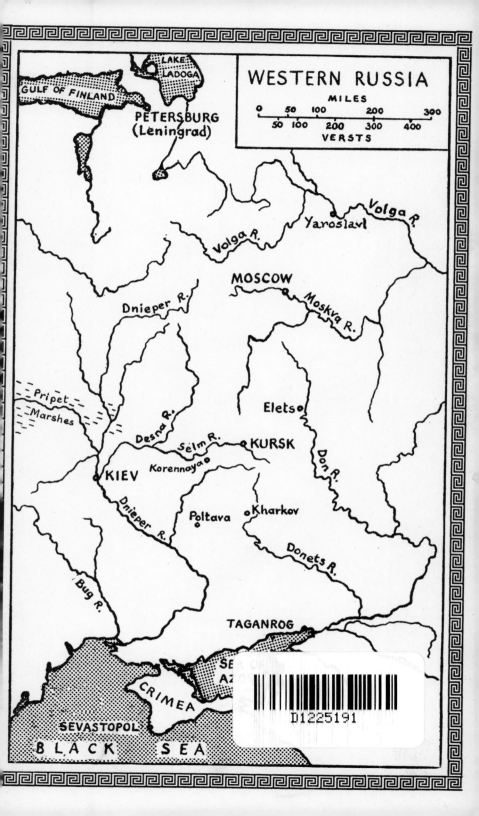

WESTERN RUSSIA

MILES

VERSTS

GULF OF FINLAND

LAKE LADOGA

PETERSBURG (Leningrad)

Volga R.

Yaroslavl

Volga R.

MOSCOW

Moskva R.

Dnieper R.

Pripet Marshes

Desna R.

Selm R.

Elets

KURSK

Don R.

Korennaya

KIEV

Poltava

Kharkov

Dnieper R.

Donets R.

Bug R.

TAGANROG

SEA OF AZOV

CRIMEA

SEVASTOPOL

BLACK SEA

THREE GENERATIONS

Vladimir Polunin.

THREE GENERATIONS

Family Life in Russia, 1845-1902

by

VLADIMIR POLUNIN

Translated by A. F. Birch-Jones

1957

LEONARD HILL [BOOKS] LIMITED
9 Eden Street, London N.W.1

BY THE SAME AUTHOR

The Continental Method of Scene Painting
(Cyril Beaumont, 1927)

PRINTED IN GREAT BRITAIN BY J. W. ARROWSMITH LTD., BRISTOL

CONTENTS

Prologue

———————

1845-1880

Chapters I-XVII

pp. 5-146

∾

1880-1890

Chapters XVIII-XXV

pp. 149-246

∾

1890-1902

Chapters XXVI-XXXVII

pp. 249-396

———————

Epilogue

ILLUSTRATIONS

Vladimir Polunin, *frontispiece*

Grandfather and Grandmother, *facing p.* 118

Family tree, *facing p.* 119

Yasha, nineteen years old, *facing p.* 134

Olya, about seventeen years old, *facing p.* 135

Old postcard view in Moscow, *facing p.* 150

Vera and Volodya, in 1883 and in 1889, *facing p.* 151

Father, thirty-five years old, *facing p.* 166

Volodya as a schoolboy, *facing p.* 166

Volodya as a student in Moscow, *facing p.* 167

Father in 1894, *facing p.* 278

Father with grandchildren, *facing p.* 279

Nadya with son, *facing p.* 294

Vera with children and Tatyana the cook, *facing p.* 295

Nicholas, Colonel of Grenadiers, *facing p.* 310

Victor, the doctor, in old age, *facing p.* 311

Father with Volodya, 1898, *facing p.* 326

Family group, 1900, *facing p.* 327

Father at Pushkino, with himself, 1901, *facing p.* 390

Last photograph of Father at Pushkino, *facing p.* 391

Vladimir Polunin, by Picasso, 1919, *facing p.* 398

PREFACE

Many thanks must go to my friend A. F. Birch-Jones for undertaking voluntarily the difficult task of translating my manuscript from the Russian; and to my son, Professor Nicholas Polunin, for all the trouble he has taken to further the realization of the book.

Vladimir Polunin

PROLOGUE

MANY years ago, quite by chance, I happened to be travelling by train to that little corner of provincial Russia where all our family originated.

An ungainly, boxlike house of the time of Emperor Paul; a spotless courtyard surrounded by various outhouses and enclosed by a boarded fence; some stunted poplars planted by Grandfather's own hand—the whole nestling in the shadow of a brightly painted church, with resonant bells and circling flocks of rooks—all this combined to carry the mind back involuntarily to the days of Gogol's *Dead Souls*.

There was something crystal clear yet stifling in the atmosphere of the place, which had its counterpart in the human inhabitants. To the ineradicable impression of still waters induced by times past and people departed was added a feeling of suffocation. It was as though the grey shadow of Ostrovsky's *Dark Kingdom* were engulfing the lucid brilliance of still waters.

Especially was this so at noon, when somehow everything was blended and softened. The old houses, the little streets, the country town straggling below with its dusty gardens, its cathedral, and its inevitable 'Nobles Assembly', seemed then to relive the past.

They knew no press of affairs. Life hurried past them with its giant strides. History turned from its course so as not to disturb their slumbers. It was theirs to reflect the past and all that had been, now relegated to archives and buried.

I walked around the court, looked up at the house, and thought of those bygone days.

Once upon a time, Grandfather, Father, and Mother had here lived their quiet, simple lives and known gladness and suffering.

1845 - 1880

I

IN the forties of the last century, in the town of Kursk, my grandfather, Akim Ivanovich Polunin, had a flourishing wholesale fish business; that is to say he was—to use the old phraseology—a *ribas*.

Having married early he lived, sedate and happy, in his own house in a modest quarter of a provincial town, saving his money against a rainy day. He was a complaisant, unexacting man, but in accordance with the custom of the time he kept the reins of government of his household firmly in his own hands. He addressed Grandmother as 'Thou' but she gave him his title—'You, Akim Ivanovich, *batiushka*'. Though possessing an exceptionally independent and original mind, Grandmother good-humouredly bowed to her husband's will, for the proverb said that 'Women have long hair and short wits'. The rules laid down in a *domostroy* were regarded in those days as containing the essence of married happiness, and any departure from them led to family strife—a grievous sin. And sin was punished by that 'Horned Beast of Revelations' so eloquently depicted in the popular prints that flaunted their message on every fair-ground. This idea of despotism was accepted by all sections of the community. Indeed it seemed the corner-stone of the edifice of the State as well as of everyday life; it permeated every family and stifled all individual existence. The following conversation aptly portrays the trend of thought of the time:

'Mama dear, who is that general on horseback?'

'That, darling, is the Autocrat of all Russia, Czar of Poland, and Grand Duke of Finland.'

'It's the Czar, then?'

'Yes, darling, it's the Czar. On earth he is God, and yonder in heaven is God—the heavenly Czar.'

'And can the Czar do anything—just like God?'

'Yes, darling, anything.'

'Can he kill people if he likes?'

'Yes, he can. But why do you keep on at me so, you little chatterbox?'

It was illogical that every representative of authority down to the local constable, while affirming with the support of the Church that there is no power like God's, should have regarded himself as infallible and any offence against himself a denial of first principles.

Not that Akim Ivanovich ever abused his power; he used it more as a warning and a safeguard for the proper conduct of daily life. Indeed not infrequently, albeit unwillingly, he surrendered to Grandmother's more forceful character.

Generally speaking, life flowed spontaneously without fixed rules: it was lived happily, in accordance with God.

In his affairs Grandfather was just and honest. Quite large dealings were conducted through the spoken word without documents or receipts. At a time when the saying 'No swindle, no sale' represented an axiom of trading life, this downright honesty brought him to the fore and established him in the first rank of merchants.

When his first son was born, Grandfather planted some poplars which for some reason or other never attained normal size. Maybe nature had involuntarily prophesied the boy's fate? However, Grandfather paid no heed, though when two years after Yasha's birth his brother Pasha came on the scene, he had already given up the idea of tree-planting.

Grandmother had no more children and Yasha and Pasha were left to their own devices to play about in the courtyard.

Yasha, the first-born, was inquisitive and vital; his beautiful blue eyes surveyed the world with wonder. Pasha, rather stocky and less interesting to look at, simply grew up and paid but little regard to what went on around him.

Grandmother frankly preferred her elder son and shielded him from all the storm and tempest which resulted from his constant restlessness. Pasha barely needed such protection, since he accepted once and for all, with good grace and no attempt at protest, the established routine of life. Indeed, this innate spirit of submission remained Pasha's outstanding characteristic, while Yasha, like the quicksilver in a thermometer, was alternately up or down.

On Sundays the boys were dressed in their silk shirts—Yasha's blue and Pasha's pink—and taken to the gaily painted church. They knew the church and everything around it by heart.

Now the swallows would be soaring almost as high as the cross on the belfry, and now they would be swooping till they all but brushed the half-burnt grass with their white breasts. They were old and dear friends—but how difficult to catch! For hours at a time Yasha would be concealed in the grass trying to catch just one as it flew low. He would reach out his hand and—surely he had it—but no, one glimpse and it had gone. For a long time he racked his brains for some ruse to help him catch one of those feathered miracles. If Pasha battered anything it was most likely to be the fence of their rich neighbour—though he did not know why.

As soon as they came into the church porch—how familiar it was—there were always the beggar woman, Matriona, with her red, tear-stained eyes; the old legless soldier with carroty whiskers, wearing an old greatcoat with chevrons on it and medals dangling from the faded ribbons on his chest; and the crafty creature, who was not so very old, in a skull-cap. They were a familiar but dreadful folk; the symbol of something pitiful and, at the same time, of petty subterfuge and veiled impudence.

The church, so gay to outward view, was dark inside and there was a high ikonostasis with three rows of ikons. Entering here produced a feeling of fear—fear of another mysterious world—but in the end this seemingly unknown world turned out to be a familiar one, since it was always inhabited by folk one knew so well.

B

There was the priest—Father Savatiy—in his gold vestments, looking more solemn than he did in his cassock, but just the same as when he was at home on big festal holidays. And Maltsev, the churchwarden, one of us, making a jolly jingle with the copper coins on his table laden with wax candles and mysterious holy wafers. And all around were the worshippers, all familiar folk, tradespeople, neighbours, workmen who lived in one's own street.

But one thing was always novel and surprising: the sonorous voices of the choir, gentle octaves of tenor and bass, fading away somewhere in the top of the cupola. It seemed as though the church could not contain all these sounds that, finding no escape, returned as if to bemoan their fate. Yasha loved these waves of sound. 'Waves and rollers' he called them, without being able to distinguish between them. Pasha was unmoved by them and picked off the drops of wax from the burning candles.

At last the service would come to an end. In the church, so soon as all was silent, the little lamps in front of the ikons were extinguished and a smell of wax would arise; the smoke from the censer hung motionless and the stern eyes of the saints looked on. The atmosphere became rather eerie, almost frightening. Then suddenly would be heard the piercing cry of the swallows from somewhere up in the roof and once more all was familiar, lovable, part of oneself. And in the porch the plaintive voices of the beggars, the chink of coin, the clear joyful sunshine, the billowy distant golden clouds, and the swallows—everywhere the swallows.

At home in the dining-room the table was covered with a snow-white cloth. Grandfather sat down first and invariably asked:

'And what have we today, Párochka?' In his good moods he always called his wife by a nickname of his own invention, changing Praskovia to Párochka.

'Well now, Akim Ivanovich! We've fish soup, egg and meat pasties, goose and cabbage, mushrooms, truffles, boiled sturgeon, some jam—and then there's melon—and that's all. It is what God has provided.'

'That's capital!' said Grandfather, with a foretaste of a good meal and knowing by experience the excellence of Grandmother's cooking.

The meal lasted long and was solemnly undertaken as though in performance of one of life's serious duties. There was no conversation or laughter. Although Yasha and Pasha had long wanted to rush out into the courtyard, it was impossible; one must sit to the end.

'Well, thank God that we have eaten our fill', said Grandfather, crossing himself before the ikon of the Saviour.

'Say grace, Yasha.'

'Thanks be to Christ our God who has given us our food', quickly gabbled the elder son. Now one could run out, after first kissing Father's hand and thanking him for the dinner.

In the courtyard they set about their simple games: skittles— home made—and knuckle-bones. Skittles was the more difficult, demanding strength and a good eye, while knuckle-bones de- pended more upon knack. Pasha invariably won at skittles, Yasha being better at knuckle-bones which called for more dexterity and co-ordination.

In the evening, when the setting sun seemed to set the windows ablaze, and the old house was drenched with a tender drowsiness and the parting beams glinted on the golden domes of the church finally to lose themselves far away beyond the Nobles' Assembly, Grandfather would come out into the courtyard to breathe the pure air after his Sunday rest in stuffy rooms.

A table was set under the meagre poplars; the samovar grew hot in the sun; the cups gleamed a transparent pink; the steam rose heavenwards in a straight unbroken column. It was quiet there in the open, peaceful, motionless.

How wonderful those summer evenings, when everything in nature is hushed; when the birds are silent and the voices of people and living creatures and the town itself are bathed in warm silence. How vain and foolish seem all the griefs and troubles of the departed day. We are all brothers, there is room for all of us.

'How now, Párochka?' said Grandfather. 'Is it not time that Yasha had some schooling?'

'Why, *bátiushka*, Akim Ivanovich! Yasha is still little more than a baby. Let him play about for a while.'

Grandfather made no reply but it was clear from his expression that he had made up his mind; and in the autumn Yasha began his studies under the deacon of the gaily painted church, who lived close by.

Education at that time, even among the families of well-to-do merchants, was very simple and, so to speak, classical; it was grounded on the Psalter. Reading, writing, the four arithmetical rules (taught by means of the inevitable abacus), prayers, catechism, Holy Writ—this was the course of education for a merchant's son. The instruction was conducted at intervals, when the teacher-deacon was free from his duties in church; and it was frequently accompanied by aids to memory of a purely physical kind—a smack on the hand with a ruler or a blow on the back with a cane or whatever else was handy. School fees were paid in kind: fish, poultry, or some other product of the homestead. Education was quick and simple; little time was wasted on schooling.

One evening in another summer, as distant clouds were gently drifting across the darkening sky, Grandfather said to his son:

'Well, Yakov, it's time you got to business. No more kicking your heels about: you've learned enough now.'

'Yes, Papa, but I'd like to go on learning.'

'You've had enough playing about. It's time you got to business. Go to the shop; you'll learn there willy-nilly.'

'But, *bátiushka*, Akim Ivanovich, Yasha has only got as far as the Council of Nicaea and—'

'Quiet, Mother! God forbid that he should hold the creation of the world in his head like that deacon's son who'll see the inside of a jail for all his cleverness! It's time the lad was in business.

1845-1865

Let him get used to it!'

To Yasha business appeared to be something grim, sombre and deep-rooted in the bowels of the town, in the Traders' Row —where Grandfather sat from morning till late evening, often returning home frowning and cross.

By the time winter came Yasha, wearing a warm sheepskin coat and a cap with ear-flaps, was already installed in the shop where, drowsy and starved with cold, he sat and learned his trade. And there he was destined to sit through all the years of childhood and youth until fate swept him to other spheres, among new people.

II

BEFORE the stately building of the Nobles' Assembly, whose graceful Corinthian columns rose up straight and tall, sprawled the vast ill-paved Bazaar Square, densely crowded with hastily stitched-up shops, sheds, and erections of all sorts. The shabby old Gostiniy Dvor or Market Hall, innocent of repair since the days of Catherine the Great, seemed to take all this square into its old arms and gaze down in bewilderment from its patched upper windows at the seething life below. In the middle, on a hardly perceptible hillock, was ranged like a rank of soldiers the monotonous line of shops called Traders' Row —ironmongers, cutlers, saddlers, apothecaries, mercers, and at the end, the fishmongers.

From the streets one could see the wealthy merchants sitting solemn and sedate, behind their counters; the apprentices on their errands; the assistants strolling around praising their wares. There was no undue haste—'more hurry, more folly'. The customers stood waiting; the goods were weighed, the cash disbursed, and the purchase delivered.

In Grandfather's shop in Fishmongers' Row business was mostly wholesale, but enough retail business was done 'to salve the conscience'.

Every morning, before the master arrived, an old servant of the Governor would make his usual call for 'delicatessen for the Governor-General's table'. In front of the assistants he gave himself the airs of a great gentleman, majestically stroking his 'Nicholas' side-whiskers with a caressing hand, and thrusting out his lower lip to impart emphasis. He spoke through his nose and continually peered at the appetizing food-stuffs displayed around the shop in vats, barrels, and tubs. He was blue-shaven; red

veins in his cheeks and nose enlivened his face; and his little bloodshot eyes blinked moistly.

The amber flesh of smoked salmon and the delicate pink of the fresh salmon never failed to impress him. Having subjected the different kinds of fish to numerous tests, he invariably stroked a smooth chin in obvious satisfaction, and straightening his stiff cravat proceeded whole-heartedly to enjoy a ritual. In these matters he was a recognized connoisseur, and in holding on high the banner of the Governor's authority, he not only benefited his master but his own pocket as well.

After a brief chat with the chief salesman, he would regally receive the Governor-General's salmon, fresh or smoked, deftly and tidily wrapped up in an old matting bag. Without a word he would take a small parcel for his personal consumption, some of the same fish, willingly presented for his expert judgement; and then, unhurriedly and majestically, he would depart until the morrow. He was disliked in the shop, though all paid deference to him because of his close proximity to the person of the Governor. Sometimes, also in the morning, the caterer of the Nobles' Assembly, Perepelkin, blew like a gale into the shop. He was a miserable, ill-favoured fellow, possessed of boundless energy, a shifty character, and a stentorian voice.

'Hi! You there!' he would bawl in the doorway. 'I'm to provide dinner for a hundred people, including the Marshal of Nobility, and you stand there doing nothing.'

Rapidly, and as it were casually, he would poke at a sturgeon, point an indicative finger at a sterlet rolled ringwise, frown at a smelt—and never stop talking for a moment.

'Sturgeon to be sure—a bit frozen—well, weigh me up forty. Sterlet? Throw in a couple of hundred, and see that they're fresh! I know you! Put some smelt in, too, say about sixty! Salmon? Smoked salmon, brother, is a 'bird of some importance'. It lies on the dish in all its beauty and majesty like a newly-laid-out corpse! Laid out in its bridal crown of parsley and celery and cucumber—makes your mouth water! Put me in five.'

'And how about some Maltsev trout? Still not got any? What's

THREE GENERATIONS

the matter with you? And the Marshal mad about them! Well, can't do anything about it. Give me some carp instead. Solid fish, carp, lives to a great age. I'll have good big eyes for appearances' sake. Send it along quickly, fresh condition and so forth.'

Then as he hurried out:

'I've a hundred nobles to dinner and you stand there doing nothing!'

'We'll hurry, Perepelkin', asserted the chief salesman with a laugh, and turning to his fellows:

'You've heard about his buying another house and making the property over to his wife, too?' The apprentices laughed. 'Seems that he must be worth his weight in gold!' said one.

Sometimes a peasant from the country would wander into the shop. He would stand for a long time at the counter in acute discomfort with no one paying any attention to him, and at last in a barely audible and almost apologetic voice, would say:

'Maybe I could have about a couple of hundred dabs.'

'There's a tuppenny ha'penny order for you!' the chief sales-man would exclaim. 'What fools these people are! Coming to a wholesaler's for their bits of stuff. All right, give it him.'

'Yes, and tell him to clear off. We've no time to waste here.'

About seven o'clock in the morning Grandfather arrived. He would cross himself three times before the ikon and proceed in silence to his own half of the shop, making no reply to the greetings of the salesmen standing respectfully at the counter.

'Ugh—he's in a temper', mused the chief salesman. 'Evidently had a tiff with his "Párochka".' Then just to show his master how keen he was, he would shout out: 'Now you, Michael! Why are you standing about? Look livelier with that unloading! Get Perepelkin's stuff ready and dispatched! Deliver those seventy tubs of Astrakhan herring to Korennaya!'

From his office Grandfather could see through a glass screen all that went on in the shop; he could hear every sound, and sense all the variety of fishy smells. Here he was inside his own shell. Here he represented strength and unquestionable authority.

Here he was law-giver and administrator: his word was law. No one could joke with him in here.

The office was tiny; a mahogany desk and two boxlike arm chairs took up almost all the room. He had grown accustomed to the lack of space. 'No shame in close quarters', he would often remark to customers, as he set a heavy arm-chair more conveniently for them. On his right, Nicholas I glared down from a gold frame on the wall. From the window giving on to the street could be seen the whole of Bazaar Square.

Beneath the covered arches of the Gostiny Dvor, life bubbled like a stream. Customers went to and fro, beggar women hobbled along, officials passed by, noisy children ran in and out between people's legs.

The tall constable strutted into a neighbouring tradesman's. Grandfather could see how this staid merchant, who a minute before had been sitting sedately in the full splendour of his commercial dignity, crawled under the counter to avoid meeting the custodian of order.

By experience Grandfather knew that such meetings ended not infrequently with fisticuffs. To avoid a thrashing, it behoved a man to untie his money-bags. But in any case one would be the loser.

Occasionally convicts from the town gaol passed through the square. They marched in small squads, rattling their chains, and begging the merchants to give them something 'for a bite of bread'. The bystanders gaped, the shop assistants made game of the wretched convoy, while the old women piously crossed themselves and handed out some coppers. Some of the convicts were employed in repairing the road in Konny Square and, at twilight, they returned the same way.

Sometimes the Governor-General, Dehn, astride a white charger, rode through the square at a gallop. With his clean-shaven cheeks, brushed-back curly hair, and majestic presence, he was the living portrait of Emperor Nicholas. He was unpopular in the town and feared like fire; yet, all the same, people were somehow proud of him. Certainly he was strict, but then his

THREE GENERATIONS

military bearing was worth something; and he was the symbol of autocratic power in the midst of the humdrum life of a provincial town.

Settling well down into his chair, Grandfather opened his fat ledger and turned over the thick blue leaves covered with close-written columns of figures. He pushed forward the abacus, knocked its beads to and fro, squared his totals and became absorbed in thought.

'Yes, that's a matter involving thousands,' he said to himself meditatively, 'and only suppose that Pospolitaki should die to-morrow: the whole lot would disappear into thin air! There are no documents and he won't listen to anything. A queer fellow, pretty well crazy.'

Once Grandfather had gone to see him in the evening and had discovered him sitting in a filthy old dressing gown, unshaven, and unwashed, cutting investment coupons by the light of a solitary candle.

'Well met, Akim Ivanovich,' he exclaimed. 'Sit down and make yourself welcome.'

Pospolitaki locked his cash box and put out his candle.

'I'm an old man,' he muttered, 'and we've known each other these thirty years. Why should we spend money on candles? A candle costs money. We'll sit so—in the dark.'

Yet he had bags of money, being the autocrat of the fish-kingdom of the Azov Sea. Why did he save? It made no difference—he would not take it with him to the grave. It was both farcical and sinful.

Rousing himself from his meditations, Grandfather turned again to his accounts. Energetically he flicked the round beads of his abacus, filled up columns, entered sums in a note-book and again paused. Pospolitaki's millions hammered in his brain and refused to allow him to concentrate on the figures.

A wholesale buyer would look in; long wearying conversations would begin, in which each tried to outwit the other. They would discuss discount, and draw up guarantees against default, but the deal would never be finally concluded in the shop but in

again familiar, known, and homely. In intervals between business

ing voices. Then his fears would slip away and everything was
presence of healthy young bodies and the sound of merry, laugh-
shop would somehow become more warm and friendly with the
crept nearer to his fellows. But gradually, as it grew lighter, the
fishy monsters; involuntarily he shrank from them in fear and
To Yasha there seemed to be something cruel in this realm of
along the walls.

grinned with their ravenous jaws. Shadows chased each other
bellies of the great sturgeon loomed white, and evil-looking pike
cheerless and hostile. In the dim half-light of the lantern the
—and then the deserted shop, semi-dark, and cold, waiting
rusty bolts, the rattle of padlocks, the clatter of opening shutters
of drowsy assistants borne on the frosty air; the grating sound of
The sleepy streets of the lazily waking town, the harsh voices
sunrise to dusk.

like all days, would be spent sitting in the shop from almost
Still half asleep, he dressed and got ready for a day which,
would be worse then.'

'No, laddy, you mustn't. Papasha would find out and things
'Can't I sleep just a little longer, Mother?'
the boy was wakened: 'Get up, Yasha! It's time to go to the shop.'
changeless, and wearisome. Daylight had hardly stolen in when
For Yasha life in the shop followed its monotonous course,
father's business was based on mutual understanding and on trust.
ness were the chief factors of success in these dealings. Grand-
Simple diplomacy, unassailable reputation, and absolute frank-

'Good! First rate. Well, let's drink to the bargain.'
ha'penny to the day.'

'About payment?' 'As God is my witness you'll get every
spoken word 'And you'll deliver? Done!'
The deal was concluded, without any documents, on the
hands on the bargain. 'Cash on the nail. No waiting.'
misunderstandings, opened their hearts, embraced, and shook
mechanical organ, over tea and a glass of vodka they cleared up all
the private part of the Patrikeev Inn. There, seated beneath a

THREE GENERATIONS

they would relate the news of the preceding day. The master had not yet arrived and youth was unbridled:

'Say! Yesterday,' began a young apprentice, 'a soldier at the prison knocked a woman's eye out with his bayonet.'

'Go on; that's a lie.'

'God punish all liars! I tell you I saw it with my own blinkers.'

'So, that's it—same old game, lads!'

'And yesterday Governor Dehn caught a devil at the bridge with three bags of coin on him!'

'Now we'll hear the millstones chatter!'

'He's off now!'

'Who's off? it's true I'm telling you. Ermeliy was talking about it and he's not the sort to tell lies for nothing.'

'They say that yesterday evening our Governor went out in a towering rage. Ermeliy was coachman and he asked, "Where to, Your Excellency?" And he answers, "To the Devil. Drive to the Devil," says he. Ermeliy whipped up the horses, thinking to himself—"Here's a fine to-do! Drive to the Devil, and where does he live?" They cleared the town. The horses were going at a trot. On the right was a pasture and in the distance the old bridge. Suddenly Ermeliy had a bright thought, remembering that the old bridge had been known for years as "Devil's Bridge". His Excellency wanted to have a bit of a walk to stretch his lordly legs after sitting all cramped up. So Ermeliy reined in the horses and said to him, "If you please, Your Excellency, we've come to the Devil's".

'The Governor-General smiled, looked around and then said "Turn back".

'He'd hardly started when His Excellency whispered, "Stop! Can you see anything?"

'"Not a thing, Your Excellency," says he.

'"Look under the bridge—can't you see something moving? There's something wrong here!" His Lordship jumped from the carriage, about turned to the left, and dived straight under the bridge—and there he caught the villain red-handed!'

'That's our Dehn! There's a chief for you! He's not a German for nothing—and smart too! You'll get no quarter from him!'

'He's a clever one to have in command. Remember how he managed in the cholera year! When people started rioting and there was a real shindy, and they chucked the doctors head-over-heels out of the windows and smashed up the hospital! Dehn arrived looking like a two-headed eagle, and he just thundered, "Get down on your knees!" and he had everyone quiet.'

'Son of a bitch!'

'Cut out your lies here, you young devils,' barked out the chief salesman angrily. 'The master!' Boots could be heard scrunching heavily on the thick snow. Conversation ceased.

It was cold in winter in the unheated shop, and Yasha was lonely at heart. His father kept clicking the abacus in his office; the assistants bustled about the shop and got very busy, or at any rate pretended to do so, over their jobs. Everyone was busy and Yasha alone had no real work. Sitting solitary behind the counter on a high chair he would begin to muse, from sheer inactivity.

'Let him get used to it from boyhood! And get used to what?' he would ask himself. 'To the cold? To endless hours of sitting in this frozen atmosphere? You'll never get used to that. And the boredom of it!'

Buyers came rarely. If wholesalers came, that was the master's business. You would not have the brains for it; it belonged to Father's department; he was the clever one. You, lad, sit by yourself and gape at the fish. Fish! Fish were all right in a way, even curious. Smelt, for example, lying there in batches of ten, pressed so close to each other in tidily packed boxes, glistening in the sunshine like jewels on an ikon. Lovely! Where would you find colour like it? Or take salmon, so large a fish, expensive, too, and hardly any bones in it. White only at the innermost core. And its skin so thin, thin and strong like Caucasian-worked silver. And inside so delicately pink, soft, silky—just like the flesh of a child. Two roubles a pound it cost.

Dace, too, a cheap bony little fish, unsightly in appearance but having a pleasant, delicate flavour even when frozen. And sturgeon, not too big a fish, tender and savoury when boiled.

The long, snakelike, blue-black eels, Yasha could never endure. He would not even go near their tub. They were reptiles, slimy and horrible—how could people eat such filth!

But above them all you could hear the Royal Sturgeon saying: 'Here you see me, seven stone—Of good white meat all free from bone.' There was a giant of a fish! Like a cow! Where did it get such strength? Caviare was not a fish at all in Yasha's estimation. It was an almost invisible product which fetched a big price, especially the coarse-grained sort which looked just like blacking, and sold at two and a half roubles a pound.

And so gradually he got to know all the different types in this fishy kingdom and became used to them. But to the routine and the rest of it he could never become accustomed. When Grandfather went off to the inn with a wholesale buyer, or when he was travelling somewhere, the aspect of the shop would somehow change and become livelier and cosier. The news from outside would be recounted. 'Have you heard how they put those mercers in clink last night? They've been carrying on with some chorus girls!'

'You're a liar.'

'I swear it.'

The affair was avidly discussed and the blame in the matter was assigned to the ladies. Comment was made on the strictness of the police and sympathy extended to those under arrest.

At midday, a hotted-up dinner was brought in dishes from the neighbouring inn. Then a boy would be dispatched several times for hot water. Large quantities of tea would be consumed, with intervals for games of draughts, the spectators following the moves of the players with the liveliest interest.

'That's finished your king!'

'That's a smack in the eye for you.'

'You're done for, brother!'

'All right! You go and sit in the latrine till judgement day!'

The onlookers laughed.

'Well played.'

'Say, Vaska, run out for some hot water. Don't you see that the kettle's empty?' and the boy would be off like a shot.

Our Czar's a German-Russian
In his uniform so Prussian

hummed to himself handsome, impudent Michael, unabashed by the presence of his senior, who stood thinking 'Michael's a lost soul. He's fated soon to become a soldier. What can you do with a cheeky fellow like him? He's a real outlaw.'

From his distant corner Yasha looked out on life and longed to be home with his mother and his books.

At last they closed the shop with heavy padlocks, crossed themselves in the frosty air, and Yasha ran home, where he arrived late, tired and numb with cold.

Hurriedly he sat down to his supper, and even more hurriedly went off to his warm bed in a well-heated room.

On Sunday came the customary long stand in church, the toothsome pasties, the after-dinner nap. In the evening, after a good supper, he sat under the ikons and nodded.

'Well, well! Time for bed,' said his father, stretching himself.

'And tomorrow the shop again,' thought Yasha mournfully.

To sit in the shop in summer was even more wearisome; it was intolerably hot, the outside air was like the blast from a furnace; the fish rapidly went bad and made their presence known. And he longed to be out in the open meadows where the white-breasted swallows were flying.

III

THE days and weeks and years sped on. Yasha passed into handsome boyhood; only his eyes retained a beauty that was childlike. One dull day Pasha remarked moodily, 'I don't want to study. I'd rather go into the shop.' And to the shop, its wares and its inmates he quickly adapted himself, as though he had been born there. He deftly trundled herring tubs, broke open crates, and with no apparent effort would sit at the counter for hours at a time, enduring the cold easily and noticing no monotony. He fitted, in fact, into his new surroundings like a hand into a glove.

'You've fish in your blood, Pasha,' said his father, 'I'll see to it that you're a fish merchant.'

As for Yasha, Grandfather apparently took so little notice of him that he might not have been in the shop at all.

By and by, under the counter there began to spring up a little family of books whose pages, when business was slack, Yasha would pore over in rapture. The adventures of Count Cagliostro, and the trials of the Count of Monte Cristo, with all their breathtaking hazards, fortunes and misfortunes, captured his imagination to such an extent that they seemed to be real life, while the shop, with its customers and wares, was nothing but a dream without beginning or end.

Dumas' hero in the Château d'If seemed more real, more alive than even Grandfather himself, sitting there in his office; while Governor Dehn, for all his enterprise, cut but a sorry figure in comparison. Thus wider and wider grew the abyss between Yasha's inner world and his grey work-a-day existence.

Occasionally, but only rarely, did everyday life approach that real life created by imagination and culled from books.

In the autumn, when the days grew shorter, and in the orchards were harvested the big-breasted pears, shining emerald and

mottled with brown; when the bright emerald-skinned Antonov
—the apple of apples, Grandmother called them—began to fall
from the trees, Akim Ivanovich would announce his intention of
going to the fair at Korennaya, where the Monastery was.

Thereupon in the shop, every remnant of dried, smoked, and
salted fish was collected, and countless barrels of herring, and
ponderous sacks of salt cod sorted out; while at home Grandmother brushed and pressed Grandfather's ceremonial long-skirted
frock-coat and her own silk dress—'as old as Paul's steeple'.

At last, after much preparation, Grandfather took his seat in
the lumbering coach wherein packages, bottle-cases, and cash
boxes had been safely stowed. Grandmother, Yasha, and Pasha
were packed in, the horses whipped up, and the coach set off in the
wake of three wagon-loads of fish which had been dispatched
earlier in the day.

It was early morning, the sky a greenish-yellow, translucent
and clear. The air was cool and Yasha's heart was light. It seemed
as though he might become possessed of wings and go soaring
away to the skies where a flock of white pigeons was flying;
in Korennaya there would be pigeons, he remembered, real
beauties. The coach came to the barrier, where a striped bar
raised and lowered its long neck like some monstrous heron.
Here the paving came to an end and the levelled highway unrolled its peaceful length before them. On either side were fields,
field after unenclosed field. In the distance would be seen a
little hill crowned by a wood, in the lee of which nestled some
poverty-stricken hamlet, and then again fields without number.
The sun began to blaze down, inducing drowsiness. Yasha dozed,
woke up, looked about him. The sun was now low in the sky,
and birds were wheeling around seeking some place to roost. As
evening drew on, the weary horses, scenting rest, quickened
their pace to a trot until the inn was reached.

The inn was crowded. People lay stretched out on benches or
in the open fields. They represented every calling—merchants
with their families, traders, and all manner of humbler folk—and
all had been drawn as though by a magnet to the fair; some urged

c

by necessity, and some by business, some bent on pilgrimage, and some just wandering 'on their own'. 'Tomorrow,' thought Yasha, 'we shall be in Korennaya,' as, tired out, he fell asleep on a bench.

On the morrow, when it was barely light, they took the road again through the monotonous and seemingly endless Russian fields. With every mile the press of traffic increased. High, laden wagons, carts piled with household goods, droves of frightened cows and heifers, squealing pigs, bleating sheep, and neighing colts made their way laboriously along the road. Alongside on the footpaths marched in a grey crowd the pilgrims, time-expired soldiers, and other nondescript folk, with packs on their backs and long staves or crooks in their hands.

The hubbub and confusion delighted Yasha's heart. The road ran on through a forest until, on a distant hill-top, glistening and beautiful, the monastery was revealed, ringed round by oaks centuries old, and girdled by the swollen waters of a river which lay gleaming below like a silver mirror.

The glorious expanse of Russia! Scalding tears welled up in Yasha's heart. He wanted to cry, to be borne aloft like the pigeons and the swallows.

It was stiflingly hot on the fair-ground, where, in hastily erected booths, on tables, and on bare earth, was displayed a veritable ocean of wares—pigs' carcases, children's toys, dried mushrooms, gingerbreads, mugs, harrows, pots, 'dog collars and cravats for the gentry,' everything, in short, that the heart could wish for. The air resounded with confusion, laughter, and cursing. Dashing remount-officers with tunics unbuttoned and caps awry savagely cracked their whips; swarthy gipsy horse-dealers whooped like wild beasts; hucksters and small boys lustily endeavoured to outshout each other. A veritable inferno raged without pause from early morning to sunset.

The din, the novelty, and the strangeness of it all at first attracted Yasha, but after a while it jarred and jangled on his eyes and ears and wearied him. Instinctively he edged his way to quietude and fixed his gaze on the high walls and belfries of the monastery, while his thoughts strayed back to days that had been.

The Korennaya Monastery was founded in the distant past and was built at that time almost entirely of wood. Increasing in size and importance, it was now famous throughout Russia.

By this time its monastery buildings, its churches, granaries, guest-houses, and outlying homesteads composed a town peopled by well-fed, bearded monks whose silk cassocks lay sleek upon their bellies, and by handsome lay-brothers who looked more like the heroes on some provincial stage than young men devoted to piety. The proximity to this cloistered life of huckstering, wantonness, and swindling, seemed to Yasha to be scandalous and shocking. And yet, notwithstanding its obvious disharmony, it could not mar the beauty and majesty of this holy spot.

Leaving the fair, Yasha wandered among the churches and chapels, gazing at the rich vestments and the priceless ornaments and treasures. He looked in at the monastery bakehouse, from which arose an appetizing smell of new-baked bread. For hours he read the sentimental inscriptions on the gravestones, with a feeling that in all this lay some inherent truth and meaning, the deep meaning of human life. It came as a shock to hear Grandfather say in the evening, 'Worship's all right for worshippers. But a man must needs think of his business if he's not to return with an empty pocket and a load of tainted fish! That's what I say, brother. But you—' and he paused and looked at Yasha, who had disclosed his thoughts to no one.

At the close of the fair a visit was always paid to Father Vasiliy, the fattest monk and priest in Korennaya, a jolly and hospitable man, and a distant relative. The newly painted floor, still reeking of linseed oil, the white mats, the broad space between the low-hung windows and the pictures of the monastery on the whitewashed walls, together contrived to give a blatantly festive appearance to Father Vasiliy's modest cell. He too, as it were, radiated from within and bravely carried both his corpulent body and his sixty years. No one could entertain as he did. He could devise a complete liturgy of different *zakuski*, choicest delicacies, and appetizing dishes. It was all 'lenten' fare, meat—God forbid!—was not offered, but the different courses in their variety, inventiveness, and delicacy induced such an orgy of gluttony that, had a goose in all its fleshiness been set upon the table, it would have seemed but a shy little fellow in company with Father Vasiliy's 'lenten' food. To laymen, good friends, drink—on the quiet of course—was permitted. Father Vasiliy, slyly winking a mischievous eye, would go to a far corner, move a frame and open a secret door, revealing to the astonished gaze of his guests an earthly paradise—of bottles! This apparition included almost everything: gifts of fine Hungarian Tokay, old Polish mead, Zimlansky champagne from the quietly flowing Don; the products of Widow Cliquot of France, and, standing guard in serried ranks, vodka, liqueurs, spirits, infusions and the rest.

Vasiliy, the indigent monk and humble slave of God, always had at hand the finest and best reserves 'in health and for sickness'. Yasha, without knowing why, disliked these visits. He would again go off alone, beyond the Monastery walls, and wander pensively through the cemetery, looking at the monuments and reading the inscriptions.

Antonin, Priest, a man of most excellent piety,

he deciphered, and

A priest and shepherd rests beneath this stone,
Who thirty years guided his flock alone.

Or that of Clafera Edrenovna, a major's wife whose inscription read: 'The Genius of Life is burning out its torch':

From grief retired to seek repose,
She lies in marble here concealed;
In love she mingled truth and virtues rare,
And, witness of her innocence revealed,
To her this monument is built.

Yasha was miserable, and looked up sadly at the doves wheeling so freely over his head.

IV

THE Emperor Nikolai Pavlovich had had some disagreement with the European Powers; the incident arose out of a trifle—because of some monks in Jerusalem by Our Lord's tomb—but the dispute ended in a real war. The provinces were to hear of it, too.

The start of the Sevastopol campaign completely transfigured the normally peaceful countenance of Kursk, which was on the main road from Moscow to the Crimea. It became a convenient concentration centre for troops and transport, a mobilization point for newly called-up recruits, and a base depot for supplies and hospitals. Sleepy and indolent though it had been hitherto, it rose from slumber, and with a shake of its head, embarked upon a hectic life quite foreign to it.

Now along every road there moved an unbroken column of infantry, artillery, ammunition trains, ambulances, and commissariat wagons. The air rang with the cheery laughter of soldiers chaffing civilians and exchanging bawdy jests. In endless defile army followed army, swinging along to the music of their bands or the lilt of ribald songs—regiments of infantry, cavalry squadrons with multi-coloured pennons, and in the rear the artillery, whose ponderous weight set all the buildings shaking. Outstanding, of course, were the crack regiments of the grenadiers, and the cavalry of handsome hussars, dragoons, and fierce Cossacks. Looking at them, it seemed impossible that the allies could resist their strength, and the cry went up:

Let the thunder of victory resound
Let the brave Russian people rejoice!

'Come on, hearties!' shouted the townsfolk, 'Just throw your hats at the enemy and they'll run away!' And indeed why not, when such was their courage, physique, and fine healthy complexion? As the State institutions and prisons could not house even a fraction of the civil and military officials who descended upon the town like a snowstorm, accommodation had to be found in monasteries and private houses. In Grandfather's part of town an immense camp of gleaming white tents, surmounted with flags and pennons, was established for the rank and file, while the officers were temporarily quartered in residents' homes. On Grandfather himself was billeted a young officer awaiting his command, a handsome, tall, well-educated ensign, obviously of good family, who immediately adapted himself to the life of the household and made himself universally popular. He held Grandmother's wool when she wound her skein, talked politics to Grandfather, and made a real friend of Yasha, with whom in an attic he would read Rocambole, share the thrills of Monte Cristo, and recite Pushkin. He loved poetry, and read aloud his own compositions, while Yasha listened amazed by such talent, and unable to comprehend how anyone could write in verse. 'I can imagine people writing stories,' he would say, 'but I can't understand how they make them rhyme.'

And so, while somewhere on the sea-coast a battle was raging, and Russian folk were being killed, these two, sitting in Grandmother's tidy room, read *Poor Liza* and Marlinsky with his diabolically sinister heroes and mawkish heroines, or lost themselves in Polezhaev. Life here followed its old, quiet course, and war seemed something unreal. The one real and inexplicable feature was that trade, formerly so brisk, had come to a complete standstill, followed by soaring prices and general want. And all night, with nerve-wracking monotony, wagons went lumbering through the town depriving folk even of the blessing of sleep.

Indeed the obverse side of the medal was soon revealed. The first contingent of wounded arrived, to be followed by a second and a third, until from dawn to dead of night was heard the rumble of ambulances packed with pale, dejected men, many of whom died before their jolting carts could reach a hospital. For though that great surgeon, Pirogov, worked miracles with his daring operations, his efforts could only affect one minute part of the vast amount of suffering under which Russia was submerged. True, news came of victories at Inkerman and on the Alma, but rumour said that they had really been defeats. Moreover, the demand for recruits took more bread-winners from their homes, and the cost of living rose still higher. One hope remained, namely that Sevastopol, whose beleaguered heroes still defied every onslaught by the allies, would hold out.

The charming ensign at last went to the front with his regiment and no one heard of him again, or knew whether he survived. Everyone missed him, for he was such a gentle, affectionate lad.

The town continued its hectic activity, but its strength seemed to be failing. Even Governor Dehn was worn out, and though he was frequently to be seen riding with customary vigour, he seemed to lack something of his old fire. The merchants, with secret protests, surrendered vast sums of money, in the cause of patriotism, to his constant demands, muttering as they did so, 'You should be off to the war yourself—who sooner?—instead of dragooning and tyrannizing over us.' The nobles mortgaged their estates to raise troops, while at their assembly never a day passed without the arrival or departure of some exalted personage. Meanwhile Perepelkin, the caterer, waxed rich at their expense, and cast around for yet a third house.

In the taverns, the army contractors continued to get more drunk than ever, to treat the harpists to champagne, and to squander the taxpayers' money either on gipsy singers or at the gaming-tables. Soon the first prisoners of war made their appearrance—Turks with red tarbooshes, swarthy, passionate-eyed fellows who were received as 'Mohammedan scum', and set to work sweeping roads. These were followed in turn by a few lean Frenchmen—as usual, the ladies made a rush for them—and they were apportioned among the houses as tutors or hairdressers. Some French prisoners even opened barbers' shops and dancing academies on their own account, and contrived to live as comfortably and contentedly as they did in their own country in peace time. An Englishman, apparently a solitary specimen, signalled his advent by strolling into the Nobles' Assembly groomed and pomaded and wearing his full regimentals and top boots. He disappeared, however, after a little while, rumour having it that he had been dispatched further into the interior.

The heir to the throne, the young Czarevich, paid a visit to the town, and was entertained by the nobility to dinner at the Assembly. Perepelkin bought from Grandfather the finest salmon, trout, and sturgeon, with mountains of caviare, and was reputed to have made a fortune, albeit by honest trading. The President accorded him a formal vote of thanks. But they say that Governor Dehn received a reprimand from on high. Evidently such indoor heroes, who rattled their weapons and only appeared in drawing-rooms, were not to the liking of His Imperial Highness.

With the arrival of the Heir Apparent there was a feeling of something new and refreshing in the air, but the inhabitants could not say exactly what it was. Only the die-hard nobles and serf-owners were somehow quieter and growled in their lairs.

Time passed. Convoys of wounded kept arriving. So the days dragged on, each adding to the number of legless, armless, blinded, ragged, and workless soldiers who haunted the town, no longer arousing pity as before. The novelty had worn off; only the news from Sevastopol, stale, official, and fragmentary though it was, was still greedily consumed. Rumour announced divers misfortunes. The whole army was said to be without boots. The contractors had supplied them promptly enough—but with soles of cardboard, so that the troops could not march. Contractors and purveyors were forthwith court-martialled, but this was useless to an army which had been brought to an abrupt halt. Then there was the story of how millions of roubles, representing the voluntary contributions of a whole province, had somehow stuck to the palms of the officials' hands in the game of grab, which had now become universal. There were, of course, more courts-martial, but the hospitals remained without lint. Thus, at every turn, the discipline and heroism of former times gave place to wholesale and barefaced robbery, with generals squabbling over decorations and venting their spleen upon the backs of their poor common soldiers. Only Admirals Kornilov and Nakhimov, with the gallant defenders of Sevastopol, retained their honour and were the repository of every hope.

With the suddenness of a bombshell came the news that the Emperor Nicholas, before whom all Europe had trembled, had rendered up his life in peace to God, though secret rumours darkly hinted otherwise; and this, added to the fall of Sevastopol after eleven months' heroic defence, broke down the nation's will to resist and led the young Emperor to conclude peace. Thus 'Let the thunder of victory resound' concluded with a requiem. The honour of Nicholas' fighting forces almost at once lost its lustre—and even Governor Dehn was turned out of his snug berth.

V

POSPOLITÁKI the Greek, like some giant spider, gathered into his greedy maw the whole output of fish from every shore of Azov, and entangled in the close meshes of his web all traders great and small. The country for hundreds of miles around lay cowering under threat of those millions hoarded in his lair at Taganrog.

'I'll do as I please. If I wish, I'll give. If I don't you can die of hunger,' this unkempt, unwashed plutocrat would remark to humble merchants with an ogrish grin. Nor were these the words of some half-witted dotard; for Pospolitáki was accounted a power in the land, flattered by clergy and fawned on by common folk, seeing that all Azov sent its harvest to his warehouses in the wretched little god-forsaken town of Taganrog, which reeked alike of fish and the lucre he derived from them.

Grandfather usually took in his stock in late autumn or winter, when the roads had hardened and a definite sleigh track had been established along which a long convoy could proceed to an appointed rendezvous. It was an operation which entailed long, arduous, and responsible work on the part of the master, demanding his constant vigilance over the loading and transport of the frozen fish; for if this vigilance were once relaxed there was a risk that the fish might become frost-rotten, and fit only to be abandoned on the roadside.

'Frost-rotten fish are no fools—they know their own limit.'

Again, it might happen that a driver would doze off and have his tow-ropes cut, thus losing two or three loads. 'And money doesn't grow on the road,' Grandfather would observe from the wisdom of long experience.

For some years past, being unable to leave his shop without supervision, Grandfather had not himself made the journey to Taganrog but had put the chief salesman in charge of the buying party, although during his absence he was beset by constant anxiety, imagining either that the man had bolted with the money or that the convoy had got lost. 'Murder will out,' he would exclaim, 'that fellow always had a crafty look!'

One day after supper, when the boys were in bed, Grandfather, as though suddenly remembering something, began to mumble to himself. 'It's high time, yes, high time.' Then, turning abruptly to Grandmother, he asked 'How old is Yasha now, Párochka?'

'Well, let's see,' began Grandmother. 'He was born in 'forty-five—the Feast of Assumption it was—so he'll be fourteen now.'

'Then it's high time,' Grandfather repeated, and became immersed in his thoughts.

'Yasha's not quick at his job,' he mused, 'he's for ever woolgathering. Still, he's one of the family and so won't swindle us. His eye is the master's eye and he'll keep it on the convoy—well, all is not gold that glitters,' he remarked abruptly and relapsed into silence.

So it was that when winter came Yasha was equipped for his long journey and stuffed like a capon with advice on the importance of the undertaking, while Grandmother, between her sobs, sewed and packed his belongings.

'Akim Ivanovich,' she cried reproachfully, 'what are you thinking of to send your own son "like a thief in the night" on so long and bitter a journey?'

'God forgive me!' she added, crossing herself unseen.

'Don't fret, he'll be all right. Why, he's grown up. He's got a head on his shoulders,' Grandfather interrupted, quite unshaken in his resolve.

When at last Yasha set off for Taganrog with the chief salesman, he felt so homesick and miserable that his first impulse was to throw up the whole business and run back to his mother as fast as his legs would carry him.

Taganrog—when they finally arrived there—with its mean little wooden houses buried in a boundless wilderness of snow, and its constant bitter winds from the sea, was dismal and lonely. Heavy loads of fish passed in procession along the frozen shores of Azov, and crowds of traders—merchants, fishmongers, buyers —wended their way among the drifts with never a thought, as they swarmed over the snow-covered ice, that only a few feet beneath where they stood the waters of the sea lay hidden.

Having nothing else to do, Yasha went down to the distribution centre. In hastily erected wooden sheds, mountains of fish of every sort, sturgeon, sterlet, and salmon were displayed. It was a kingdom of whiteness—white fish against a background of white snow. The chief salesman busied himself with Grandfather's orders, conducting the while an expert examination by touch and smell of the different varieties.

'Say, brothers,' he exclaimed with a sly wink, 'here's a "small heap, but stinking cheap". Well, "you can't swindle us, we've got moustachios!" God protects those who protect themselves,' he concluded, going away from the suspected fish. Then, catching sight of Yasha, he jokingly greeted him as 'Master!'

'Greetings, your Excellency! Little chicken-legs, are you taking the air?'

Yasha stopped in the shed only a few moments before making his way back to the room at the inn where he was warm, quiet, and comfortable, removed from the pervading smell of fish and the rough voices of traders. He had brought with him his favourite books as a travelling library, and he wanted nothing more.

The book which chiefly interested him in Taganrog was a little paper-bound edition picked up by chance in the market. 'The story of the life of the hermit Theodore Kuzmich, who died in Siberia near Tomsk, on the estate of the merchant

Khromov.' Could it really be true? Was it really possible that the autocrat of all Russia, Alexander the Blessed, who had conquered the invincible Napoleon and driven him out of Russia with ignominy, should have met with such an end? This was a miraculous tale indeed, of how in the zenith of his glory such melancholy descended upon him that, without a word to a soul, he drove away in his carriage, bidding goodbye to St. Petersburg and returning to his capital no more.

He had come there, to that same Taganrog, and there mysteriously and with unexpected suddenness he had died. Yasha remembered as a child hearing stories of how the body of the dead Emperor had been taken from Taganrog in unseemly haste, and buried without pause or ceremony and quickly forgotten. Yet a rumour had persisted throughout the country. 'The Czar is alive and to this day concealed in an appointed place. Alexander the Blessed did not die, but the corpse of a soldier was buried in his stead.' Governors and police alike tried to suppress these mystical rumours by the most 'positive' means in their power. But after some time, on the estate of Khromov, a merchant in Siberia, appeared a hermit who, in face and figure, bore a striking resemblance to Alexander I, having the same characteristic stoop, a similar stature, the same voice, and the same penetrating blue eyes. On his person, too, were 'secret marks' and his speech was not that of common folk'.

'If,' he said, 'I declare myself and tell the whole truth, the world will shrink in horror: and if I keep the silence of the confessional, the very heavens will weep.'

For a long while, until the evening shadows fell, Yasha sat brooding over this tale of Theodore Kuzmich.

With the dusk the assistants returned, and after a supper of sturgeon, all went to bed.

Yasha's days in Taganrog were monotonous and long, but at last the chief salesman came in, saying, 'We've finished, and, as for you, your Excellency, you'll be getting quite swollen-headed! "Job done, have your fun," as they say. We'll soon be home now.'

From his face it was easy to see that his master's and his own affairs had been concluded to his satisfaction, and that he was now waiting impatiently to set off. The loading of the sleighs was therefore begun, the fish being sewn up in sacks of matting, disposed according to their kind on long sledges with a layer of felt on top, and the whole was then covered over with a tarpaulin, to prevent freezing and jolting over the rough snowy road.

The return journey promised to be long and wearisome, and would call for much skill and patience with the cargo, before a full six hundred versts could be traversed, step by step, through snow, and storm, and thaw, and frost.

Wrapped up from head to foot, with fur caps drawn down over their ears, in bearskin coats, and in tightly-fastened jerkins, the carters, like antediluvian monsters, plodded on for days, weeks, and months—for ever keeping a watch on their loads and cursing their fate.

The convoy of forty sleighs with creaking traces stretched its sinuous length in and out of the bare ravines of snow like some immense snake. At its head, and towering high above all, was erected a look-out in which was ensconced a watcher whose password had to be 'More haste, less speed'; and throughout the whole journey this watcher could not even doze, lest a sudden mischance should befall some careless driver or a collision occur on meeting the lumbering four-horse coach of a wayfaring landowner. He had to lead the way for all, and keep an eye on everything. A moment's carelessness or absence of mind might mean a good cut from the whip of a passing courier, or a breakdown in the convoy, involving a delay in which all forty sleighs would halt like a regiment, while the drivers crowded to one spot as black crows on carrion, bawling and shouting in an effort to get some warmth into their frozen throats amid the steam from the breath of man and horse which lightly floated over the whole convoy.

Yasha loved sitting near the look-out man. Swathed in scarves and shawls to the proportions of a market woman, he would settle well down upon the planks until it was difficult even to turn around, and give himself up to his dreams.

But the monotonous sameness of the white fields and the creamy sky lulled his imagination to rest and quickly induced sleep. He began to nod, dropped off to sleep, and then awoke with a start. On opening his eyes it seemed as though the caravan had long been standing in one place, while fields and banks of snow stretching far away on either flank were revolving slowly through an immense circle like a relentless roundabout. A spell of sitting still made his feet swell and stiffened his limbs, filling him with a desire to wave his arms and get some exercise. Chafing himself, he clambered down from the sleigh and marched a long while with the drivers. The crumbling snow was soft beneath the tread of his comfortable felt boots—it was just like going barefoot along the frozen road except that one's feet were not cold. Only his hands were always cold, notwithstanding his mother's fur gloves.

When at times the sky frowned, the sun hid itself, and winds blew, Yasha felt uneasy. As soon as the low leaden clouds drove across the sky and the thick snow danced through the frozen air in great woolly flakes, hiding the countryside from view, he was terrified. It seemed then as if the convoy, and even the whole world and every living creature in it, had disappeared, and as if all that remained was snow, endless snow, soft, feathery, treacherous snow.

Horrible thoughts would haunt him, memories which sent a shudder down his spine. He would recall how, once long ago, in some obscure corner of boundless Russia, a convoy had been overcome by a blizzard and had just disappeared—no one knew where or how—until spring came and the snow melted away, and men and horses, frozen stark, had been discovered standing or lying down just as they had been in life. Then he would call to mind stories of wandering packs of wolves, though these were no longer frightening. In fact, the thought that the wolves

37

had now been driven away from those parts brought some consolation, and under the influence of the monotonous movement he dropped off to sleep again.

And thus the journey went on, until at night the inn was reached. Oh, what joy it was after a long monotonous day's march, to sit before a glowing stove, to move one's arms and legs in freedom and forget, with soul and body forget, the existence of convoys and snowdrifts!

A samovar boiled and bubbled on the table as though at home, and the round-bellied kettles, the vast cups, the pies, and the griddle-cakes seemed to chuckle to themselves at the noise of the storm without. Hens clucked in the passage quite undisturbed; dogs whimpered from cold; and everywhere was life, everything as it had always been, in contrast to the life in death outside.

It was jolly, too, to watch the chief salesman quizzing a buxom landlady, or endeavouring to beat down a porter's overcharge for lodging.

Yasha fell asleep in the cosy warmth of his bed, stretching his young body in complete abandonment. Yet on the other side of the wall where the storm was howling, the watchmen on duty, guarding the convoy, were never silent, and their long-drawn-out shouts rang over the snow.

'Listen! Listen!' And in reply from somewhere quite close to where he lay drowsing, 'Listen!'

And so through the night in relays they kept watch over the freight. Then in the morning, when it was hardly light, off they went again. Once more the ravines of snow, the sparse rime-covered hamlets, and the striped barriers of little towns, right on to Kharkov.

And the nearer they got to home the more cruel became the frost. The sun was bright and full, but gave no heat. The air was dry and clear but so cold that it caught the breath. The snow became firmer and the sleigh-runners glided over it squeaking like an ungreased axle. Blue shadows fell athwart it, and over all was the boundless expanse of the sky.

'Don't open your mouth, master, or you'll have a jackdaw flying in,' the carters called out laughingly to him. 'And don't choke from the cold,' added the chief salesmen. 'And see that you don't let your nose get white. If you do, it will fall off like a tramp's, who has been crunching along in the snow on the Moscow road.'

Yasha thoroughly enjoyed these sunny, frosty days. Such a crackling frost—'Grandfather frosty Red Nose' himself! He wanted to match his strength with him, to play leap-frog with him, to fetch him a box on the ear. At such times he would jump down from the sleigh and run along the singing white road. Screwing up his eyes in the sunshine, he would deftly plant a tightly made snowball right in the middle of the look-out man's red face! That would be a signal for all sorts of sport which enlivened the whole convoy, and snow-fights would start amid roars of laughter. They neighed like young colts.

'You've no guts, Egorka!'

'Well, Ginger, here's your change, anyhow,' challenged Egorka, catching the senior assistant on the ear with a lucky shot and chanting cheekily:

> *Sandy asked old Ginger-head*
> *How do you paint your beard so red?*
> *It isn't paint, old Ginger boasted—*
> *I sit in the sun and get it toasted,*

and they neighed again like horses.

After they passed Kharkov the frost became even keener, and Yasha was happier than ever. In two weeks, with God's help, they would be home again, and he would again see Mother, from whom he had received no news for two months. With this thought he snuggled down into his sleigh-rug.

The closer the measured tread of the carters brought him to his home, the more keen and bitter was the enveloping frost, and the warmer became Yasha's heart. He imagined himself taking wings like a bird and quickly speeding home.

They reached the monastery of Korennaya, empty and deserted in winter; and then, at last, that well-loved quarter of his own blessed town. There it stood, muffled in its white kerchief, like some dear old woman in a storm showing her gap-toothed smile of welcome to a friend. There was the market square, and there in the distance, the gaily painted church he had known from childhood.

'Yasha! My first-born! How you've grown! Oh, how you've grown! Why, you're quite a young man,' exclaimed his mother with tears of happiness, as she clung to the excited boy.

But Grandfather returned from the store-house with a look as black as thunder, and severely reprimanded the chief salesman —a load of dace was frost-rotted.

'You were careless, you sons of bitches! You scoundrels!' he muttered fiercely, throwing an angry glance at his newly returned son.

VI

TOWARDS the spring, after much talk, deliberation, and fuss, Grandfather prepared to set off for Moscow. 'It's no joking matter,' he said almost boastfully over the tea-table, looking across at Grandmother's frightened face, 'to risk knocking off five hundred versts with one's own horses, and in these times, too!'

At last, when the snow finally disappeared, and the earth, drenched with the showers of spring, bared her soft bosom to dry in the warm beams of the sun, when the silver-birch trees were thickly covered with sticky leaves and the happy songs of the birds filled the air with sound, the day for his departure was fixed.

'And would Yasha like to go to Moscow?' he jokingly inquired of his son.

'If you like, Papasha.'

'All right, then, get yourself ready. And Pasha, you can look after the shop and be the master!'

'Yes, Papasha, I will.'

On the morrow the horses were brought round by Simeon the coachman who, dressed in holiday clothes, sat on the box and gazed lovingly at his well-groomed team, while the whole household, including the servants, knelt in the hall before the ikon. Before a long journey, in the face of an unknown venture, one must needs ponder, concentrating one's thoughts, and silently praying. All sat together with serious, tense expressions, as though each was thinking the same thought. 'One chapter of life has closed. Another is beginning. What has the future in store?' This was a fine Russian custom—to unite in thought and ponder together over the future. In front lay life's road, unknown and strange. The past, whether it were good or ill, has already ceased to be, and all that remained of it was a feeling of grief. But in the immediate present, within a minute of time, something new was beginning. Who knew whether it would bring happiness?

'Now, it's time to start,' Grandfather's voice broke in upon them after the silence.

'Happy journey, Akim Ivanovich!'

'Yasha!—take care of Yasha, he's only—' but copious tears coursing down Grandmother's agitated face cut short her speech.

What is it that the Russian rhyme says?

> *A mother's tears are as a flowing river.*
> *A sister's tears are as the trickling brooks.*
> *A wife's tears are as the falling dew:*
> *The sun appears, the dew all dries away.*

They were off! It was good at this time of year to be out among the ordered fields. Larks trilled in the sky, rooks preened themselves in the sun, and the road ran on ahead like a white ribbon through a surrounding wealth of common, ploughland, meadow, and coppice. They entered a pine forest, whose trees towered majestically above them, straight and tall, thinking the thoughts of centuries. Except for the horses' hooves, it was as quiet there as in a cathedral, so that one wanted to speak in whispers. There was a smell of resin and of wild flowers; the vivid foliage shone like an emerald against the soft meadow grass; and all the time the horses kept up their brisk trot along the beaten tract.

The forest came to an end as they reached a river, there to encounter new forms of life and a new environment. They could see the long-legged wading-birds, and from afar could discern the river bed among the darkening reeds. Then came the thrill of crossing the ferry with the carriage and horses, while one sat quite at ease on the high box-seat, watching how slowly the ferry-boat was moving and listening to the melodious burble of the water. Somewhere a fish leapt; ducks swam out from among the rushes on the bank. It induced meditation. Above the steep bank, in the huts of some village, the first lights of the approaching evening began to twinkle; plaintive songs, fragments of talk and laughter, and the sound of evening bells stole across the water. Then came the night's halt, talk with strangers, the long tea-drinking under blossoming apple trees; and when all talk was ended, the magic of the night. It was a long time before Yasha could be persuaded to go to bed; he could not tear himself away from the fascination of the distant stars, the tranquil silence, and his own young thoughts.

The nearer they got to Moscow the more frequent became the hamlets, villages, and little towns. At the inns landlords began asking unheard-of prices for a night's lodging; everyone was preoccupied, hurried, and somewhat dishonest. It was a case of each for himself, of watching how 'to take the little more and give the little less'. They reached Serpukhov, from which, as Grandfather pointed out, Moscow is only a stone's throw. 'Come on, Simeon!' he exhorted, 'Use your whip!' Simeon nodded, and for appearance' sake gave the wheel horse a cut, exclaiming, 'Stop your fooling, you scamp,' but with a look as though to say to his master, 'Don't you worry! You'll get there in fine style.'

As they came over the Sparrow Hills the whole city lay open before them, the multi-coloured monasteries around its rim, then parishes and wards all thick with houses, and then in the very centre the great gleaming Kremlin with all its palaces, belfries, towers, and battlements.

At the Serpukhov barrier, where all had to present their documents and submit to various formalities, they found a press of people and wagons. At last, however, the parti-coloured boom, striped black and white, was raised, and a sentry with a badge and halberd thrust himself right under Simeon's chin and shouted after him 'Keep more over to the right, you ignorant lout'. Though Simeon nodded violently, he had no intention of keeping to the right, and indeed drove all through Moscow as God put it into his heart to drive, thereby more than once on the journey earning a drubbing from enraged sentries. After which he would rub himself and call back, 'We're not country folk. We come from a county town. We're not bumpkins!'

The crooked streets of Moscow, its countless churches, its noise, bells, sentry-boxes, and taverns astonished Yasha. They stopped on the far side of Moskva River near Bolotny Square, on which stood stone-built warehouses with long rows of covered archways enclosing thousands of wagons, which contained all sorts of merchandise from poultry to tanned hides, the latter looking like withered bark freshly torn from huge oaks.

Their lodging was a little wooden house belonging to a fellow-townsman, and there they deposited their leather trunks ('Our trousseau', thought Yasha) in a vestibule smelling of new wood and oil paint, which opened on to the small living-room. This was furnished in mahogany, and boasted a leather sofa and some round tables covered with hand-crocheted cloths, where tea had already been laid. The samovar gurgled merrily, the *zakuski* were all set out, and the old faces depicted in the ikons in silver settings, and each illuminated by a coloured-glass lamp, looked on in wonder from their corner of the room.

The hostess proved to be a kindly old lady with whom Yasha soon made friends, feeling altogether at home at her tea-table. She asked after old acquaintances and advised on the sights of Moscow and how to reach them. 'You must not forget first of all to visit the Iverskaya chapel,' she asserted, interrupting her knitting. 'It is a holy spot, famous throughout the world, revered even in foreign parts. It is our intercessor with Heaven.'

Her pleasant, kindly talk made the time slip by imperceptibly until the evening, when their host came in. He was grey-headed and lame in one knee. Grandfather and he were friends and old school-fellows. For the last twenty years they had rarely met. The claims of business had separated them, and life with its

constant anxieties had hardly ever caused their paths to cross.
None the less, they greeted each other as though they had only
parted on the previous evening.

'Well met, Akim Ivanovich! Did you have a good journey?'
asked Saveliy Zakharich, embracing Grandfather.

'Yes, so-so, Saveliy Zakharich, thanks to your prayers. And
now look you, here is my son Yakov, whom I commend to your
love and sympathy.'

'Why, it's a fine young fellow you've got there, Akim
Ivanovich,' said the old man, grasping Yasha by the fore-arm and
gazing with curiosity at his young, smiling face. 'He's quite
a man, quite a man! We must see about finding a wife for him
while he is here!'

At this Yasha was overcome by shyness, and the old lady came
to his aid.

'What are you saying to the boy, Saveliy Zakharich? Only
fifteen, and you all for getting him married! And now, dear
friends, draw up to the table for what God has provided.'

Yasha's life in Moscow was quiet and restful. Every morning,
as soon as the bells rang out for early service from the 'forty
times forty Moscow churches', he leaped out of bed and, quickly
putting on his clothes, stole out of the door to wander about in
streets, and alleys, and churches and monasteries. He climbed
the belfry of Ivan the Great, and for hours at a time gazed at
Moscow spread out like a map below him. There was the Czar's
Palace, there the Red Stairway, and there the window from
which legend said that the populace had hurled Dmitriy the
Pretender. There again was the Metropolitan of Moscow's
residence and sacristy, while far away, beyond the countless
houses, the monasteries of the Virgin and Andronev, with their
gardens and orchards, came into view. The belfry on which he
stood was not without its associations, he remembered, for it
had been built by Boris Godounov in a year of famine, to give
work to the starving. And though many years had passed, and
man's memory was poor, it still stood as a permanent memorial
of those days, and would yet stand. Then there was the monstrous

exotic Cathedral of St. Basil, looking as though it was squatting on all fours, its fluted onion-shaped cupolas and pointed windows decked out with every hue, lending it the appearance of a Persian rug. It was sheer Asiatic magnificence! Yet St. Basil himself, when here on earth, had been a beggar, going about in a shift imploring alms, and he had died as naked as when his mother had borne him.

Yasha spent whole days of his visit in the dimly lit Archangelsky, bowing before the old ikons and hearing the masses. The singing of the cathedral choir so gripped his heart that at the first strains of the 'Song of the Cherubim' he could barely restrain his tears. The deep bass chords seemed to sink into the depths of the earth, while the tenor descants soared heavenwards. The fair-haired deacon in his gold vestments began the prayer in a soft, low voice, which gradually rose higher and higher, until at last a clarion note sounded through the length and breadth of the vast building and was caught up within the lofty cupola, from which the stern eyes of the God of Hosts looked down.

In the heart of the cathedral was a rostrum bearing a high throne on which, crosier in hand, sat the prelate, wearing gold vestments and bejewelled mitre, and seeming almost unearthly in his splendour. And yet, when to the intoning of *Ispolati Despota, Ispolati Despota*, they unrobed him, divesting him according to ritual of mitre, pectoral image, and outer robes, leaving him there in his purple cassock, he was seen to be just an ordinary, feeble old man, weary from having stood so long.

The service over, Yasha mingled with the crowd in the cloisters, and there distributed coppers among the hordes of beggars, cripples, and starvelings. He watched the prelate mount his carriage, to be borne away at a brisk trot behind a team of six sturdy, well-groomed horses, and then he wandered homewards still dazed by the impressions received from deep reverberating chords of the singing, fragrantly scented incense, and all the splendour he had witnessed. For in Moscow, as in his own provincial town, it was by monasteries, quietude, and old-time integrity that he was fascinated, while Grandfather for his part preferred the proximity of Traders' Row, the tavern, and the busy stir of men: and here in Moscow was all the bustle of business on a large scale.

In endless vaulted galleries and buildings, built on what used to be the Bolotny marshes, sat bearded merchants in top hats far less sedate in manner than their provincial brethren. Their young assistants, dressed in the latest tradesmen's modes, would, even in the open streets, hurl themselves upon the passers-by, tugging at their coats like dogs, in their effort to attract some customer to their shops, shouting at the tops of their voices, 'By your leave, merchant. We have the very finest wares; the real city quality; the same price for one and all: our prices cannot be questioned. By your leave, Sir.'

It was impossible not to go in and purchase some little present for those at home. 'We mustn't return empty-handed,' Grandfather remarked—and so they bought a picture of the Emperor Nikolai Pavlovich in white buckskin breeches and plumed shako astride a charger, a new coat for Grandmother, and a sable cap for Grandfather. Though the proprietor vowed that he was selling at a loss, for 'we never bargain with fellow-townsmen', they haggled together for half-an-hour, and he reduced his price by half; keeping up his incessant babble of talk while his assistants were wrapping up the parcel.

'I am giving the goods away, merchant!' he said with a twinkle in his roguish eyes, as he handed the wrapped-up parcel to Grandfather. 'It has pleased me beyond measure to be able to oblige a fellow-countryman!' and with that they went off with their purchases through the Saviour's Gate into the Red Square.

'Heigh you! Boy!' shouted a sentry to Yasha, 'Take your hat off when you go under the holy gate!' At first Yasha failed to understand, but then remembered that this was a local ordinance of the first Romanoff, and that he must comply.

In the Red Square there stood the scaffold, a circular structure surrounded by an iron railing; and they involuntarily paused there. It was from the Kremlin walls that Ivan the Terrible had watched the mass executions here beneath, and though now quiet and deserted, it was, thought Yasha, a place of horror over which still brooded a heavy oppressive atmosphere from times long past. Evidently human blood leaves traces of itself, and there is no escape from it.

The feeling of oppression induced by the place did not leave them, nor did their nerves become steady again until they had reached Bolshoi Moscow Tavern, where waiters in white trousers, and long shirts gathered in by magenta sashes, were bustling round with dishes; guests were sitting decorously at little tables, and a barman of majestic presence was lording it over a buffet loaded with *zakuski* of all sorts. By the time sun-dried and smoked sturgeon, borsch with Moscow *kalatch*, and roast chicken were set before them, they were completely happy and content again. Grandfather had a glass of vodka at the bar, sampled the *zakuski*—pickled gherkin, mushrooms, salmon, soused apple and other such delicacies—and returned to the table, wiping his hands before helping himself to sturgeon. 'They know how to live in Moscow!' he said. 'Aah!'

As for the waiters, they kept running to and fro between client and bar, uncorked small bottles of vodka, jingled the change, and if, as sometimes happened, a merchant became tipsy and made himself a nuisance, they deftly bundled the offender to the door and handed him over to the tall 'chucker-out' to expel in a manner befitting his station: either, that is to say, with fatherly affection, or with painful severity and a parting kick.

Before their departure from Moscow, Grandfather and Yasha, with hair well pomaded and wearing long black frock-coats, long black ribbon cravats, and narrow watch-chains looped across their chests, attended a birthday party at a merchant's house. There were many guests—gentlemen wearing frock-coats and displaying their watch-chains, and ladies wearing silk or velvet crinolines, their fingers covered with rings, their long pendant ear-rings dangling, and pearls round their bare necks. All of this wealth they had taken out of their jewel-cases to flaunt in its entirety like so much window-dressing in a shop. The gentlemen crowding round the table of *zakuski* drank their host's health, while the ladies, sitting modestly in the chairs ranged round the walls, toyed with their handerchiefs and rarely exchanged a word with each other. As it was considered improper for ladies to take part in the general merriment around the table, the hostess would find some pretext or other for inviting each in turn to her bedroom, where 'just as a secret' she had put out apple-jack, cherry brandy, sloe-gin, and various *zakuski* and bon-bons, and where without a blush one bottle after another was disposed of.

Dressed in white frocks, the young girls tended to go about in pairs, while the youths—merchants' sons, minor officials, and the like—stood after the *zakuski* in groups around the wall; both sides alike, in their own way, were stiff and shy, until some happy chance remark broke the ice. As Yasha was good-looking, besides being a stranger, he was at once surrounded by the white frocks, 'And they were all so pretty and dainty,' he said afterwards, 'All in tarlatans and full of fun! I said to them, "I'm itching," and they burst out giggling and ran away. Then they all came round again, still laughing. It was not till later that I discovered that in Moscow "itching" was itching, while at home in Kursk, it meant "bored".'

It was good to be at a party, but home was better! When Grandfather had completed his business, and Yasha had taken a final look at Moscow from the belfry of Ivan the Great, they set off for home again.

'Moscow's all right, and it's good to be there. But home's best,' said Grandfather as they approached the 'Blessed City'. It was cosy and snug at home.

'Look you, Párochka,' cried Grandfather, full of joy at seeing his wife again, 'I've brought a new coat for you. Come along, Yasha, undo it! Careful, now! Don't spoil that picture or break its frame! I've bought a sable cap for myself, too! Terribly dear it was. A hundred roubles in notes it cost!'

49

'Is it really possible, Akim Ivanovich?' gasped Grandmother in astonishment.

They undid their parcel. They found instead of the sable cap only some feathers, which flew about in all directions, and instead of the picture of Nikolai Pavlovich only an old broken frame!

'Thieves! Swindlers! They changed it under the counter when the proprietor was talking his ridiculous nonsense!' exclaimed Grandfather, brandishing his arms. 'God forgive me, it's true that they're all thieves in Moscow! "Moscow thieves!" I used not to believe it, but now I see! They've swindled me! The rogues!'

For a long time Grandfather, unable to calm down, stormed from room to room in a transport of rage. But it was of no avail. The presents had been paid for. Grandmother, as always was able to quiet him, telling him of domestic affairs and relating the town's news. At intervals she referred again to the unfortunate purchase, 'As for the money, Akim Ivanovich, that's no great matter! And some day they'll have the tables turned upon them. "The cat that feasts today will mew tomorrow!"'

VII

WITH the end of the Crimean war had come strange rumours, and the talk was all of great reforms, of a new judicial system, and, above all, of changes in the rights of serf-ownership. Already in Fishmongers' Row, even into Grandfather's immemorial domain, were penetrating new sounds and portents. The constables no longer bore themselves so arrogantly; the shop-assistants became less servile; and under the counter among Yasha's constant and well-thumbed favourites appeared suppressed pages of *The Tocsin*, *The Life and Opinions of Iskander*, and Hertzen's *From the Opposite Bank*, which were shattering as with a succession of mighty hammer-blows the old foundations, and forging a new Russia. More than ever Yasha's lifelong friend, Vanya Puzanov, the handsome son of a merchant in Mercers' Row, would run round to the shop to slip into his hand revolutionary pamphlets like *The Improvement of Affairs*, under cover of crudely illustrated little books such as *The Major's Wooing*.

Yasha had always been instinctively responsive to physical beauty and, since he regarded them as beings apart, venerated beautiful people as though he looked to them for something out of the ordinary, some beauty of character to rival their beauty of feature. And, without exaggeration, this Vanya resembled a Greek god with his tall, upright carriage, his mass of thick, black curls, his darting eyes, and his gentle, polished manner. Indeed, it was incomprehensible why such pure classically Greek beauty should have descended on a grey, humdrum provincial town. This beauty, moreover, was not confined to the physical, for Vanya's heart went out to beauty of all kinds, and his effort-less talents embraced literature and drama and covered the intense and restless activities of a young 'patrician'. It was invariably he who discovered anything interesting, new or unusual, and he would dart into the shop, quickly whisper the news to Yasha, and be off in a moment so as to escape Grandfather's notice.

'Come round to Maltsev's place,' he said once, 'There is a magic lantern there. It's really lovely.' Thereafter at Maltsev's, in a darkened room crowded to suffocation, were found his young companions, watching with bated breath an illuminated screen, where stars, spheres, and cubes of different hue became transfused with all the colours of the rainbow, and assumed every gradation of shade and shape. There was something wonderful in this threshold of another as yet unexplored world. Geometrical figures and revolving spheres wove moving patterns like those on a Persian carpet. The celebrated 'Struwwelpeter' began to pick his nose till it grew to such an extent that his Papasha advised him to carry it in a barrow. So for many years he trundled his barrow before him, jeered at by all the urchins everywhere he went. In the end his nose ripened and fell, and he appeared with his normal nose once more, with a slogan coming from his mouth saying, 'Children, don't pick your nose.' The colours were bright and crude, except for the geometrical designs, which were projected in tints like the reflections from stained glass in old western cathedrals and churches.

After the demonstration, in the same darkened room, they applied themselves to spiritualism and table-rapping, and became absorbed in the hidden mysteries of life beyond the grave, only to return with equal facility to careless mundane happiness, with Vanya, their leader and pioneer, infecting all with his boundless energy and good nature.

One day Vanya took Yasha to see a new acquaintance of his, of whom he talked incessantly all the way to his house. He proved to be a young doctor, Briliantov by name, who, having just completed his course at the University of Moscow, had now come to live in the attic of a shabby house, the property of a country squire, which stood in a narrow little street. With a shock of curly hair crowning his giant's head, Briliantov gave the impression of all-embracing knowledge and ability. He was, too, a born enthusiast and an authority on every subject under the sun, from beetles to the structure of roses, and he could discuss at length the habits of any wild beast, the life of the bee, or the differentiation of species throughout the animal and vegetable kingdoms. When his memory was for a moment at fault he would take a book from one of the shelves, with which his walls were lined from floor to ceiling, and without interrupting the clear and orderly sequence of his discourse, would look up a reference and conclude with a summary wherein his every point was made crystal clear. He it was who first introduced his youthful friends to a strange-looking instrument called a microscope, through the lenses of which appeared a new world inhabited by tiny creatures that moved and swam about, globules which chased each other, mites which devoured each other. He, too, displayed to their admiring gaze the wonders of a Rumford coil, while under the magic of his dissecting knife an ordinary frog revealed the ingenious mechanism of its circulatory system in delicate colouring, and became an object of wonderment.

The young host himself never lost his air of mystery and omniscience, but calmly and confidently would explain physical laws, bacteriology, or the origin and evolution of life. Occasionally, too, he would gently direct his talk to current affairs and the question of serfdom; or, without cant or hypocrisy, would launch into a passionate plea for honesty in living and obedience to the voice of conscience. At such times the professor of the attic university became the preacher of Virtue and Justice, whose spiritual gifts left his audience with an abiding memory of his personality, and not merely of his profound knowledge. Briliantov was so transparently good—a real 'diamond', as Yasha used to say—and his love of knowledge was so genuine that in Yasha's heart he implanted a respect for science and scientists which was to last his lifetime; and though in after-years Briliantov's name became famous for work in research, he himself remained the same simple, kindly soul, refusing all honours and high-sounding titles. The young people came to him for a solution of life's problems, and the townsfolk admired his learning, simplicity, and sound medical advice, unostentatiously and gratuitously given. Even the authorities turned a blind eye to his liberal opinions.

It would, however, be a mistake to imagine that this attic university was the sole diversion of the young members of the merchant class. But 'all young fledgelings come alike from the same nest', and to this particular flock it was always Vanya Puzanov, with his intimate knowledge of every aspect of provincial life, who supplied the initiative. It was he who organized the boat race on the sluggish, shallow river and offered prizes for the crayfish-catching competition. The boat race was the signal for a veritable campaign, during which hours were spent in sounding the depth of the river, noting the shoals, studying the currents, erecting distance-posts, and practising far into the evening. Vanya was best when endurance was demanded, and Yasha was a clever cox, who could contrive to avoid the shoals and other danger spots without adding to the length of the course. The opposing crew was recruited from the young smiths of Iron-mongers' Row—strong, hefty fellows who could easily beat Vanya's boat over a straight course, but who lacked any technique for negotiating bends in the river, and thus frequently went aground on the shoals.

As the day of the race approached, Vanya noticed with alarm that his opponents, besides being the more powerful crew, had acquired a modicum of style and were no longer rowing like a rabble. The loss of the race would, he considered, be a catastrophe, especially when he imagined what would be said down in the Mercers' Row, and what laughter would be caused by his discomfiture. On the Saturday of the trial race, when the smiths moved really easily and never went aground, Vanya recognized that his crew were in for a beating. His rivals now revealed a turn of speed which they had never shown before. They were, in fact, themselves already celebrating their victory. It was essential, therefore, that definite action should be taken, but exactly what to do he did not know. At last he hit on an idea, and at night, without breathing a word to anyone, went out in a small boat, and not only altered the distance stakes, thereby appreciably shortening the course, but also moved the flags which marked the shoals. No one noticed or suspected anything. His crew, as a result, reached the post a full three minutes ahead of their rivals, who were left gasping. He duly celebrated his triumph, and only Doctor Briliantov guessed the truth, and gave him a severe lecturing in the attic, after which he made a full confession.

Sometimes the young friends went out together just to carouse. Meeting at a remote inn of the town, they ordered drinks, and on the production of a pack of cards, started to gamble. Supper followed, at which they told each other anecdotes and discussed women. As always, Vanya commanded the attention of all. His complete candour, his knowledge of the ins and outs of tavern life, and his inimitable sense of humour, opened all hearts to him and gave piquancy to those merchant bacchanalia. He was a past master at relating funny stories, giving thumbnail sketches of merchant life, or declaiming Schiller in the true histrionic tradition:

'Oh, people, people, progeny of Hell, breed of crocodiles! Lions and leopards tend their offspring—but you?' he would sob aloud while his audience shuddered with bated breath.

His recitation ended, and perspiring from his efforts, he demanded wine, and champagne was served before the appearance of the harpists, all of whom he knew and had captivated by his charm. After rendering indifferent love-songs to the accompaniment of harps, invariably out of tune, they took their fee and departed. To follow them Vanya had secured some gipsies, of whom a whole troupe now tumbled noisily in. Having tuned their guitars, they struck up a melody, while the women jingled their coins, preened themselves before the mirror, postured, or flirted with the audience. Everyone was in high spirits, and when at last the chorus, flinging restraint to the winds, broke into some wild, rousing song to the passionate thrum of the guitar,

E

everything vanished into nothingness, and forgotten alike were the grey monotony of life, the Traders' Rows, and the changeless daily round.

> *The gipsies came from the fair, from the fair,*
> *They halted under an apple tree.*
> *A lad in a gay red shirt was there*
> *And jolly and ruddy and ruddy was he.*

So sang the chorus, and as the basses joined in, there was conjured up a complete picture of gipsy encampments and the life of freedom.

When the song crashed to its end, having roused the audience to passion, Styosha, handsome, dark, stately, with great black languishing eyes, took her stand in the midst of the singers and, to the accompaniment of soft muted guitars, sang in her rich contralto:

> *Two guitars beyond my wall plaintively were ringing*
> *Oh, melody I long have loved 'tis you that they are singing?*
> *Yes, 'tis you whose yearning notes now thrill my heart with pleasure*
> *As in my ears resound again your harmony and measure,*

and the full chorus caught up the refrain

> *Once again, and yet again!*
> *And many, many times again!*

An eerie feeling came over Yasha, causing him to creep away into a distant unlit corner, where in silence he could sit and listen, while his dreams bore him to strange, unexplored domains, or carried him away into boundless space before bringing him back to earth again. Meanwhile Vanya, his eyes bloodshot, scattered money broadcast and prostrated himself in a transport of passion at Styosha's feet, in wild tones declaiming

> *Now die by the knife*
> *Of Prokopa Lapunova*

until pacified by a bottle of Donskoie.

An old gipsy woman, Turchykha, then sang the lively little song, 'Lieutenant, pray why are you under arrest?'

She was followed by tall Khapilo, who flung himself into a dance with such frenzy that the stout floor-boards bent beneath him, and on the table the bottles and tinkling glasses seemed to dance in sympathy.

In the early morning, when full payment had been made with unstinting hand, and the waiters had bowed themselves double, the party embarked on *troikas* and drove home through the remaining hours of darkness. They arrived with the break of day, and went at once to work tired but fully content.

Sitting in Mercers' Row, surrounded by silks and satins, Vanya was for a long time unable to settle down again. He dreamed of running away to join the gipsies, of visiting the country fairs with them, and sharing their free, careless life, instead of being condemned by circumstance to sit in a shop importuning customers and occasionally representing shop-worn pieces of material to be the latest fashion.

'What a fate! What a fate!' he would lament to Yasha, 'To sit in a shop counting out change! And one's soul yearning for freedom! Ah! Yasha, this is no work for men of our intellect!'

When a travelling circus or a touring company from the capital visited the town Vanya awoke to life again. He became an impresario, sparing no pains to dispose of tickets or arrange supper parties for the artists. Swelling with pride he would say to Yasha,

'Yasha, my friend, come and let me take you behind the scenes. I'll show you something, brother! You shall see a queen!' Yasha went, and in the light of smoky lamps gazed on a queen in her make-up and on Spanish grandees in their tawdry finery.

It was then that Vanya's great love and unusual talent for the stage were first manifested. He began quite by accident, as prompter, when, on the eve of a performance, the local prompter could not resist temptation and appeared dead drunk at rehearsal. As, with the exception of the leading actor, the great Shumski, no performer knew his part, a prompter was essential, and since

Vanya almost knew the play by heart, and got through a rehearsal without the least hitch, he was engaged. Jevokini the comedian, who afterwards attained fame, appeared in a vaudeville and singing act and made his public cry with laughter, while Vanya, hidden from view and bent double in his prompter's box, lived through every line and never failed to give timely cues.

When at length old Jevokini, twining his fat legs, sang in his squeaky tenor

> *Once in front of a personage grand*
> *A little official stood*
> *And said with a smile obsequious and bland—*

the audience drowned his words in their laughter at his comical miming, and when on the high notes he finished with

> *Your speech is the sacred truth itself*
> *I have never heard any so good*

there was such deafening confusion that the auditorium sounded like a cavalry stable, and the noise of stamping feet almost drowned the clapping. Ensconced in his little box, Vanya accepted all this applause for himself, with a pride which was increased by the guarantee of a walking-on part at the next performance. He was promised next the part of Hamlet's father's ghost and similar roles, on which to found a repertoire. So carefully and conscientiously did he eventually rehearse these parts, that he literally took the whole performance on himself, studying his lines in the shop, where he sold silks in the manner of a Merchant of Venice, becoming lovesick in the manner of Schiller—'like forty thousand brothers'—and bowing like a Spanish grandee. In short, he carried every part in his repertoire into his work-a-day life.

Later, when regular tours of the Moscow troupe were organized, with the participation of actors like Shepnikov, Sadovski, and others of the 'greatest attraction of the age', they began to rely on Vanya's services. Often he was entrusted with some share of the production, and as a reward for his pains, was given a more responsible part. Later he became famous as the mayor in Gogol's *Inspector-General* and as Nesheslivtzev in Ostrovsky's comedy. The youth of the town patronized the performances not only to see the stars but also to admire their homebred talent. Ladies got into the habit of dropping into the shop in Mercers' Row, not so much to make purchases as to have a word with the good-looking merchant-actor, and since their conversations generally ended with their buying something, the mercery business, so far from suffering from Vanya's stage activities, gradually increased and prospered. Old Puzanov made no protest, although he kept a strict eye on his son who, now that his fame was growing, had fully decided to throw up everything and become an actor, just as once he had decided to join the gipsies. The final resolve was, however, put off from day to day, and to the end of his life it was never his lot to escape the toil of drab, tedious existence in his shop in a provincial town.

VIII

TIME passed, and Yasha had just turned eighteen. He was of medium height, with brown hair, which he parted in the middle, a high forehead, a straight, well-proportioned nose, and beautiful blue eyes, flecked with brown. As always, he was conspicuous among his drab fellow-townsmen; and though he remained absorbed in his thoughts, he was in no way to be pitied, for he faithfully performed his duties in the shop, even when his heart was far away, somewhere on the mountain tops.

Grandfather, though he was ageing, still kept the reins of government in his own hands, and attended to all business matters. Pasha, however, now went to Taganrog to collect the fish, Yasha remaining behind in the shop. On his return with his task successfully accomplished and his convoy safe and sound, Pasha, who had thought but little of the hardships of the journey, began to assume a personal responsibility and control. In shops the assistants bowed and scraped before him, and Grandfather was loud in his praise. But Yasha, who had apparently sold his birthright for a mess of pottage composed of dreams, was neither distressed nor worried thereby.

More than ever he felt that he would find the truth of life in Doctor Briliantov's attic. Life was lived but once, and one must live it with as much truth and enlightenment as possible. There was room in the world for all sorts and conditions of men, and to his thinking, at any rate, happiness lay neither in making money nor in having it. Had not Alexander the First turned his back on wealth and unbelievable power in order to live as a hermit, unrecognized and alone? And yet, to escape from the world into a monastery seemed to Yasha to be wrong, since it was precisely in the world that truth was needed, and it was one's duty to irradiate the world with the light of peace and justice. So when doubts assailed him he betook himself to Doctor Briliantov's attic and sat for hours with him, solving life's problems, constructing new worlds, and building castles in the air.

About this time carefree Vanya Puzanov began to look worried. He was constantly depressed, moody and listless; and a rash appeared on his body. The handsome young Italian apothecary, Torciani, was summoned to his aid, but despite his fame as healer, sorcerer, and magician—for he was a Russian Cagliostro—his efforts were quite unavailing. Vanya would go to no doctors because he had no faith in them, and when Yasha did his utmost to persuade him to consult Doctor Briliantov he refused point-blank, saying that he had greater belief in folk-medicine, the accumulated wisdom of ages, and in native common sense. When therefore he heard that there was a 'wise woman' living somewhere in the countryside, he gladly and without more ado repaired to her. This 'wise woman' was a typical old crone, who received him without ceremony. She examined him. Then with a sigh she said, 'Young merchant, yours is a grave disease. It is the black disease. I know a secret remedy, but it is difficult to get and to prepare. Give me a hundred roubles, and you will be well again. If not—' Such was his faith in her, that Vanya accepted these terms, and having settled in a lonely peasant hut on the outskirts of a village, applied himself to the cure. Looking for all the world like 'the striped devil from the black marsh', he sat in his hovel, stark naked, and plastered with a sticky, blackish-brown pitchlike concoction, the revolting stink of which could be discerned a mile away. Within three days he was on the road to recovery, and at the end of the week was fully cured. 'It just vanished,' he used afterwards to relate, 'as though I'd been licked clean by a cow's tongue—and you talk of your doctors!' he would add, throwing a triumphant glance at Yasha. Within a few days the black disease was forgotten, and Vanya was running about the town, as usual ferreting out new interests and arranging evening parties.

At that time a distillery, fitted with all the latest foreign equipment, was being set up near the river, on the outskirts of the town. The company was a German one, and the manager of the concern was a dandified young Russian man-about-town, by name Pavlusha Gushchin. With him Vanya soon struck up a friendship, for both knew and appreciated the good things of life, dressed fashionably, and were acknowledged lady-killers. Gushchin was quite an insignificant person, but could bluff others into thinking him their superior, and when it came to arranging suppers or drinking parties he surpassed even Vanya, since he was entirely without shame.

Once these two determined to organize a drinking party in the really grand manner, somewhere in the country air; and to this end chartered the factory's boat, a flat-bottomed paddle steamer, which was still accounted a wonder in the town, and with music and refreshments on board, everyone set off down the river. Their goal was the monastery of Tolkhov, where it had been decided to spend a night ashore, returning at about noon on the morrow. A large number of friends, young fellows with good voices, made up their party, so that a chorus was automatically selected, without any need for preliminary rehearsal. They started to the strains of 'Down Mother Volga', the traditional song sung by Russians everywhere at each place of halt. Their young voices rang out clearly, and a wave of melody was borne along the river banks, to lose itself at last among the meadows, startling the water-fowl, which rose protesting from the reeds, and with a flurry of wings flew away to quieter havens. The singing ended, and only the splash of the paddles and the chugging of the engine was heard, as the boat ploughed peacefully forward on its placid course, while peasants at work in the fields stopped to gaze in astonishment at the crowded decks.

At last, in the distance, down the silver ribbon of water the monastery appeared in hazy outline, on a high bank. A cuckoo was calling, counting out the time. They demanded, 'Cuckoo, cuckoo. How long shall I live?' The cuckoo counted seventy-five.

'Well, Gushchin, you're twenty-five now, so you'll see the hundred!'

The question was repeated, and this time the count was only three. 'Poor Aksentiev, you've only three years left,' they jokingly sympathized. 'Well, you'd best drown your sorrows and sing us something from "Askold's Tomb". That song—you know—"In the days of our fathers of old", or something like that.'

Ivan Aksentiev, a light-haired clerk from the distillery, took his guitar and, striking an attitude, sent his resonant tenor notes to join the birds among the clouds.

> *Near Slavyansk city*
> *On the top of a steep hill*
> *There lived a famous Boyar*
> *Whose name was Karachun*
> *And in his dizzy eyrie*
> *Like a bird caught in a gin*
> *Languished in captive sorrow*
> *The heart of a beautiful maid.*

The words and melody, the sound of a soft guitar, the setting sun, and the scent of the fertile fields, blended into one harmonious whole, and lulled all to listening silence.

Have you ever chanced to hear, on a quiet summer evening, a distant song, a Russian song, soaring heavenwards? Have you ever heard the water softly murmuring to the silver note of a guitar? When you listened, did not your heart seem to well over with a happiness which, had it endured but a moment longer, was like to shatter it and to put an end to earthly existence?

Vanya Puzanov was the first to break the spell. Leaping up with wild abandon, his eyes expressionless as a madman's, he began time and time again, without restraint, to declaim hissingly through his teeth:

> *Now die by the knife*
> *Of Prokopa Lapunova*

63

until, drenched with sweat, he collapsed exhausted and almost unconscious on the deck.

All was then quiet again, until someone hurled into the water a plate which, falling pancake-wise, sped over the ripples before sinking with a gurgle to the bottom. This was voted capital sport, and in a moment all the plates on the table were likewise sent skimming into the river, and any thrower who succeeded in making one perform 'ducks-and-drakes' before slowly disappearing into the depths, was greeted with rounds of applause worthy of a theatre. Another dozen plates were procured from the buffet to go after their fellows, until not one remained on board. The merchant-discoboli were still throwing the discus into the shallow waters, to the amazement of the gentle monks gathered together on the landing-stage, while the boat came gently up to her mooring.

Sacks of provisions, bottles, crockery, and a samovar were in turn dragged up to the monastery wall, where a camp had been established and a log-fire kindled, and all joined in a stupendous feast, to an accompaniment of vulgar choruses. Gushchin essayed an obscene story, 'Once upon a time a fellow was—' but was shouted down when he reached the savoury part:

'That's enough of your nastiness, Gushchin.'

'Better shut up altogether.'

'Come along, let's drink.'

A few moments later, despite general laughter and interruption, he essayed some dirty little tales about monastic life. Imitating the monks' nasal intonation he began:

> *'Name the three sweets of life'*,
> *The Hermit they asked*
> *And this the reply that they heard:*
> *'Sugar and wine are two, brothers mine,*
> *And a fine country wench is the third!'*

'That's enough! You're a low fellow, Gushchin. You wallow in dirt. Let's have just one more drink "to drown the worms"!'

Tempted by the sounds of revelry, some monks now joined the party; they had quietly scaled the monastery walls without being seen. They were received with open arms and warm embraces, and without more ado the remaining bottles were broached and more food unpacked. Feasting and drinking were prolonged throughout the night, and when dawn broke most of the guests were asleep under the willows; only Vanya Puzanov, who had out-drunk everyone, was to be seen conducting with a fork a group of monks gathered round the fire intoning in monastic manner:

> *We shall not go to early Mass,*
> *We'll be down in the cellars deep*
> *Trundling the giant barrels out*
> *And, filling our glasses to the brim,*
> *We'll sing the songs of Yaroslavl.*

and changing suddenly to the jolly everyday catch

> *And when I come upon the river*
> *And see it swiftly flowing by,*
> *Then, maybe, I there shall see*
> *My dear beloved pass my way.*

IX

GRANDMOTHER was aware of Yasha's dissipations, but never reproached him; she laid all the blame on his companions. Indeed, more than once she supplied him with funds, saying to herself as she returned to her housework, after having extracted some money from under the mattress, 'A young man must have his fling. We must bow to God's will. He will return to his senses and see for himself.'

Under the leadership of Vanya Puzanov a new diversion had been discovered, with the result that every night was now spent in a club, gambling for stakes which, though trifling at first, had latterly become extremely high. After one whole night of gambling, during which Yasha had experienced a continuous run of bad luck, Vanya, just as dawn was breaking, jumped up, shouting,

'God in heaven! There's a fire on Moscovskaia Street!' and truly enough from the window could be seen an ominous red glow. The cards were at once thrown down, and everyone rushed out to find that already half the street, including the best shops and the detached houses, was ablaze. Firemen wearing helmets and carrying axes were working like men possessed, scaling narrow ladders, hacking through window-frames and forcing their way into houses through the belching smoke. The devastating flames alternately died down and rose again, roaring with savage cruelty. The brave figure of the Fire-Brigade Captain was to be seen in all places at once, now shouting out a direction, now giving an order, vanishing one moment and reappearing the next in some totally different spot. The police and the garrison infantry endeavoured to keep back the crowd. Suddenly, maddened by the noise of the bystanders, the horses attached to the fire-engine broke their traces and bolted, and a pair of dapple greys, plunging wildly, fell and pinned Yasha painfully against a fence. He lay there thinking that his last hour had come. Before him he saw the quarters of a heavily breathing panic-stricken horse. At the same time he felt a gnawing pain in his leg. God grant that the beast did not kick again and smash the life out of him! He called to mind those heroes of his—Rocambole, Monte Cristo, and the rest. What fine fellows they were! They would never have lost their heads in a jam! Exerting all his strength he managed to seize the horse's crupper in both his hands, just as with a frantic struggle it rose, to its own evident surprise, and stood up on all fours. For a moment Yasha was suspended in mid-air, but, collecting his wits swiftly, succeeded in slipping to the ground. Rocambole had saved him! His leg hurt for a long time, but no damage had been done, and on his arrival home he never breathed a word about his adventure.

For the increasing energy of his young manhood, life still offered no outlet. More than ever, he spent his time gambling. It fascinated him to pit himself against Fortune, ignorant of the issue. Once luck favoured him; throughout a whole night's play he won. A countless number of notes overflowed from the table to the floor. When the game ended at daybreak Vanya, pale and trembling, rose and gazed vacantly through the window. Gushchin, though hiding his emotion, remembered with terror in his heart the sums he had embezzled from the factory's funds, and the thought of what would happen on the morrow struck him like a blow. Contemplating his last ten-rouble note, he consoled himself with the expectation that somehow he would manage to clear himself. Aksentiev continued to drink vodka as though nothing had happened.

It was already daylight when Yasha went out into the street. He had still to change from his evening dress before going to the shop. Street-cleaners and sewermen were already at work. The bells were ringing for morning mass. He knew that his winnings had been considerable, for his pockets bulged with notes, and even his top hat was stuffed with them. He had no idea of the total, since he had not troubled as yet to count.

He stole on tiptoe into the house, praying to God that his father would not hear his arrival. Apparently the house was asleep. It was quite light in the hall. The cat was dozing on the sofa. The muslin curtains fluttered gently. The waxed floor-boards creaked. Suddenly the door leading to his bedroom opened and Akim Ivanovich, attired in a dressing-gown and frowning fiercely, appeared in all his majesty. They met face to face.

'Yakov—Again!' The stern voice brought Yasha to a standstill. 'Look here, Yakov, I have stood enough from you! Do you imagine that you can go on gambling with card-sharpers? You seem to know how to lose my money. Scoundrel!' he added angrily.

'But, Father, it's nothing! Tonight, thank God, I won a bit'— and to his father's amazement Yasha turned out his pockets and scattered bank-notes in all directions, adding to them the contents of his wallet and top hat. Akim Ivanovich, in his astonishment, broke off his harangue in the middle of a word, and before he knew what he was doing, was on the floor, helping to gather up the money which, when counted, yielded a total of fifteen hundred roubles. In his confusion Akim Ivanovich did not know whether to praise or blame his son. At last he said:

'Well, that's all right now. But look me in the face and say that you will never gamble again. And now be off with you!'

It turned out that Grandfather had for a long time been on Yasha's track, and had discovered his new-found passion. He remembered how, many years ago, a landowner whom he had known had lost the whole of his fortune to card-sharpers and had shot himself when reduced to beggary. He knew that a passion for gambling was dangerous—'For every fool his folly'—and must be nipped in the bud before it was too late. There was no sin to which gambling did not eventually lead. Such were his thoughts as he paced his room restlessly.

'Yasha! Yasha! And always so quiet a lad! Well, there is no grief but that the devil sends it.'

For a long while the old man sat with bowed head, and at last decided that if it were impossible to put an end to the business, then at least everything must be changed, and changed absolutely. At last he hit upon an idea, and getting up, went to dress. It was time to set off for the shop.

X

IN the same street, but a little lower down the hill than where the gaily painted church flaunted aloft its ornate belfry, there stood in a spacious garden, surrounded by its servants' quarters and out-buildings, a detached house of considerable size, which had evidently once belonged to a country squire. It was built of wood on a stone foundation, and was faced by four tall columns, well-proportioned long windows, and in the middle an unusually broad porch. The style was that of the period of Alexander the First, that beautiful neoclassic 'Empire' style which had been imported into Russia from the west, and here simplified without any loss of essential dignity.

Stone had been replaced by any wood which lay ready to hand, and all the columns, capitals, and friezes, while conforming to the classical order had, when rendered in wood, a homely and intimate appearance. This type of wooden 'Empire' architecture had become so thoroughly established on Russian soil that it developed a native individuality all its own. Seen from a distance these houses, which were generally painted light ochre, with white columns and cornices, were in no way inferior to stone, and indeed wood seemed somehow to soften the hardness of outline inherent in that material. Apparently only in Russia and in the United States did this 'Greek Revival' style become so naturalized as fully to conform with its environment, whether in farms, manor-houses, or villas.

The interior of a house of this kind was always in complete harmony with its façade and general exterior appearance. There was the same strict regard for proportion, the same wealth of light admitted by high windows, and the same deep rooms with lofty ceilings and doors.

On the ground floor, leading from the broad porch, were found a lobby and footmen's rooms, which opened into a main hall, sparsely furnished with round tables, bureaux, and the like, against a background of pilasters, a painted ceiling, and a central chandelier. This hall was practically never lived in, and had the chilly atmosphere associated with formal receptions.

Adjoining it was the drawing-room, with an imposing array of hospitable armchairs, settees, stools, cushions, and work-boxes. Its wallpaper of blue with gold stars was relieved by portraits in heavy gilt frames, engravings mounted in blue-and-gold passe-partout, and mirrors in narrow frames hung symmetrically over the divans and in the spaces between the windows. Long comfortable sofas with backs and arm-rests of carved mahogany were set in the corners, and before them were round tables with crocheted covers. A fireplace or tall blue-tiled stove would be there, and in the evening, when the last rays of the setting sun fell upon the sombre portraits and were reflected in a glow upon the glass of the engravings, one felt a sensation of complete isolation from the world outside.

Next to the drawing-room was the study, which invariably revealed the character of the master of the house; and then the dining-room of strictly conventional type.

The upper floor was given over to bedrooms, boudoirs, and store-rooms. The attic storey was in most cases placed at the disposal of the younger generation, and here in small, narrow rooms life followed a different course, as often as not at variance with the traditions of the house.

Some twenty years previously the house of which we are now speaking had been put up to auction by a bankrupt country squire, and purchased with all its grounds, furniture, and fittings by one Okorokov, a merchant of the first rank.

He had made but few changes: he hung some indifferent family portraits in the hall, and replaced a partially nude Psyche by a portrait of a bishop of his acquaintance; Psyche was relegated to the attic. He also unwittingly ruined the noble proportions of the dining-room by partitioning it and adorning it with oleographs of Mount Athos and Korennaya, but on the whole he left everything else as in the days of the hapless squire.

Nikolai Alexeivich Okorokov belonged to a new race of merchants, since his frequent and often prolonged absences on important business ventures had brought him into contact with new men and manners, and had rendered him contemptuous of merchants of the old patriarchal type. He thought nothing of incurring risks in his undertakings and, whenever luck came his way, attributed it solely to his personality, his intelligence, and his knowledge of current affairs and of the weaknesses of the pettifogging folk around him.

'They have no initiative! They're dull! They pray to treestumps,' he would say unkindly of his neighbours, 'They hide their money under the floor-boards because they have never even heard of banks.'

He passed arrogantly from one speculative enterprise to another, until his self-confidence gave place to self-idolatry, obstinacy and tyranny. Thin, tall, with muscular hands, and black eyes peering from beneath beetling grey brows, he was always fashionably and carefully dressed, and looked more like the vice-principal of a department of state than a provincial merchant. In the few months that he spent with his family he succeeded in bending all its members to his iron will.

It was a large and noisy family consisting of twelve sons and two daughters, of whom the elder, having long been married to a prosperous landowner in a distant province, had now practically severed connexion with the parental home. Its remaining members were disposed in the attics. The younger daughter, the fourteen-year-old Olya, her father's favourite, was virtually mistress of the house.

Okorokov's wife was a small, ailing, prematurely old woman, who had long ago relinquished the reins of government. The despotic power of her husband, added to her constant childbearing, had made her a completely forlorn creature to whom nobody in the house paid the least regard. Outwardly, for decency's sake, she was accorded some of the respect due to a mother and mistress of a household, but even this concession seemed superfluous to Okorokov, who simply ignored her existence and was frankly intolerant of wife, children, and home alike. Only in the case of Olya did he make any exception, even going so far as to bestow an occasional caress on her. Though he spoke but rarely to her, and never admitted her to his thoughts or aspirations, he never failed, on coming back after one of his absences, to bring her a present or to remark on how she had grown, and on how pretty she had become.

Every now and then Okorokov would suddenly set off on his travels without giving a word of warning and, after staying away for any period from one to six months, during which he vouchsafed no news of himself, would return equally unexpectedly. It was known that he had business interests in the Black Sea ports, even as far away as Turkey. In the town, it was alleged that on the Black Sea coast he had another home and family, and that his absences were not therefore so much due to business as to new family responsibilities. Whether this was so or not, no one knew for certain, and certainly no one had courage enough to ask. By some the story was credited and by others doubted. For God alone knows what men will say between themselves, especially bachelors.

Once, for instance, a story was circulated about a number of friends of the merchant class who lived in harmony and love at Elets with their young wives. Everything went well with them at first, but at last there came a time when each successive day grew more tedious, with the result that they all decided to exchange wives. Thus, quite as a matter of course, they started brazenly to live with new wives! But lo and behold! Within six months all the wives had with one accord returned to their lawful husbands themselves, preferring apparently to be at home under the wing of someone they trusted! Only one, so went the story, took the wrong turning, 'slipped', and vanished. Everyone talks in a town, and what is true and what is false no man can say. So in Okorokov's case it may have been nothing but idle slander.

But, be that as it may, it once happened that Nicholas Alexeivich came back after a long absence in Turkey with a cartload of swarthy, black-eyed children. 'We were looking out of the window', Olya used to relate afterwards, 'and we saw Papa sitting in the barouche in front of the steps, but in a tilt-cart behind there was a crowd of swarthy children with eyes like coals. They grinned and showed their white teeth just like little animals. Our boys saw them from the balcony above and shouted, "Look! Look! Someone has brought a load of young devils! Hey you! You're devils—and some other god's devils at that!"'

Nicholai Alexeivich gave no explanation, but simply quartered the new generation from the East among the out-buildings on his ample estate. He had them all baptized into the Orthodox faith, gave them all Christian names, clothed and shod them all, and sent them to school. Gradually the members of this olive-skinned tribe settled down and made themselves completely at home, eventually entering various business concerns in the town, where in course of time many of them made their fortunes. Nicholai Alexeivich treated them all as sons, and never ceased to look after them.

More than ever before, the house now echoed to the sound of happy voices; quarrels, pranks, and games went on incessantly, and were only automatically interrupted as soon as the tall autocratic figure of Okorokov was seen in the distance, it being known that he did not like jokes, and punished even the most trivial act of disobedience by confinement in a dark box-room on bread and water. The true-born young Okorokov boys, the whole dozen of them, were subjected to exactly the same discipline, and in this respect no difference was ever made between them.

In the early morning, after breakfast, all twelve burst from the house like a flock of sparrows, and scurried off to the town. Carrying their reading and exercise-books, they ran along to the Provincial School, striking terror en route into the hearts of all small boys, who reckoned the united strength of 'Okorokov's dozen' invincible. Even grown-ups avoided their playful attentions. To smash in passing two or three panes of glass in an empty factory building; dexterously to filch an unripe apple from the orchard of the merchant Bakharin; to turn adrift a boat on the canal, were all in the day's fun to them. But as soon as they were within a couple of streets from the school, the 'dozen' pulled themselves up and assumed the innocent demeanour of novices hastening to mass. Quietly, and sedately, they entered the building and took their proper places in class, for in this school the cruel discipline of the Czar Nicholas's time, founded on the cane, the birch-rod, and solitary confinement, was in full force.

This tradition of Nicholas's permeated the whole school and shackled it hand and foot. Everything that was done was done for show. Lessons were learned by rote without any real understanding of their content. Religion was regarded as a subject apart, and in it pupils were failed their examinations by the dozen. The responsible priest was an oily-looking old man with a voice of honey, who meted out generous punishment left and right, and with sadistic sensuality invariably entered, with an almost caressing hand, the lowest obtainable mark in his pupils' books. Moreover, he made special note of absentees from church on Sundays, the punishment for such being especially severe. The Headmaster, a retired major, was responsible for deportment, to induce which he sweated the boys with drill-exercises as though he were preparing a provincial school for a military inspection by the Czar himself. The arts were taught on an out-of-date basis, and the composition of the teaching staff was lamentable. The teacher of literature openly drank to excess, and neglected his lessons. Besides, he had, when sober, a violent temper, for in such a condition he remembered his own drunken, wasted life, with its ruined hopes, and avenged himself on the young lives before him. But when he was only slightly tipsy there was not a better fellow, for he would then give up cramming his class with the intricacies of Russian grammar, and hold it spellbound by his talks on Karamzin and Sumarokov, or even by the occasional introduction of some censored work of Pushkin. The mathematics teacher, though invariably sober, was a dry-as-dust pedant of limited imagination.

Then there was Eremov, a retired sergeant-major, who had seen service under Nicholas I; a picturesque, talkative fellow who could not instruct in the military arts without physical application. Every Saturday, therefore, under his supervision the boys prepared a large collection of birch twigs, so that there might never be any lack of instruments for punishment, and armed with the same pedagogical equipment Eremov forthwith proceeded with his own hand to conduct 'operations' without a shadow of ill-feeling, after which he would chat amiably with his victims and console them with such proverbs as 'One boy beaten is worth two unbeaten'. 'Even a four-legged horse can stumble sometimes', and so forth. These punishments were never resented, but were rather regarded as an established custom, which constituted an important part of the school curriculum. Incapable but subservient pupils quickly established themselves in their master's good graces. The gifted either continued to attend 'operations' or were expelled from school without mercy.

'Okorokov's dozen' was a united band, the members of which never gave each other away or told tales to masters. Regarded as invincible by their fellows, any party to which they transferred their allegiance at once obtained leadership and emerged victorious from all scrapes and contests, including the pitched battles behind the brick works. The three eldest brothers, Nikander, Dmitry, and Platon, were renowned for pluck and ability and were, in addition, all tall, upstanding, and big-fisted; Vasily and Victor were cool and decisive strategists; and Peter, Alexei, and the rest constituted the second-line troops. The battles generally started out of almost nothing. An Okorokov scout would run and give some boy from the Parochial School a smack over the head, thereafter retreating under cover to his own forces. The Parochials retaliated and the fight was on. Were the Provincials in danger? Then Peter and Alexei restored their fortunes. Did the Parochials launch picked troops into an attack? Then Nikander, Dmitry, and Platon repulsed the invaders. The two ranks advanced against each other, skirmishing with varying success. They got to grips, and at last it was man-to-man! The struggle reached fever pitch as Nikander, his strong legs planted firmly on the ground, battled like Ilya Murometz and warded off blows from all directions. Platon was down! A shrewd blow was landed on Dmitry! The Provincials wavered, and were even battered into ignominious retreat. But then came the long-awaited moment when Vasily, rushing his reinforcements from the flank, swooped like a hawk from the sky, and with a cheer charged clean through the enemy ranks. The Parochials, unable to withstand this onslaught, faltered, broke, and finally fled in disorder to their own territory. Bravo, the Provincials! Hurrah for the Okorokovs!

Nikander, Dmitry, and Victor were soon dispatched to St. Petersburg and assigned to different businesses. Their absence noticeably decreased the fighting strength of the Okorokovs, and when, some time later, Vasily, Alexei and Peter followed them, the battles between Provincials and Parochials stopped automatically.

Most of the boys quickly set themselves up in the mercery trade. The eldest, Nikander, on leaving school entered the important firm of Goloftaev, a well-known St. Petersburg millionaire, and having been speedily promoted to a position of trust, gradually arranged for nearly all his brothers to be transferred to him. For Vasily alone did fate ordain a career of different sort. Even as a child he had outshone the others by reason of his exceptional ability and retentive memory, and he soon surpassed them both in school-work and in general conduct. His tall, shapely figure and wide-open blue eyes invited confidence, and his quiet energy, habitual tenacity, and powers of reasoning enabled him easily to surmount difficulties, and win the respect even of his teachers. His features had something aristocratic in them and his manners, though natural, carried an air of distinction.

Shortly before the Crimean War, a distinguished general had come down from St. Petersburg to inspect the Provincial School. The royal cipher on his massive epaulettes and his moustaches worn in the manner of Nicholas I inspired awe in the hearts of all the boys, and even filled the masters with alarm. Vasily Okorokov alone was as collected, polite and easy as ever. On entering the classroom where the boys were standing stiffly at attention, each in his own class, and hardly daring to breathe, the general greeted them by barking out in military fashion 'Greeting, lads!' to which they shouted the reply in unison like troops on parade, 'Greeting, your most High Excellency.'

Satisfied with this response, the general put a few questions to the headmaster, and surveying with a glance of disapprobation the crowd of teachers slouching in the distance, proceeded to summon the pupils individually to his presence, calling out their names, asking them trivial questions, and entering his observations in a morocco-bound note-book before passing on to the next boy. When the answers had been given, each was supposed to click heels, salute, turn smartly left about, and march to his own place, but most of them, in their excitement, forgot these military customs and executed their turns as awkwardly as bear-cubs, thereby causing the general to smile and the headmaster to show visible signs of annoyance.

When Vasily Okorokov was called, he was completely self-possessed, and even graceful in his movements, and having replied to all that was demanded of him, marched back deliberately to his place. Such show of spirit in a young boy, together with his prompt answers and unflinching eyes, delighted the exalted personage. The headmaster, too, beamed with satisfaction, and with a respectful bow ventured some remarks to His Excellency, as in a contented frame of mind the general made a brusque adieu to the boys who, lined up again at attention, shouted with one voice, 'Fare you well, your most High Excellency!'

Everyone breathed freely again, and as a result of the inspection, it was announced that Vasily Okorokov, for excellent progress, exemplary conduct, and manly bearing, had been awarded a State scholarship at the First St. Petersburg Cadets' College in order to study military science.

Vasily was quickly equipped for the journey, and went off like a duck to water. He was gone for many years.

For Platon, who had always been a surly and unsociable boy,

a less brilliant future was in store. Even from childhood he had loved to hoard money and carry all his capital on his person, so that whenever he was alone he could retire to some secluded corner and count over his coppers by the hour. This done, he would shake them up in a box and count them again. He showed no special aptitude for commerce, but everything that concerned figures, especially if money was involved, came easily to him, and would cause his eyes to glitter, his knees to shake, and transform him into a talkative and sociable boy. Okorokov, noticing this peculiarity, put Platon to work at a money-changer's in Elets, where within fifteen years he became proprietor, advanced loans, and opened almost the first pawn-shop in the town. He speculated, too, on a large scale, and had no scruples regarding risky or even shady transactions. To a certain extent he resembled old Okorokov, but he lacked his father's character and was more devoted to money, loving it for its own sake and never spending a penny on himself. His miserliness gradually developed into a mania, which at last completely dominated him. Despite the nearness of Elets he rarely went home, for he was aware that he had nothing in common with his family.

Nikander, tall, dark and clean-shaven, save for his carefully tended black side-whiskers, continued to enjoy Goloftaev's confidence. He, too, came home but rarely. He blossomed into the complete dandy, affecting the latest fashions of a Parisian *bon viveur*, with rings, checked waistcoats, befrilled cravats, striking neckerchiefs, and trousers strapped beneath the instep. Even his speech became interlarded with French idiom. He enjoyed great success with the daughters of the provincial merchants, though he spoke so affectedly and floridly, after the manner of a half-educated student in a seminary, that much of what he said was unintelligible to the local inhabitants. Nevertheless, he generally left a marked impression on more than one solitary female heart. Years later he met an unexpected end. While still in Goloftaev's confidential employ, and at a time when fortune seemed to smile, he apparently committed suicide. He was on business in a remote little town, and was occupying the best suite in the hotel, where he was seen to be in high spirits and chaffing the landlord. In the morning he rang for a valet, ordered hot shaving-water, and had already started shaving when, with a single slash of the razor, he cut his throat. The valet returned to find him clad in his sumptuous Persian dressing-gown, lying dead in a pool of blood, in the middle of the room. It was never discovered what had been behind this untimely end to his life.

Handsome, delicate, kind Alexei, who was loved by everybody, burned out like a candle, and died of consumption at the age of nineteen.

Peter, always a little strange, died in the Obukhovsky hospital.

And thus began to melt away that invincible force—the 'Okorokov dozen'.

XI

WHEN, following Vasily's departure to the Cadet College, all the young members of the terrible 'dozen' had one by one dispersed, peace reigned in the Okorokov home. Its rooms were deserted, its attics no longer resounded with voices, and as old Okorokov continued to absent himself, the only occupants of the big house, aside from the servants, were young Olya and her forlorn Mama, who rarely left her stuffy room, where even in summer the double window-frames for winter use were left in place.

Here, the leather-bound trunks filled with all kinds of stuffs, and furniture of every different style, were so piled up in every nook and corner that there was no space left in which to move. Such was the senseless and wanton profusion of vast chests of drawers and bloated armchairs, that the distinctive appearance of the Empire room had been completely lost, and it resembled nothing so much as a curiosity shop. And yet, to the heart of the old woman, all these possessions were precious because of their association with the past. She had never really liked the big, chilly house; to her it had always seemed unfriendly and its spaciousness superfluous. Only here, in her own little niche, surrounded by her own things, did she feel at home. Lying on her big wooden bed, with a mountain of pillows at her head, she was able to give herself up to mournful recollection of those past times which alone seemed to be endowed with beauty and tranquillity.

The present was incomprehensible to her, and full of anxiety. The past awoke memories of spring.

She saw herself again in her little white frock, sitting under the flowering cherry trees; her father, an arch-priest, seated on the verandah reading his *Episcopal Intelligence*, and waving an arm to drive away the insistent midges; her home full of peace, and plenty, and love.

'Where has all this gone?' she asked herself. 'How can it have vanished away like smoke?'

Before her arose another picture, that of her courtship—young Okorokov in his black frock-coat and bow tie, standing gracefully beside her chair, chatting to her father, the arch-priest; then their engagement, and later, the wedding and the honeymoon. And after that children, children, almost every year, and the agony of bearing several sets of twins. And then the constant absences of her husband, his cold severity, culminating in anger and contempt. 'Why? Why?' she asked herself, and found no answer.

She was profoundly depressed. It was too hot in bed. She had cramp in her ribs. She got up and wandered aimlessly about the room, stumbling against the furniture. At that moment Olya knocked at her door, coming instinctively to her aid.

'Lie down and rest, Mama', she said anxiously, endeavouring to comfort her.

The old woman climbed back into the bed she had just left and embarked upon an interminable lamentation.

'Olya, little Olya, how will you all get on without me?'

'Do not worry, Mama. We will live somehow or other,' Olya replied consolingly, smoothing the while her patchwork quilt.

'I do not know, I do not know,' the old woman mumbled pensively, apparently doubting anyone's ability to exist without her care.

So day followed day as she lay there, complaining, and yet taking not the least interest in the life of the quiet household.

At last Okorokov, on one of his return visits from Turkey, despatched Olya to the Finishing School for Young Girls of Noble Birth, founded by a French lady, Mlle de Muchel, and housed in a stone building, standing in its own grounds, opposite the Nobles' Assembly. This school was controlled entirely by the grasping hands of Mademoiselle, whose whole heart, nevertheless, was given up to her work.

Good manners, music, French, and handwriting were regarded as the corner-stone and fixed foundation of genteel upbringing, and the establishment was graced by the presence of the daughters of high provincial officials of aristocratic family. Olya was not, therefore, admitted at once, but only after much persuasion and argument, reinforced by Mademoiselle's appreciation of the value of money, and her knowledge of Okorokov's financial position.

It was, indeed, only after protest against breaking the rules of the school that Mlle de Muchel finally agreed to admit the daughter of a merchant as an exceptional measure and 'in deference', she added, 'to the sterling worth of M. Okorokov,' this sterling worth being the more obvious, and even tangible, because at the moment she was holding two bank-notes for considerable sums, which Okorokov had gently pressed into her tender hands.

Olya's fortunes were thus decided, and to her delight she took her place in the school where she was soon on good terms with the other girls, seeing that these young folk themselves did not attach much importance to questions of origin.

Life, which in the deserted rooms at home had at times seemed to her unendurable, had here the glancing sparkle of a fountain, and even Mlle de Muchel, for all her severely official appearance, was discovered to be an old maid with a generous heart and a real love for children, despite her own irretrievably lost hopes of motherhood. Certainly she did what she could, and, in the end, gradually supplanted the angular movements of growing girls by rounded suppleness, on which she grafted the manners of the solid French bourgeoisie.

Sciences were not treated seriously, being as it were just brushed with gentle wing, but dancing and music were accorded the highest places in the educational hierarchy; and when twice a week Monsieur Pique, a retired ballet-master of the Imperial Theatre, paid a three hours' visit to the school, the plaintive note of the violin was heard throughout the building. This Monsieur Pique was a little man with a bald head and incredibly developed calf muscles, who used to astound the girls by his athletic agility, his subtle ballet *pas* and his remarkable vivacious manner. Judged by his years, it would have seemed more appropriate for him to be sitting by a fireside with dressing-gown, carpet-slippers, and pipe, musing on earthly vanities, than tirelessly executing pirouettes for three hours at a time on a slippery floor. But, evidently, such was the nature of things, that the extraordinary *joie-de-vivre* of his legs defied the established laws of life, and would not leave the old man in peace.

In all his lessons, Michael Ivanovich, a decrepit old fiddler, accompanied Monsieur Pique. Entering the hall, black case in hand, he would deposit his ancient top hat under a seat, mop the perspiration from his brow with a checked handkerchief that was not very clean, open the case with yellow trembling fingers, bring out his fiddle from a cover like a patchwork quilt, and tucking it under his wizened chin, fill the ballroom with its rhythmically wailing notes. Fixing his eyes on one spot, generally somewhere on the ceiling, he could continue thus to play without pause throughout the whole of the lesson, as if he were a fully-wound-up metronome. The class was drawn up in four rows, the pupils wearing white frocks and ballet shoes. To the accompaniment of the fiddle, and with a chorus of 'One, two, three, four', all glided in unison over the polished floor, imitating the movements of Monsieur Pique and then essaying more difficult *pas*, maintaining a pose with feet outstretched. Many of them, however, failing to keep their balance, would fall down, whereupon Monsieur Pique would pick them up and demonstrate how a classical *chassé* should be done, for to him it was all entirely easy.

Exercises and *pas* did not enjoy much popularity with the girls, who adored the mazurka, quadrille, and lancers. Even the Irish jig which Monsieur Pique transplanted to Russian soil, though generally accounted strange and incomprehensible, was to everyone's astonishment executed with remarkable success by Olya.

At the close of the lesson Monsieur Pique demonstrated some

really breath-taking *pas*, relics of his former greatness, when he had appeared at the court of Alexander I. This done, he wiped his brow with a lace handkerchief, bowed graciously to the the company, and flitted like a butterfly from the ballroom, whereupon Michael Ivanovich, having played out his last note, wrapped up his black fiddle like a baby in its quilt, carefully laid it in its case, and with shaky steps made his exit.

The teaching of music was entrusted to an experienced and talented man, Monsieur Debuc, whose ballads and compositions had once been the vogue in the aristocratic drawing-rooms of two capitals. A virtuoso and talented composer, Debuc had been well trained by his father, a French *émigré*, and had shone in the highest society, but just when a brilliant future was being predicted for him something happened, no one knew precisely what, which caused him at once to withdraw from society, refuse all pupils, and eventually vanish from the horizon.

It was said that he had fallen madly in love with one of his pupils, the lovely Countess V., and that on proposing to her had been deeply insulted by her father, the haughty old Count; and that this treatment had so deeply wounded his Gallic spirit, offending both family pride and professional status, that he had, without another word, left the capital for ever. According to another version the Count did not come into the affair at all, and Debuc was expelled and banished to the provinces because at some very distinguished gathering he had forcibly expressed himself as opposed to serf-ownership in the hearing of the chief of the gendarmes. The first version was credited by the ladies, while the second found currency among men. But, whatever the truth, it was abundantly clear that his humble post in Mlle de Muchel's 'Institute' in no way accorded with his talent or his former reputation.

Debuc was now an old man—indeed for some reason all the teachers in the 'Institute' were old and venerable—and though he no longer appeared on the concert-platform, his beautiful ballads continued to be recognized and sung at evening parties, while his *Guide to Piano Playing* was known to every school-child. Yet owing to his obstinate refusal to enter society, no-one in the province had ever heard him play. His classroom manner was invariably rather serious, but he was able to instil a love of music into even the dullest pupils, and not one of them ever passed through his hands without having acquired real musical knowledge, including the ability to read music quickly, and a critical appreciation of the beauty of the classical composers.

Tall, invariably neat in appearance, with white hair falling down to his shoulders, Debuc was strict, though kindly, but as soon as he discovered in one of his pupils any spark of real ability he bubbled over with life, and spared neither time nor effort in kindling it further. On these occasions he adopted the animated, natural, and easy manner of a near relation, and such behaviour, when coming from him, contributed greatly to his pupil's success.

At first he seemed to pay but little attention to Olya, but one day, arriving somewhat earlier than usual, and pausing outside the door of the music room, he was surprised to hear from within the soft chords of an accompaniment and the natural, naïve phrasing of a young, and as it were muted, voice in whose sweet rendering of his own romance, dedicated years ago in St Petersburg to Countess V., was some quality which stirred his memory. Quietly opening the door he went in, and, even more quietly drawing up a chair, sat down and surrendered himself to the enchantment of his long-lost happiness. Olya, meanwhile, went on singing until, blushing to the roots of her hair with confusion, she suddenly discovered her severe instructor.

'Good! Mademoiselle,' he greeted her with a voice full of emotion. 'Yes, very good, little one. But here we must have that B minor,' and approaching the piano he indicated to Olya the offending passage. 'And here—not quite like that, but rather this way.' And unconsciously he sat down on the stool and played through the whole piece. Then, discarding the music, and brushing his hands through his hair, he began to improvise, while Olya, sitting some distance away, deep in meditation, drank in the flowing melody with all her heart.

The theme he had chosen was apparently the same, but on its canvas, as on a tapestry, was woven a pattern whose beauty amounted almost to pain, and whose phrases rose in elaborate counterpoint and then fell away to a barely audible *pianissimo*. Yet throughout the whole, with clear insistence, could be discerned a background composed of the same simple melody which Olya had just sung. Its effect was almost frightening, bordering on magic.

For the first time Olya was recognizing the majestic power of music. For the first time since his departure from St. Petersburg Debuc was playing in front of someone. There followed a long pause, during which both were silent—Debuc at the piano, Olya seated in the armchair—and from that day dated an understanding, and even a feeling of intimacy, between the stern musician and the young girl. It was indeed evidently in memory of that moment that Debuc dedicated to Olya one of his loveliest and most pathetic ballads.

Many years afterwards, while turning over some old music on a stall near Sukharev Tower in Moscow, one of Olya's old friends came across the yellowing pages of the complete collected works of a long-forgotten Debuc, and found inscribed on Opus 16, 'Dedicated to Olga Nikolaievna Okorokov'. Debuc had always been exceptional.

The other members of the teaching staff of the Finishing School for Young Girls of Noble Birth were undistinguished gentlemen of advanced years, who left little impression on the memories of their young pupils. But old age in her teachers was looked upon with favour by Mlle de Muchel, and with good cause.

A number of years previously she had made an experiment by introducing an educated young teacher of literature from the Cadet's College, and the result had been well-nigh catastrophic: indeed, the reputation of the school had been severely shaken, and the whole of that noble educational establishment had almost fallen in ruins round Mademoiselle's astonished head. It had happened in this way. Things had gone very well at first, and there had been a remarkably increased interest in native literature, especially among members of the senior class. Mademoiselle had been triumphant, and had even had thoughts of completely changing her staff. But the final results had been terrible, ending as they did in a full-blooded love affair, and almost in the open abduction of a pretty brunette, an advocate's daughter, from under the very nose of the vigilant Mademoiselle herself. A scandal indeed!

Since then the good French lady had resolved to be more careful, and hence revered old age alone received full right of entry to her establishment.

Oldest of all was the Professor of Calligraphy, M. Astapov, an ailing and boring old man, with enormous spectacles on his nose and a magnifying glass in his hands. It was somewhat curious that his copy-book work was regarded as of the very highest importance, and that handwriting demanded not only the greatest expenditure of time and patience, but also received still further encouragement by the award of the most valuable prizes.

Despite his antiquity, Astapov's steady hand, and the upright and beautiful letters traced by it in his pupil's copy-books, won universal admiration. Letters and sentences were copied an incredible number of times, until approved by the ever-dissatisfied taskmaster. The ability to copy in letters as straight and upright as a rank of soldiers a word like 'Attestation' was looked upon as the crown of calligraphic art, and the best examples of handwriting were displayed upon the walls for posterity's edification.

Olya used to come home from the school vivacious and excited, but the old, deserted house soon laid its heavy hand upon her and brought back a restless and despondent mood.

From her mother's bedroom the stream of tedious lamentation was now increasing all the time, for the old woman either talked to herself or carried on conversations with the canaries, which alone shared her loneliness and kept retiring in fright to the bottom of their cage, just as they were preparing to burst into song.

Olya would tiptoe to the bedroom to see whether she was required. From within came the droning voice of one bewailing her fate.

'You see, Nikander has gone away to St. Petersburg. Is that nothing but a trifle?'

Silence. The canaries chirrup. Again the droning voice.

'Goloftaev is a wealthy man, but what of it? Nikander is hot-tempered. He will not sit down under anything. Not a bit of it.'

'All right, Mama,' said Olya entering the stuffy room, 'Nikander has a head on his shoulders. No harm will come to him.'

The old woman, in no way deterred by Olya's sudden appearance, let her thoughts follow the same trend as when she was alone.

'Head or no head,' she mused in answer to her own thoughts, 'it is all the same. No good could come of it.'

A prolonged silence, the old eyes fixedly staring at the now silent canaries as if to hear their opinion. And then a sigh and:

'How will you all manage without me?'

Silence again, and then a sudden return to animation. Sitting up in bed as though some dear and near person were standing before her, she would continue to think out loud: 'Vasily, dear Vasily! My son! Your honour! A nobleman now. No commoner now. Serving the Czar! What a joy and consolation to your parents! But supposing war breaks out? God save us from war! What suffering there would be! But if you had kept a shop instead,' she continued monotonously, as if answering her own thoughts, 'there you'd sit quietly and sip some tea.'

'But, Mama,' interrupted Olya, trying to sooth her, 'Vasily is now a nobleman, an officer in the Guards, and his general is fond of him.'

'But we are still humble folk,' she added pathetically.

'Yes, Olya, but it all frightens me,' the old woman complained. So for a long time she would continue to fret as her memory turned to those twelve sons scattered to the four corners of the earth, living lives which she could never know. To her it seemed that without her maternal care and anxiety all must be engulfed by the temptations and misfortunes of the outside world.

At last she gave a yawn, and making the sign of the cross over her mouth with a wrinkled hand, mumbled, 'It's time to go to sleep.'

'So passes another day,' thought Olya mournfully as she nestled down in her own fresh, clean little room.

XII

IN her own light room Olya felt happy and free. Here everything remained almost as it had been in the days of the bankrupt squire, whose young and coquettish wife had used it as
her bedroom. Along the friezes Cupids disported, their anything
but innocent poses still symbolic of innocence. A bronze chiming
clock, a beautiful example of Empire craftsmanship, supported
by a bronze youth as handsome as Adonis, still indicated the
passage of time with ornate hands on a dial now growing yellow
with age. The four-poster bed, with its silk canopy resting on
lions' paws, and ancient metal adornments, called to mind the
Trianon and the Gardens of Versailles; and even more did the
narrow silk-upholstered armchairs set round a polished oval table
carry the imagination back to the far-off days of the Great
Revolution.

Olya's room, if one disregarded the family ikons, maintained
intact the spirit and ideals of a long but unforgotten past, though
to Olya it was a part of herself—a little intimate world which
she had known from childhood. The big oval mirror, in a frame
with a carved design inlaid in brass of torches and Roman
armour, faithfully reflected her familiar expressions, the way she
brushed her mass of flaxen hair, her little narrow-waisted white
frock, and her tiny silver-buckled shoes secured with black
ribbons. The morning sun peered in at all the windows and shone
upon the walls or glanced along the mirror to set the sunbeams
dancing among the trinkets on her little muslin-covered dressing-
table. Gloomy thoughts induced by her mother's illness, her
father's absences, and her own household cares, were then
alike dispelled, and gave way to faith in life with its joy and
gladness.

Every morning Olya leapt from bed, went to the washstand, and taking off her night-dress sponged her slender immature body with ice-cold water. Then, slipping on a lace wrap, she brushed her light hair, gazing the while with curiosity into her mirror. For every day she seemed to notice some change in herself. Sometimes she appeared to herself a little strange, and even remote, and she would ask her reflection: 'Heavens! Is that really me?' At other times she knew herself. Her greyish-blue eyes were her own, the parting of her hair was the same, and her breasts were as prominent beneath her thin wrap.

Agafia, the old housekeeper, came in with a tea-tray.

'Little one, are you up already?' was her astonished greeting. 'Come, little pigeon, and have your tea. What a fine day God has sent us! The air is so fresh.'

She sat down on the bed for her usual morning chat, and though Olya well knew that all the household management was really in Agafia's hands, she gave no sign of this knowledge, but rather like an Eastern princess, reclined on her bed and deliberately sipped her tea, as she commented upon the day's arrangements, and issued her customary orders. When this was done, she put on with Agafia's help the modest uniform of Mademoiselle de Muchel's 'Institute', consisting of a blue crinoline gown, white apron, and a broad white turned-down collar, and arranged her hair in heavy, snakelike plaits, which made a frame for her face and set off the graceful curve of her neck. Meanwhile Agafia stood by, listening to her final orders.

'Don't forget Mama's gruel,' Olya reminded her, putting her apron to rights and bestowing a hearty kiss on her kind old face. 'And don't let it get burned,' she added with a smile, hurrying into the hall while Agafia waddled after. Then, lightly gathering up her skirt, she tripped happily along the boarded foot-walk, for the street was unpaved and difficult to traverse in spring, while Agafia stood for some moments in the porch, watching her departing footsteps, before disappearing with a little involuntary sigh into the depths of the house. Agafia truly had her 'mouthful of worries'.

Olya was especially happy today. It was the height of spring. The new grass was sprouting at the bottom of the fence and the dandelions were bravely poking their modest little yellow heads through the crevices in the boards under the very feet of passers-by. The buds were bursting on the trees. The sky was one mass of translucent blue. Rooks, joyfully cawing, were flying in flocks from the trees to the lamp-posts. A white cabbage butterfly had settled on the old grey fence.

She fell to thinking of the rapidly approaching holidays and the end of her school-days. She was now in the top class, and only six weeks were left until the final examinations. She was glad, and yet a little sorry, as she thought of saying goodbye to her friends. They would all disperse, and who knew when they would meet again? It would be sad, too, to say goodbye to M. Debuc. Lessons with him had passed so happily, and she had put her whole heart into her music. In class she had done well, and even in French, which had been her worst subject, she had made good progress. Debuc was satisfied with her playing, and even praised her, impressing upon her the need for hard work as a means for success, and the iniquity of wasting her talent.

'You, Mademoiselle, will go out into the world and forget an old man like me,' he said half-jokingly, 'you will get married and give up your music. You will not be the first nor the last to do so.' 'Dear child,' he added, marking on the score her allotted task.

And she wanted to tell him so much, to convince that pensive old man that she would never forget either her music or himself, but she could not find the words.

Even Astapov, scanning with a magnifying glass the Bristol board submitted by Olya, on which had been written out beautifully many times the word 'Attestation,' remarked laconically but encouragingly, 'An excellent copy!' before putting her specimen of calligraphy at his right hand, as sure proof of his satisfaction.

She returned home excited, confident that some great event was impending, and sure enough, on the little round table in the hall was waiting a letter whose large envelope addressed in an elegant, even handwriting, betokened her brother Vasily, whose rare letters always possessed a special significance for her. So it was now. Impatiently tearing open the envelope, she read with delight that Vasily had completed his course at the Engineering Academy with distinction; had passed out top, and that his name would accordingly be permanently inscribed on the Golden Honours Board; that he had now been appointed to the Caucasus in connexion with the construction of the Georgian military highway, and that soon—chief cause for joy—he would be coming home for a few days on the way out, with one of his comrades.

To Olya the arrival of her brother Vasily, whom she loved above all the others, was an event of the first magnitude, and the news so excited her that she wanted to laugh, cry, and run wild, all at the same time. Rushing through the hall she reached the piano, and played with much gusto the Artillery March, with its vivid impression of galloping horses; then, jumping up from the stool, she deftly caught up her skirt and executed an Irish jig until she collapsed on the floor from sheer dizziness. The important sentence kept dinning in her head: 'I am coming home with a comrade on the way out.' Getting up, she returned mechanically to the piano and sang 'The Red Sarafan' in order somewhat to calm her nerves before she began to think things out. How to receive and dispose these guests? What sort of a man would be this mysterious comrade whom the letter so casually mentioned? And how to arrange everything so that young Guards' officers, spoilt by the life of the capital, should not be displeased? Would they criticize and poke fun at a little country miss?

Much to Olya's surprise, Mama did not display any visible pleasure on being told of her son's arrival. Truth to tell, the news did not greatly interest her, for the excitement, worry, fuss, and exercise of thought which it entailed, left no room for other emotion. 'With a comrade?' she exclaimed with a look of alarm. 'Where can we put him? How could he do such a thing with never a word of warning? With a comrade indeed! Does he think that this is a roadside inn?' In this strain the old woman chattered pointlessly on, while Olya consoled her by reading through the letter again, and explaining that not only would so large a house with so many rooms accommodate a regiment, but also that she would take all the necessary arrangements upon herself. 'You lie down and rest, Mamasha, and do not fret yourself,' she concluded soothingly.

Thereafter, in the evening, she discussed every detail with Agafia—where to put the noble young master and where the comrade, and the orderlies. What were Vasily's favourite dishes, and what his habits. At last, tired out by these long deliberations, she plaited her hair and went lazily to bed, where she was soon happily asleep, and dreaming that brother Vasily, as tall as a steeple, and his mysterious comrade, as handsome as the Adonis on her Empire clock, were singing a heavenly song, and that for some reason Astapov was there, too, dancing a jig with his magnifying glass in his hand.

On the morrow, at break of day, the floors of the spare rooms were scrubbed, the furniture rearranged, the muslin curtains changed, and over the bed in the room allocated to the stranger was draped a Turkish rug which depicted, on a pink background, two turbaned horsemen slashing at each other with curved swords—*ytagans*. Finally, a large collection of pipes with long curved stems was introduced, and a rich Bokhara dressing-gown of all the colours of the rainbow hung over the foot of the large bedstead.

Vasily's room was made gay with orange-blossom, and its whole floor covered with the rare and magnificent carpet which Okorokov had brought from Turkey along with his blackamoors.

Olya impatiently counted the hours until her brother's arrival. At last came the day when, looking out of the window, she saw a carriage, bearing two handsome officers, drive up to the door. She was too overcome by excitement to distinguish which was Vasily and which his comrade, or see Vasily quickly jump down and help his fellow-traveller to alight, while the orderlies busied themselves with the trunks, boxes, and dispatch cases. On seeing a beautiful young girl standing gracefully by the pillars Vasily flushed with excitement, and was so dumbfounded that he took an involuntary step back, unable to believe his eyes, thinking, 'Olya! can this really be Olya?' For he had left her a child, and now before him was standing a young woman.

Brother and sister ran to each other. Olya threw her arms round her brother's neck. The mysterious comrade, slender and sleek as a thoroughbred, surveyed the scene, feeling that he had no part in it.

'Why, darling!' Vasily exclaimed at last, 'you must permit me to present to you my friend and colleague, and I beg you to be kind and sympathetic towards him,' he added, apologizing for his earlier neglect with a flashing smile which showed his strong white teeth. Lieutenant Pereverziev brought his hand to his forage cap in a salute, and clicked his heels so that his spurs jingled. Olya curtsied with such grace as still further to astonish Vasily, who, as he watched the pair, was wondering, 'Where does she get it from? Only the other day she was just an ugly duckling!'

When they sat down to dinner Olya played hostess with tact and humour. She adroitly directed the channels of conversation and was discreet in her laughter. Vasily's amazement was more than ever intensified, since he had never even suspected the existence of that powerful arbitrator of fashion—Mlle de Muchel. In his secret heart he had been more than a little apprehensive about this meeting, and had felt somewhat shy about introducing so meticulous a friend into his unpretentious family circle. But now, sitting at table with Olya, he was as completely at ease as in any fashionable Petersburg salon. Even the conversation tended to centre round the capital, as Olya inquired about the Academy, the ceremonies at Court, the balls, and the latest fashions. Vasily narrated how once or twice it had been his good fortune to meet His Imperial Majesty, and how once he had been privileged to be questioned by him. The court balls he had attended but rarely, and then only as a matter of duty, since they held little attraction for him. 'And as for fashions,' and here he made a little deprecatory gesture, 'they do not come within my department!'

Changing the subject, Olya asked after all the brothers and Vasily addressed himself to giving a full account of them. Victor was married, and had set up in business on his own account, and apparently was doing well. Nikander had made a fortune, and was now generally out of town. Vasily had, however, caught glimpses of him sauntering along, dressed in the height of fashion, with diamond rings and cravats of fantastic cut, and invariably surrounded by a crowd of provincials.

Alyosha? Alyosha often dropped in to see him. He came ever so quietly and ensconced himself in a corner, where he listened in silence to what Vasily's brother officers were saying. They would call out, 'Come along, Alyosha, tell us something, and let it be good and strong!' and he would retire still further into his corner, smiling that sweet smile of his, and say, 'What stories can you expect from simple folk like me?' and again relapse into silence and listen. 'Yes, he has the gift of listening, which is more than we have! He is a quiet, lonely, unassuming fellow,' concluded Vasily as, with a glance towards Olya, he rose from the table, well satisfied both with his sister and the meal.

Coffee and pipes were handed to them in the drawing room, where the young officers sat with unbuttoned tunics, feeling as much at home as in their flat on the Ismailovskai Prospect. After a while they were joined by Olya, and the conversation turned on the Caucasus. Olya was alarmed by the thought of its dizzy precipices, surging mountain torrents, and fierce marauding tribesmen. That romantic 'fatal Caucasus' depicted in the poems of Lermontov and Pushkin, and the stories of Marlinsky, frightened and at the same time fascinated her. The officers laughed at her fears, and Pereverziev with deft broad strokes sketched picture after picture to illustrate the dangers of its life, its wild gorges, mountain rivers, and crazy bridges. The tale lost nothing in the telling as he spoke of blood-feuds, silver daggers inlaid with black enamel, Kabardinsky horses, lovely but unapproachable Caucasian girls, and the dangers which were for ever lurking behind every rock and tree. Olya listened with a sinking heart. Vasily smiled, twirled his moustache, puffed at his pipe and said little, confining himself to matter-of-fact enquiries generally concerning the Georgian military highway.

In the evening after supper they all went into the garden, Olya wearing a mantle and a little round hat, and the officers broad cloaks picturesquely thrown across their shoulders. It was cold in the evening, notwithstanding that it was the eve of Whitsun. In the garden all was quiet. The bright young moon was like a silver sickle suspended in the lilac-blue sky. The avenue of lime trees, deprived of shadow and relief, looked like an impenetrable wall. The weeping willow growing near a broken obelisk bowed down its branches in humility. The sand-covered paths turned left and right until, completing a circle, they came back to their starting point. There was neither motion nor sound. The young people were themselves silent. Vasily was thinking of his meeting with his mother, and of his shock at finding how old and infirm she had become in the last few years. He had not expected to find so great a change. It would, he thought, be impossible to present this infirm mother of his to a comrade. 'I will explain that she is too ill,' he decided, looking towards Pereverziev.

Pereverziev was walking along, with his hands clasped after the manner of Napoleon, thinking of the Caucasus, of the new life which he was about to start there, and of the sweetheart he had left in St. Petersburg. Though he loved her deeply, he found himself on this peaceful evening acutely aware of the proximity of another young girl, Olya, whom he barely knew. Olya was silent, immersed in her own thoughts and unable to explain the new sensations which were welling up in her heart.

The crescent moon, the mist blowing like steam across the garden, the stories of the Caucasus, and above all, the presence of the two young officers had produced in her a feeling of excitement such as she had never previously known. Everything now seemed to her to be moving to some determined, as yet unknown end.

So, almost without a word to each other, they paced mechanically several times round the garden.

When they got back to the house, the candelabra were already lit, a fire was crackling in the hearth, and Martishka the cat lay curled up, sleeping peacefully on the rug in the warmth of its glow. The officers, pleading fatigue after their journey, soon withdrew, leaving Olya sitting thoughtfully at the fireside, still under the influence of their silent walk. What was disturbing her? What had happened? Nothing! Why, then, this feeling of anxiety accompanied by joy? It seemed to portend something of unprecedented magnitude, to which the present moment was only the calm before the storm, a storm which would be so fierce as to overthrow and destroy all her hitherto simple and artless life. For hours afterwards, almost until daybreak, the painful impressions of that silent evening refused to leave her bedside.

Vasily, too, could not for a long time get to sleep, owing to the emotions evoked by his sad meeting with his mother and by the old familiar garden. Memories of his childhood haunted him, his father's sternness, the Provincial School, the pitched battles. And thereafter St Petersburg; the Cadets' College; the early rising to the call of a bugle; how with towels round their shoulders the cadets used to run pell-mell to the washing place, where each tried to secure the most convenient spot and the best bit of soap; the copper trough, long and straight, which had to serve thirty cadets, fifteen on each side, like a manger in a cavalry stable. The water used to flow in a gurgling, soapy stream, until some fellow would stop up the tap with the palm of his hand and let lose a cold spray which drenched the room and soaked their uniform trousers. What laughter and what oaths! He saw them all tending their close-cropped hair with army-issue combs, standing in a bunch before the solitary mirror; quickly buttoning up their tunics as they fell in in ranks; marching in quick time along the semi-dark corridor, with their footsteps resounding under a vaulted roof, and hideous shadows stalking along the walls beside them; the sergeant-major giving them the step with his 'Left, right, left, right.'

And then the dining-room, the immense square hall furnished with long brown painted tables and forms, with a separate table, covered with a clean cloth, for the officer-instructors; the appointed place for each cadet, before which was set a big jug of watery tea and a smallish round loaf on a tin plate.

It would still be dark outside at six o'clock in the morning, and one would long for sleep. How one longed for it! But life seemed much better after a drink of tea, or when eight hundred young voices chanted grace: 'I thank thee, Christ our Lord, who of Thy heavenly bounty hath given us our fill.'

There followed the memory of how in the senior class they had vowed to serve their country, deal justly, accept no bribe, subscribe no falsehood. Now that he was embarking on his new life, Vasily wished to prove that he had not forgotten that oath taken in the presence of his comrades.

Yet again his heart grew heavy at the thought of his sad meeting with his mother, until a sweet vision of Olya arose comfortingly to beckon him to deep and peaceful slumber.

Pereverziev in the next room for a long time tossed from side to side, at a loss to know why, for the first time, he had almost for a whole day failed to remember his sweetheart, and why all the time his thoughts had kept turning against his will to the white frock and flaxen head of a girl who, besides being a stranger, was quite outside his circle. Confused at last by his self-examination, he, too, settled down to sleep.

All were asleep, the old house was wrapped in slumber; even the canaries had long gone to rest. Only the old mother was still awake, worrying about this venture in the Caucasus. 'Is the Caucasus a mere nothing? Why, it costs a fortune even to reach it! Oh God, my God? Why must they go gadding about!' So the old woman mumbled in the darkness.

On the morrow Olya arose early in the morning. It was Whitsunday, and the cloudless sky was radiant with happiness. Everything promised a fine day, though in Olya's experience Whitsunday was rarely fine. She tried on the new dress which her brother had just brought from Petersburg. She carefully

arranged her hair with its central parting and put on her golden
drop ear-rings, also a present from Vasily. Then she adjusted
her crinoline and went over to the oval mirror, in which she
could not recognize the graceful young girl with sloping
shoulders, attired in a silk dress of faultless cut, who looked
out at her. She caught her breath and smiled at this unknown
stranger, and then quickly dropped her eyes in admiration of
the girl who faced her. Agafia, coming in at this moment with
the tray, gave one gasp of astonishment and sat down so precipi-
tately that she all but dropped the tea-things at her mistress's
feet. She fingered the material lovingly, and finally came to the
conclusion that it was of the finest possible quality, that its
little roses on a white background were like cherubs flitting
about the heavens, and that, in short, there was not in the whole
town the equal of her young mistress.

Pleased by this eulogy, Olya went away singing. In every
room, freshly cut silver-birch branches had been placed against
the walls. In all their green finery they looked like brides in
white dresses, or, when standing close together in the corners,
like groups of shy peasant girls.

The officers came out wearing their full-dress uniforms,
dazzling tunics neatly gathered at the waist by silver belts,
epaulettes, tight riding breeches, shakos with tall horsehair
plumes, swords dragging along the floor, and jingling spurs.

The church was all decorated with wild flowers and birch
branches and, as they entered, all eyes were turned on the officers
of the Guards. When, soon after, the joyous service was over,
Olya was surrounded in the porch by her friends from the 'Institute', all of whom wanted a closer view of these officers from
the capital. Proud of their general attention, as well as of her
two cavaliers, she returned the greetings of these acquaintances
with more formality than usual. Akim Ivanovich and Yasha,
standing on one side, surveyed the brilliant trio from a distance.
Grandfather had long observed this daughter of Okorokov's,
and knew everything that there was to be known about her.
Satisfied with the accounts he had received, he had long coveted

her as a bride for his eldest son, and was now only waiting for
the arrival of old Okorokov in order to agree upon terms,
shake hands on the bargain, and celebrate the marriage. As
regards Okorokov's consent he had no doubts whatever. Olya
acknowledged with a curtsey his affected bow and, with a
kindly inclination of the head to Yasha, quickly made her
departure to the accompaniment of the clinking of spurs and
the clatter of swords.

At home a festive dinner was waiting—game pie, roast goose
and kasha, a quivering blancmange, a cake as light as air, and
bottles of champagne swathed in table napkins, raising their
narrow necks in pride. Vasily was in high spirits and full of
jests. Pereverziev was pained more than once to catch himself
involuntarily stealing frequent glances at Olya, who was spark-
ling with vivacity.

After dinner Olya played for some time and talked of M.
Debuc, some of whose ballads she even sang, in a voice that
was tender and a little sentimental. Pereverziev, striking a
picturesque attitude, leaned heavily on his sword and listened
attentively, with apparent approval. Olya's joy and happiness
knew no bounds.

But all good things come to an end, and two days afterwards,
the officers set off. Vasily tenderly embraced his sister, and
promised to send her a Caucasian shawl, some silver and black
enamel bracelets, and even an inlaid dagger. Pereverziev,
before his departure, seemed to Olya to be always trying to
say something to her, and more than once he endeavoured to
be alone with her. He left, however, without saying anything
important. Only when the horses had been brought round he
kissed her hand with peculiar reverence, gave her a look full
of meaning—and, clinking his spurs for the last time, got into
the carriage.

XIII

AFTER the departure of the officers, life in the Okorokov house followed its accustomed course, only Olya used to cry occasionally in bed, without knowing why she did so.

Returning unexpectedly as usual, old Okorokov had been delighted to hear Olya's account of his son's visit, and made her repeat several times in detail how they arrived, what they did, and what they talked about. Olya tried to remember every trifling incident in order to satisfy her father's curiosity. He was proud of his son, because in his secret heart he regarded his son's success as a tribute to his own genius and personality. No other father, in fact, could have produced such a son, and this thought made every reference to Vasily exceedingly gratifying to his vanity.

After the closing ceremonies at the 'Institute', Olya came home with her diploma, in a gloomy and depressed frame of mind. A whole period of her life had come to an end. What had the future in store? For all the girls in her circle life held only one goal, that of marriage, and the idea of becoming an old maid was accounted a disgrace. As she sat at home, playing the piano, or busying herself with housekeeping, it was natural that thoughts of the future should call up visions of some noble young officer or landowner. Invariably the vision was one of a man of noble birth and not of humbler merchant origin, for more than ever after the visit of the officers did 'her nobleman' figure in her dreams, and the less interesting did she find the young men of the town. She was aware that many eyes were turned towards her in church and in the street, and she lacked no evidence that she was much admired, but as yet no firm suitor for her hand had appeared upon the scene. Now, however, they began to arrive, having first put out tentative proposals through the medium of a matchmaker.

'You have the goods and we the customers,' the matchmaker would remark diplomatically to Okorokov, as she sat sipping tea from a saucer in the formal drawing-room, while endeavouring to convince him how attractive was a certain proposition. But Okorokov would demur, saying that Olya was still young, that the goods would be none the worse for lying a while in the shop, and that in short he was unwilling to hurry her. In accordance with established tradition, however, he never interrupted the matchmaker, but gave her back proverb for proverb, and regaled her with tea, until she departed with a wry look on her face at having received no definite reply. Nevertheless, on a Sunday following one of her visits, the piebald horses of the Distillery Company came dashing up to the Okorokov house, and from the step of a light gig there fluttered like a butterfly the faultlessly attired, perfumed, nimble form of Paul Alexeivich Gushchin, who with a preliminary flourish of his cane darted into the entrance hall. With well-rehearsed courtesy, and studied self-assurance, he made his bow before a somewhat confused Olya, and in honeyed tones tendered inquiries concerning the health of her mama, her brothers, and the master of the house. Okorokov received the dandy coldly, and on learning the object of his visit, met him with a point-blank refusal. Surprised at so definite a refusal, Gushchin was at first completely abashed, and even dumbfounded, but soon recovering and pulling himself together, he ventured a few observations on the weather before beating a retreat in such haste that he forgot his cane.

'What a popinjay! Dancing about like Stryutski!' Okorokov muttered to himself as he stalked up and down his study in a transport of rage. 'A plague on his bow legs! What gentlemanly airs he gives himself! "We are," says he, "a limited company, an anonymous society." Well, brother, say I, when a business is anonymous, it's a rotten business! It's reached its

limit! *Kaput*, as the Germans have it! Limited company, for-
sooth! As like as not it hasn't fifty kopeks to its credit! Ah,
Gushchin, Gushchin! One of these days you'll be giving yourself
airs and graces without a pair of breeches to your name! And
you won't have to wait long, either! And yet you're thinking
of marriage! "Give me your Olya in marriage," says he.
"What?" said I, "Do you mean my daughter Olya? See here,
Paul What's-your-name, you've taken leave of your senses!
Good-bye—and there's the door!" And he shot out as though
he'd been scalded,' Okorokov chuckled maliciously, recalling to
mind the final scene.

Of the object of Gushchin's visit Okorokov never breathed
a word to Olya, who got to know about the dramatic refusal
many years afterwards from Gushchin himself. As for Okorokov's prophecy, it was fulfilled almost literally word for word.
The limited company shortly afterwards went into liquidation,
and Gushchin, its one-time brilliant director, lost everything,
and was frequently in want even of a second-hand pair of
breeches. On the strength of former friendship he would
often drop in on his old acquaintances to remind them of the
old days and, in the end, would be supplied with the necessities
of life.

There were other pretenders to Olya's hand, but Okorokov
remained obstinate in his refusal.

There came a day, however, when Akim Ivanovich called,
apparently quite casually, at Okorokov's shop. The two old men
had known each other from childhood, and each had a thorough
knowledge of the character and standing of the other. Though
they rarely met, there was no ill-feeling between them. Grandfather, for instance, knew of Okorokov's embittered outlook
and of his loose living in Turkey, for 'the world is full of
rumours', but nevertheless he appreciated his enterprise and
common sense. Okorokov, for his part, had scant regard for
Grandfather's antiquated turn of thought, but gave him full
credit for his honesty and fair dealing. After a business discussion, during which they both bemoaned the hardness of

the times, they rose and went off to the inn, where their
arrival occasioned great stir among the waiters, and caused the
landlord himself to come and pay his respects to two such
distinguished merchants who were rarely seen together. Grandfather opened the conversation by discussing the mayor of the
town and other matters of local interest, imperceptibly brought
it round to Olya, and then, after reference to his own Yasha,
gradually disclosed his whole plan, while Okorokov listened
attentively.

Following Akim Ivanovich's every word Okorokov was, as
the conversation proceeded, making a mental summary of the
advantages and disadvantages of the scheme; but pretending not
to understand whither it was leading, he endeavoured to escape
the necessity for a definite reply by limiting himself to non-
committal phrases, which soon broke the thread of the discussion.

Grandfather fully realized the commercial astuteness of
his companion, but considered it beneath his dignity to put
his question bluntly, and thus deferred any decision to
a more convenient time. Having settled the bill, each
went home on more friendly terms than they had ever been
before.

Okorokov on his return thought over Grandfather's project,
and found it not at all unsatisfactory and quite capable of
realization. No one had a bad word for Yasha. He was a reserved,
hard-working lad, and he was not given to drink. Moreover,
Akim Ivanovich would be open to reason in the matter of the
dowry when that point was raised, and latterly money was more
than ever uppermost in Okorokov's thoughts. His latest specu-
lation was causing him much anxiety, and there was risk of
scandal and, God forfend, of bankruptcy. 'What would happen
to Olya in such event?' he asked himself, and the idea of placing her at once in safe hands seemed both expedient and
wise. Naturally he had not wished to betray any of this
to Akim Ivanovich, lest the crafty old fellow should smell
a rat, or, worst of all, retract altogether. That was why,

when sitting in the inn, he had so adroitly avoided the main issue.

Meanwhile Akim Ivanovich, sitting in his office before his ledgers, was also thinking out the details of his inspired idea concerning Olya Okorokova. Here was a girl, he mused, who was not only young, healthy, and clever, but was also capable of running a whole household. 'Okorokov is shrewd, but no shrewder than I,' he smiled to himself, 'I could tell by his eyes that he would come to terms and surrender the girl. It is not as if she were going to just anybody, she is going to a good solid family.'

'He thought,' he added with a chuckle, 'that I could not make out how the trend of conversation changed after tea! The old rogue! It was all quite simple to me! I know all about his crazy ways, he's on a tight-rope! If not today, then tomorrow he will be proclaimed a bankrupt. Any man would give his daughter in marriage to my Yasha. He's no Treasury clerk, or starveling officer with not so much as a pair of breeches to his name! He's not just anybody. He's the son of a merchant and a future proprietor! I was shrewder than that old devil —God forgive me!' and crossing himself, Grandfather leaned back in contentment like a sagacious commander-in-chief on the eve of a decisive battle.

'Yasha!' he called to his son, pushing the door ajar, 'Will you see that a salmon—and a big one at that—is sent round as a present to Okorokov. The best piece in the shop!'

'I'll see to it, Papasha,' replied Yasha, raising his eyes from an interesting book, which he concealed under the counter, just in case.

On receipt of the magnificent salmon, Okorokov realized that Akim Ivanovich had seen through him. He thanked him in writing, but made no other sign, and shortly afterwards set off on one of his usual journeys. The betrothal, to all appearance, had fallen through and come to nothing. Even Grandfather began to have doubts, but decided to wait patiently and lay siege to Okorokov.

Winter was now gradually approaching, and by November there was already a keen frost. The snowfall this year was exceptionally heavy, and the sleigh-roads were now firm. Vanya Puzanov, now an amateur actor of repute, having appeared more than once with Fedotova and Sadovski, arranged sleigh-parties and transported all the young people to Korennaya, where the gipsies were performing.

Near home an ice-slope was erected on the frozen river, and a space surrounded by fir-trees was cleared for a skating rink. These fir trees, which were simply thrust down into the snow on four sides of a square, lasted wonderfully well all through the winter, and made the big quadrangular rink visible from a great distance. On Sundays a military band played there. Its brass instruments glittered in the sunshine; the sound of horns rang bravely through the frosty air; the trombones grunted laboriously as though suffering from cold, and failed to keep pace with the brisk melody of the lively clarionets. Everyone was gay, and the keen air was good to breathe.

Olya was like a child in her enjoyment of these hours of freedom with young friends. It was generally Yasha who fastened on her skates, or standing upright fearlessly piloted her sledge down the ice-slope. Catching her breath and inclining forward her pretty head with its cap of white fur, she frequently clutched his hand in alarm; and when the sledge, after negotiating some perilous dip, went bounding down the precipitous course, until it seemed that nothing could arrest its headlong flight, she was filled with pleasure and fear alike. This, however, never deterred her from wanting to repeat the exhilarating rush, and so, often happy and tired, they would re-ascend the slope in order once more to experience the fascinating feeling of terror.

On skates the acknowledged virtuoso and artist was little Gushchin, luckless in love, whose chicken-legs, clad in tight checked breeches, cut such capers that the onlookers could hardly believe their eyes, and were quite afraid to watch him.

On the ice he seemed to avenge himself for the failure of the fair sex to recognize his true worth. When, however, it came to racing, the winner was invariably Vanya Puzanov. Olya skated with grace and was able to dance a quadrille on the ice, and it was thus that she and Yasha often met and were unconsciously drawn towards each other. For although Vasily with his uniform and polished manners remained her ideal, she found something in Yasha's simple modesty which was far from displeasing. Every day she discovered in him a friend with whom it was pleasant to laugh.

Occasionally, too, they would meet in church and, after vespers, Yasha would see her home, while Agafia, who was not admitted to their conversation, followed at a fit and proper distance behind. It was still light when they returned after these Lenten services, with the solemn liturgy ringing in their ears, and the outside air was sweet to breathe after long standing in the close atmosphere of the church. Everything was rich in the promise of approaching spring, and gave birth within them to new and confused thoughts.

Olya loved the liturgy of Lent. When the old priest in his black-and-silver vestments solemnly recited the prayer, 'Give me the spirit of purity and meekness, of patience and love,' she would shudder and make so deep a reverence, that her head touched the cold floor as she prayed for mercy. The inexorable words of the prayer were terrible in their prophetic warning, and brought home the urgency of intercession for sin in order to escape fearful retribution.

The sombre, joyless Lenten prayers, the church in semi-darkness, the unfamiliar black vestments of the clergy, oppressed her heart, and made her feel as though from on high an unknown voice, pealing like the trumpet of an archangel on the Day of Judgment, was crying to her 'Repent'.

She almost became ill. Her body lost all sensation, her head began to swim, but her soul within was bright and as it were purified. As she got nearer home, walking over ice-covered puddles on the frost-bound road, the more keenly did she feel the pleasure of a duty done.

Throughout the course of Lent a strict fast was observed. Pasties of dried mushroom, fish, potato or rice cutlets with sweet sauce, and *kvass* to drink, formed the fare regarded as essential for subduing the sinful flesh.

During the fifth week Olya attended the early-morning service when it was still dark. Few people were then in church, and the deacon's monotonous voice repeated the long service as though it were something he had learned by rote. There followed the late mass attended by a larger congregation, and finally vespers. So it was every day for six long days, until Olya grew wan from the consciousness of sin. During this time she never played the piano nor sang, but tried to concentrate all her thoughts upon the sublime significance of the present season.

On the Saturday before Palm Sunday Olya made her confession. Behind a curtain over the sanctuary door to the right of the altar, Father Eulogy, in black cassock and a single stole, received the penitents who were standing below the lectern. Awaiting her turn, Olya tried not to forget any of her transgressions, but at the last moment she was seized with confusion and resolved only to answer the questions put to her by the priest. Her turn came, and after making preliminary reverence, she approached the steps to stand with her soul bared in the presence of her confessor.

'Have you honoured your parents?' The voice was unrecognizably severe.

'In this, Father, I have sinned,' she replied.

'Have you honoured your teachers and mentors?'

'In this, Father, I have sinned,' she answered, remembering how she used to laugh at Astapov.

Father Eulogy was so austere that he no longer seemed to be of this world. He prepared himself to put the most difficult question of all; looking from under his lids at Olya, whom he knew so well, he demanded:

'Have you transgressed in your desires towards the male sex?'

'I have sinned,' she whispered barely audibly, as, covered with blushes, she recalled how she had gazed at the handsome Pereverziev.

Father Eulogy refrained from asking further questions, and covering her with his stole, made the sign of the cross as he pronounced, 'I absolve and forgive.'

Immediately Olya felt that all her difficulties had been swept away and had disappeared. As he took her silver coins the priest looked less official. He even inquired after her mother's health. She left the church radiant. Her whole body seemed buoyant. 'Repent and pray,' she remembered. She had repented and was now as pure as an Angel of God!

On the morrow, after Mass, in the festive church where the choristers sang so well, Olya in her becoming little new frock glowed with the radiance of youth. People turned to look at her. Her friends gaily greeted her, felicitating her with joy on having participated in the sacred mysteries. Yasha, too, was among those who took communion. As Olya went home she felt serene in her freedom from sin and in her crystal purity.

On Good Friday her meditations reached their climax in the solemn church service, and in reading of the twelve Apostles. She experienced then an ecstasy beyond which the soul could not travel nor the body, weakened by fasting, endure. The services were fatiguing not merely because they were long, but more especially because of their vivid dramatization of the tragedy which they commemorated. Advancing to the centre of the church, every priest in turn read at the lectern a chapter of the Gospel, each in his own manner, giving his interpretation of Our Saviour's Passion, until the imagination welded this recital into one vast and clearly depicted representation of the world's most overwhelming tragedy. Kneeling in a semi-stupor, Olya relived with her whole heart the sufferings of the Son of

Man. The measured words of the saintly Evangelist fell upon her ears:

'And Peter remembered the word of Jesus, which said unto him, Before the cock crow, thou shalt deny me thrice. And he went out and wept bitterly.'

Before her arose a vision of Peter, 'strongest of them all', shamefully denying his Master. 'I would not have denied him,' she thought. Then calling to mind her own confessions, she shrank in horror at the revelation of her sins.

As in a trance she heard:

'And about the ninth hour Jesus cried with a loud voice saying, My God! My God! Why hast thou forsaken me?' Endurance could go no further. Without a sound she collapsed into Agafia's expectant arms. 'Come, come, my little angel, you've only fainted,' whispered Agafia, full of sympathy and comfort as Olya recovered consciousness in the porch. She felt utterly weak, her legs refused to obey her, there was a ringing in her ears. Quietly they proceeded home, Agafia anxiously supporting her young mistress, deeply touched by her weakness, which she took to be only the result of prayer and fasting.

Next day Agafia, her sleeves rolled up, was in command of the kitchen, where a thousand things were calling for her attention—roast goose and cabbage, jellied sucking pig with parsley and slices of lemon stuck in its foolish gaping mouth, various *zakuski*, pickles, and savoury dishes. All these treasures were now resting on tables, covered with white napkins, so as not to be touched before the fast was ended.

On the night before the dawn of Easter Sunday, Olya dressed herself with a special care. Her dress, as white as snow, had been lovingly laundered by Agafia's own hand, and now lay on a chair, as though resting in expectation of its owner. Her favourite drop ear-rings were set in the place they coveted. All was ready much too early, and Olya impatiently waited for her father in the somewhat chilly hall. Seeing her there, warming herself by the fire, even old Okorokov smiled to himself, and, remembering an engraving he had once seen somewhere, thought, 'She looks like "Undine".'

At midnight the church was brilliantly illuminated by a thousand candles in whose light the ikons gleamed. The clergy were robed in rich bright vestments. The congregation in their diverse dress stood in dense rows, and everywhere was manifest a spirit of joyfulness. And when a resounding voice proclaimed, 'Christ is risen!' and the cry was caught up by the choir in the sanctuary, such a transport of almost childish happiness flooded Olya's heart that she wanted to embrace the whole world.

The service concluded, the priest hastened to the porch as though to meet the end of the festival, and there blessed the *paskha* and *kulich*, which were set out on the tables. The congregation dispersed with smiling faces, felicitating and saluting one another with the Easter kiss. Yasha shyly came up to Olya, and, clasping her hand, kissed her three times. More than ever did he now find favour in her sight, and that little mark of intimacy founded on a tradition of centuries seemed to stamp him as a member of the family.

At noon Okorokov paid a call on Akim Ivanovich, though the proud old man had never before been known to pay a visit of felicitation on anyone. After spending a minute over a glass of wine, while Grandmother hospitably regaled her other guests, he buttonholed Grandfather. With frowning face, and speaking with difficulty as though his words stuck in his throat, he said, 'Have it your own way, Akim Ivanovich! Only don't be extortionate over the dowry. Business, brother, is rotten!' Then, without venturing any further details, he retired to the window. Grandfather immediately realized that his plan for Yasha had succeeded, and that its success was partly due to Okorokov's finding himself in straits. In point of fact, Okorokov's doom had been sealed one day, a week before Easter, when he had returned home stooping and looking suddenly aged. His bank in Tula had unexpectedly failed, and he was now faced with ruin. It was this that had prompted him to sink his pride and hasten to clinch the matter.

At the same moment, before an immense table tastefully laid with *zakuski*, jellies, and cakes in Okorokov's dining-room, Yasha, in frock coat, was blushingly stammering out tender words to Olya, who was neither blushing nor confused. Trustfully and candidly she looked into his eyes, and when, after eating his *zakuski*, he recited in a sing-song voice some verses he had heard in vaudeville, she laughed aloud like a child. Yasha took his leave, drunk with his love and filled with thoughts of her.

Olya could not restrain her laughter, but walked the length of the room repeating Yasha's rhyme:

> *For years have I wanted my love to declare!*
> *My devotion no longer to hide,*
> *But always at last I am seized with despair,*
> *And always lack strength to decide.*
> *If I find you alone, do my hot words come gushing?*
> *No! Like carrot or lobster I just stand there blushing.*

Her peal of merry laughter rang out afresh, despite the fact that Yasha had chosen this ridiculous verse not with the idea of causing her amusement, but because its every word represented the feelings of his heart far better than any divine flight of poetic fantasy. Olya instinctively knew this, and for all that she gave a little sigh as her memory turned to stories of chasms, and torches, and marauding tribesmen of Caucasus; she quickly consoled herself with the thought, 'But then my Yasha is such a nice quiet boy.'

When on his return old Okorokov disclosed to her his indisputable decision, he was more than a little surprised by her ready acquiescence. He had expected difficulties, and had come prepared to exercise the full weight of his parental authority, and now it was apparently quite unnecessary.

'Well, that's strange,' he thought, as he paced up and down his study. 'There's no accounting for the ways of a young girl.

Her head completely turned by smart officers, and yet when it comes to the point, she's ready to marry a merchant's son! It's miraculous.'

A month later, in the summertime, the quiet Yasha was to lead young Olya to the altar of the gaily painted church.

XIV

GRANDMOTHER, Praskovia Feodorovna, learned of Yasha's destiny as soon as Grandfather and Okorokov had reached final agreement in the matter, and the news so moved her that she shut herself up in her room in order to compose her thoughts in solitude.

Drawing the muslin curtains so as not to be seen from the street, she sat down on her bed and fell to thinking. She disliked the Okorokovs. The old man was conceited and boastful, and the stories of his adventures in Turkey reflected no credit upon him. Whether what people said was true or false she did not know, but she had learned from experience that 'there's no smoke without a fire'.

His old wife she did not blame so much as pity, but, all the same, she felt an instinctive prejudice against her. There was something wrong with the female side of the family, no one knew just what. The girls all started by being kind and reasonable creatures and ended in a sort of dotage, growing old before their time. Okorokova now was the image of what her mother had been when she had died quite worn out. It might not happen again, but nevetheless Grandmother felt grief and alarm for Yasha, her first-born.

Although Olya Okorokova was evidently and according to all reports a well-behaved, modest, and hard-working girl, Grandmother's heart did not warm towards her future daughter-in-law. 'What if the same thing should happen again?' thought the old woman, glancing up at the ikon of the benign Saviour.

The warm wine-red glow of the ever-burning ikon lamp comforted her a little, for surely God, merciful and omnipotent, would not allow such tragedy to come to pass. She had known almost a lifetime of peace and tranquillity with her husband, and during it all Christ, her own Christ, illumined by the kindly light of that lamp, had shielded her from misfortune and unhappiness.

Sinking to her knees, she prayed passionately to her dear, kind, and merciful Saviour, beseeching him from the depth of her soul to guard her first-born, her beloved Yasha from grief and sorrow.

Strengthened by this simple, fervent prayer, she rose from the floor, and settling down again on the bed gave herself up to material thoughts concerning the young folks' comfort.

Grandfather, when telling her of the early marriage, had said that the young couple would live with them, and now it was for her carefully to think out every detail, so as to ensure that both young and old should be housed with all possible comfort and yet secure the greatest independence.

As the second storey was more commodious, as well as lighter, she decided that Yasha should be installed there, and that she and Grandfather should be disposed downstairs. Although it was less comfortable there, and the windows were smaller, she consoled herself with the thought that 'we old people want nothing more'.

Yet it was hard for her to give up her bedroom, where for nearly thirty years everything had known its own place, where she had brought her first-born into the world, and where during the length of a lifetime she had found such happiness. But the thought of the young couple, of her Yasha's future comfort, made her put aside any other plan.

In imagination she was already changing the furniture around, deciding what should go downstairs and what should remain for the young folks' use; what room should be made into their bedroom, and how to contrive a hall.

They would probably all dine together downstairs. It would be more convenient that way, nearer to the kitchen.

She even began planning a future nursery, and gradually a thousand different worries crowded upon her. Unknown to herself, that moment set a seal upon her own personal existence, and marked the transference of all her love and care to making her Yasha's future happy.

When in the evening she went down to tea, her face was calm, and betrayed no trace of excitement. Her eyes gazed unconcernedly at Grandfather, and none guessed that the whole course of her life had been changed for all time.

Grandfather was in a specially good mood. He was delighted that at last Yasha was affianced, that business in the shop was good, and that Grandmother had welcomed the idea of a speedy marriage without any 'twiddle-twaddle'. 'She is beyond price,' he reflected as he watched Grandmother calmly pouring out tea.

Indeed today he saw everything through rose-coloured glasses, and never even suspected the struggle through which Grandmother had just passed.

Like a confirmed egotist—the last thing he imagined himself to be—he praised his own cleverness and common sense. He related how he had long 'got beneath the skin' of Okorokov. He expressed envy of his son, and was lavish in his promises to the happy pair.

He was also enraptured by Olya: 'A clever girl and a beauty into the bargain.'

Grandmother listened, sipped her tea, nibbled her sugar and agreed with everything.

The following morning saw a whole army of plasterers, painters, and carpenters, hammering and scraping in the courtyard in apparent confusion. A merry lot, they filled Grandfather's hitherto silent house with every conceivable kind of noise. With a few words Grandmother induced order into this cheery mob, with the result that each applied himself to his allotted task, and the work was tackled with all the fervour required to complete the alterations by the earliest possible date.

A light scaffolding was erected outside, whereon the plasterers scraped their trowels with a will, and painters, with apparent

Grandmother and Grandfather.

THREE GENERATIONS OF THE POLUNIN FAMILY

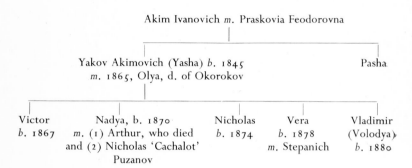

Akim Ivanovich *m.* Praskovia Feodorovna

Yakov Akimovich (Yasha) *b.* 1845
m. 1865, Olya, d. of Okorokov

Pasha

Victor
b. 1867

Nadya, *b.* 1870
m. (1) Arthur, who died
and (2) Nicholas 'Cachalot'
Puzanov

Nicholas
b. 1874

Vera
b. 1878
m. Stepanich

Vladimir
(Volodya)
b. 1880

enthusiasm, attacked the walls with broad brushes which greedily lapped up the thick creamy paint from buckets suspended from ladder-rungs. The brushes swept from left to right over the prepared surface as though pulled on strings. The painters would often start humming a song, those below leading and those above harmonizing. The result was pleasing and often very amusing, because of the unexpected changes of motif.

Whenever Grandmother was not looking, the maid poked her head out of a window to watch the workmen. It was invariably the painters who supplied the wit and the laughter, and when the cook came in sight—she was a squat little woman —they invariably chanted in chorus:

> *Oh, little mother,*
> *Chicken, aren't you short?*
> *Your lover, if you have one,*
> *Will be such another wart.*

Whereupon in exasperation she slammed down the window and disappeared into her own fastnesses. The painters, in fact, never stopped laughing and joking. An admixture of song and jest lightened their labours.

The joiners and carpenters inside the house, at work on making new partitions and rehanging doors to an accompaniment of banging hammers and shrieking saws were, on the contrary, a reticent and uncommunicative lot. With their long hair tied back with string, and their big bushy beards, they looked like so many holymen. The painters frequently chaffed them about their studied silence.

'Hello! You sinful crowd of saints! Why have you gone so quiet there? You must have your mouths full of water!' or 'Look out, Matvei, throw that away before you drop it!' they would yell to them as the carpenters set up door-frames in the second storey.

The carpenters smiled, but went on with their job without saying a word. They worked 'as though the wheels were oiled'.

Every now and then the contractor would call quickly to survey the work, and reassure Grandmother by saying, 'Don't worry! There's no doubt that everything will be ready in time,' and then he would vanish silently to another building job.

Grandfather, on his return from the shop, sniffed with disapproval. The smell of the new oil paint got on his nerves and gave him a headache. Yasha spent all his free time with his betrothed, but when at home endorsed all of his mother's arrangements.

When at last the gangs of workmen had disappeared as at the touch of a wand, the house looked almost new. Its window frames had been painted white and its walls a soft pink which, while the paint was still new, made it resemble a blancmange in a confectioner's shop. The drawing-room had been covered with a showy wall-paper, while the bedroom boasted garlands of white roses on a rose-pink background. The floors gleamed with new paint of a uniform brick colour with a black surround, and in order to save the new paintwork they were intersected by strips of matting.

The rooms, devoid of any furniture, seemed both larger and lighter, and Grandmother quite failed to recognize her old bedroom, so greatly was it changed by the new wall-paper and the absence of the familiar bedstead and large presses. When bright shafts of sunlight shone through the five windows of the empty drawing-room and glinted on the milk-white dutch tiling of the new stove, she took heart, and for a moment, at any rate, felt confident that Yasha would find happiness in this bright little corner.

Meanwhile at the Okorokovs', too, everything was bustle and confusion. The trousseau was being prepared. Samples of materials were brought, dressmakers flitted up and down the stairs carrying their dainty handiwork in immense boxes, and they were busy cutting out materials and trying them on.

The big drawing-room, which alone had sufficient light and space, was littered with lengths of material and with trimmings of all sorts. Lace undergarments were stacked upon all the chairs. Bobbins and scissors lay scattered underfoot. There was a serious and workmanlike atmosphere about this gentle trade.

Every other minute, Olya had to take off a dress in order either to fit on another one or to have some alteration made.

She stood patiently in a petticoat and shift, with arms bare and neck uncovered, while her minions tightened corsets, adjusted a crinoline, or slipped one of the many dresses over her head. Then there would be trouble over a train, some pinning at the waist would be needed, a hem would call for discussion, and the whole thing would be started all over again.

Olya surveyed herself in the big mirror, which had been transported from her bedroom on the previous day. She turned here and there in front of it, assumed different attitudes, and finally remained always satisfied with the novelty.

When they had finished with the dresses—the wedding dress, those for visiting and feast-days, and the cotton frocks—it was the turn of the fur coats and mantles. And so the work of fitting went on until far into the evening. The effect of all these matronly garments, so strange to a young girl, was to make Olya look older, more serious, and more reserved.

Agafia was always at her side, and was as always her only adviser and friend, as well as nurse. Her old mother never came out from her room, but remained in bed as usual. Okorokov, having set aside a substantial sum of money for the dowry, 'so that everything,' to use his own words, 'should be in the best fashion,' paid no attention to the details, considering such women's work beneath him. Moreover, he had other worries. One after another his anxieties crowded upon him. His every effort and care was directed towards preventing any rumours of his imminent bankruptcy reaching the ear of the town before the day of his daughter's wedding.

He knew that he would in any case be forced to sell his house and furniture, and as he paced mechanically up and down

his study, he realized with despair that he would have to part
with everything else he possessed besides.

If only his creditors would agree to ten kopecks in the rouble,
if only he could manage to keep something from his estate, he
might perhaps start life anew. 'But suppose they won't?' he
asked himself. The restless pacing ceased. There was no reply.
A faint gleam of hope died on his embittered face.

Sinking heavily into the chair in front of his little writing
table, he fixed his dim eyes upon the papers which lay scattered
in confusion before him, cheques, bills of exchange, receipts, all
fateful witnesses to his active life as a speculator.

But the imminent threat of poverty did not daunt him.
'What is poverty?' he mused. 'Poverty's nothing. Devil take
poverty! Let it go hang. One can always get money,' he added
comfortingly to his paper audience.

His vanity rose hydra-like and gnawed at his heart. It was the
loss of respect, the forfeiture of the confidence of the business
world which was unendurable to him. It was this that caused
him to burn with shame. It was this that filled his heart with
poisonous gall, and created a hell from which there was no
escape.

He had no blame for himself, for his speculations and for his
lust for easy profits. It was all the fault of others—'Friends!
Devil take them!' or if friends were clearly not at fault, it was
due to the unfortunate concatenation of circumstances. And so
on these, on friends and circumstances, the hapless old gambler
now vented his boiling anger.

It was already light when he woke from his hopeless reverie.
It was too late to go to bed. Picking up his hat, he went into the
garden.

The garden was in rapt, attentive silence. The sun was
gilding the tops of the trees in the avenue.

Not a sound was to be heard.

XV

VANYA Puzanov was nominated Chief Master of Ceremonies at the forthcoming wedding, and for his friend 'Andrashy', as he had now nicknamed Yasha after a Hungarian Member of Parliament who had caused considerable stir in the newspapers, he was ready to make every sacrifice. He chased round the town, calling at the livery stables to engage carriages, interviewing the priests, holding discussions with the caterers, and even personally selecting the more responsible of the waiters. In all directions he exerted his remarkable energy, feeling that he was in his element. For it was only when he was organizing something for somebody that his enthusiasm was fully aroused, and life became interesting and purposeful.

He gave careful consideration to every detail of wedding ritual, having regard to local custom; for in order to maintain his own high standards in the capacity of best man it was essential for him to keep his eyes open, the more so because upon his efforts rested the reputation of a whole household. A wedding was invariably a public function, and any oversight in the arrangements was a matter for censure by malicious tongues. Among his multitudinous duties was one which lay specially close to Vanya's heart, namely the 'Bachelor's Farewell Party', that is to say, the final dinner and talk to which were gathered intimate friends and contemporaries of the bridegroom, all of whom without exception had to be bachelors. This was the occasion when, his 'last hour' upon him, the young groom bade goodbye to his independence before voluntarily submitting his neck to the yoke of matrimony.

To strike one false note at so important a rite was physically impossible to Vanya; his artistic sense rebelled at the mere thought, and drove him to spare himself no trouble. The 'Flykillers' Club', which he had founded and of which he was President, with Yasha as one of the chief members, owed its origin to functions of this nature. The club met in a specially reserved room at an out-of-the-way tavern. Its members wore a prescribed uniform consisting of a white night-cap with an embroidered fly in the middle, and any defection of duty was visited by belabouring fellow-members with fly-whisks. At times when flies were plentiful, competitions were arranged and prizes awarded to the most successful fly-killers. Membership was confined to bachelors, and married men were ignominiously expelled, their night-caps and fly-whisks being confiscated and themselves debarred from all future meetings of the club. A better scene for a 'Farewell Party' could not well be imagined, but it was essential that every detail should receive attention to ensure that such a party should be different from one of the ordinary meetings, when members dined together at regular intervals.

Vanya became completely absorbed in his task. Having first chosen the menu, he passed to the more difficult problem of the wines. Gushchin advocated that the symposium be limited to vodka; Vanya insisted upon the best champagne. A majority vote decided that Yasha be feted with Veuve Cliquot. 'It is no mere nobody whom we are depriving of membership. We are expelling our Yasha Andrashy from the Club,' asserted the President, 'and you advise us to confine ourselves to vodka! Ah, Gushchin, Gushchin, you have a soul of water, and no genuine feelings! Yasha? Vodka?' and he surveyed Gushchin disdainfully from head to toe.

After a stormy meeting, a motion was carried to the effect that 'the farewell party of the honourable member Andrashy be conducted with all pomp and ceremony.' 'It shall be a gala performance,' added the President, 'without regard to expenditure of whisks or flies.' This resolution was duly recorded in the minute book, and verbal announcements were sent round. The meeting broke up at a late hour with the consciousness that duty had been done.

On the eve of the wedding a small but intimate company was assembled at eight o'clock. Gushchin had long ago concealed any feelings of resentment over his own unhappy courtship, nor could anyone discern a trace of it. He seemed as happy and as witty as ever.

Ivan Aksentiev, in his Flykiller's night-cap, cast covert glances towards the waiting *zakuski* and uncorked wine bottles, while Vanya Puzanov chatted with fellow-members standing round the tables awaiting the arrival of the cause of this little tragi-comedy. They delayed eating, since it would hardly have been proper to proceed with the programme before the arrival of the leading actor, and as Yasha was late, they watched the door with impatient hunger.

At last Yasha, accompanied by his younger brother, was seen on the threshold, and the whole company, with feelings of relief, dashed to the tables. Copying Vanya's easy manner, all now called Yasha 'Andrashy', as they clapped him on the shoulder, commiserating with him on his fall, and jokingly warning him against marriage. From every side he was assailed with such greetings as 'Look out, Andrashy, before it's too late!' 'There's still time. All is not lost yet!' 'You can still get out of it. It's been done before!'

All these insinuations and warnings against the married state were intended as no more than chaff and banter along tradi-tional lines; none the less they had a noticeable effect on Yasha, whom they served to remind how serious was the step he was taking and, though he joined in the fun, he was not his accus-tomed self.

After drinking a preliminary glass and sampling the caviare, they took their places at the long tables in order of seniority. Vanya, as President, occupied the head, wearing an immense night-cap with three embroidered flies. He beat the table with a fly-whisk to open the meeting, and after the minutes had been read, picked up his speech and turned to Yasha. All listened attentively.

'In this civilized age of ours, an age of railways, of bridges, of electricity, and balloons; in this period of inventive genius, the discovery of gold in America, and so forth, and so forth, it is to be noted with shame and horror that there have been criminal infringements of the very essentials of our Statutes— those mighty Statutes of the Flykillers. Tempted on the right hand and on the left by the suggestions of the devil, our best members are fleeing our hospitable home and disregarding their sacred covenant! And whither do they flee? And why? I ask you!

' "Is it true I tend you not, true I feed you not?" ' he quoted.

'No gentlemen, the fault does not lie in me, it lies in loose thinking, it lies in weakness of character, it lies in empty-headedness.

'Even at this moment a woman's skirt has obscured the proudly unfurled standard of the Flykillers.

'Members, like silly sheep, are stretching out their necks in droves to the yoke of matrimony!

'Soon, we may suppose, there will not be in our ranks a single genuine Flykiller!

'Where are we going? I ask you.

'Take heed before it be too late! There is still time.

'Show the whole world that there is still powder in your flask!'

The President mournfully subsided into his chair and drained a glass of champagne at a single draught, all the other members following his example. Aksentiev, having poured out a fresh glass, rose to his feet and addressed himself directly to Yasha.

'As Secretary and member of the honourable Flykillers' Club, I rise to administer to you, Sir, in the name of all here present, a most severe reproof. Is it true, Sir, that you have forgotten your tempestuous youth, and how we have made merry here over a glass of wine,'—here Aksentiev swallowed the contents of his glass at a gulp—'how we have killed flies in their hundreds and by one means or another striven to divert our President, Vanya? We were all told, Sir, that in you we were dealing with an outstanding Flykiller. And what now? What do we see? Ah, Andrashy, Andrashy! A fruit rotten before ever it was ripe! Before ever you attained those heights of single bliss which thrust themselves into your hand, all was over! Neither our tearful assurances nor the sobs of those who have suffered have availed to turn you from your resolve.

'Away with you! "Horseless to horseman cannot be friend." Away with you!'

Aksentiev drank down a second glass and made a gesture of command.

Yasha's night-cap was taken off, he was deprived of the title 'Honourable Alcoholic' and for ever banished from the Club.

To him it all seemed like a requiem. They would now start drinking to his successor. Behind this farrago of jest and boyish mockery at the foundations of life, lay something serious. A strong connecting link was being severed, a good fellow was passing a milestone. Here among the friends of his childhood the very last moments of independent youth were indeed slipping away.

The official programme having come to an end, Vanya discarded his night-cap, knocked thrice on the table, and closed the session. They then proceeded to the 'Farewell Party'. Mounting the platform, Vanya proposed toast after toast, and every time they drank to the future happiness of the Andrashy whom they had just expelled, Yasha's eyes filled with tears. He imagined himself a guest at his own funeral, rather than as standing on the threshold of a new life fraught with purpose.

The conversation turned on a bachelor's lot, the immeasurable delights of single blessedness, and the charm of freedom. As each related his own experiences he lied like a trooper, as he recalled his amorous conquests, or depicted horrible examples of married life. This was in strict accord with tradition, the object being to make the future happy owner of a domestic hearth so appalled by his fate that he would drink himself almost unconscious. The intoxication of the young bridegroom was part of the fixed plan on the farewell programme so that, in the words of the song:

No shame it should be to remember
Those years when once we were young.

Without it the party would have lost its meaning.

They now started drinking to anything and everything—to the limited company, to the watch-tower at the fire station, to Perepelkin, the caterer. The atmosphere was thick with the fumes of wine.

Vanya, radiant as the sun, clinked glasses with his friend who was the cause of the feast.

Simultaneously with Yasha's 'Farewell' a parallel party for girls at Olya's house was just drawing to a close. Some friends from the finishing school, some neighbours, and two or three merchants' daughters, sat decorously in a row in Okorokov's hall, and sipped coffee. The trousseau, tidily disposed around the hall, had been inspected long ago and discussed in detail, and the timely-dispatched presents from brother Vasily, with a fine Caucasian shawl as the chief, had made a unique impression upon all the guests. Everyone congratulated Olya times without number, and kissed her. Sweets, mint cakes, almonds and nuts were passed round, and conversation became less restrained, as they discussed young men and future suitors, surveying them at all points as if they were race-horses. A party like this formed an excellent pretext for young girls to have an intimate talk about marriage and the advantages and disadvantages of married life. All declared themselves in favour of holy wedlock, and looked on their girlhood as being but a transitory stage, preliminary to the selection of a husband. Marriage they accepted as the aim and object of their existence. When at last her friends departed, having bestowed kisses on her by the dozen, and Olya was left alone, she pondered for the first time on the seriousness of the future, and tears dropped down her cheeks, though she was at a loss to account for them.

By the time Agafia came to help her undress, no vestige of her grief remained, and as she quickly undressed and sprang into the familiar bed, the thought that she was spending her last night in her parental home no longer troubled her.

XVI

IVAN Puzanov, dressed with an elegance of fashion such as had never before been seen in the province, complete with silk check waistcoat, curled hair and powdered face, lay stretched out on a sofa critically regarding Yasha from head to foot. Yasha was standing before his mirror parting his fair hair, straightening the long ends of his necktie, and adjusting a narrow watch-chain around his neck; he looked nervous and preoccupied. The wedding was now only two hours off.

'Why be afraid, brother Yasha? There is nothing to be afraid of! True, a wedding is a complicated affair, and when it's the first time and a fellow lacks experience it's not all plain sailing. But you have nothing to worry about, my boy, because I have arranged everything, seen to everything, and inspected everything. My ingenuity has been incredible, and I haven't the strength left to tell you about it. Well, as you are nearly dressed, I think that I will review my forces. Then I must escort the bride. Punctually at twelve o'clock, absolutely on the tick, we will drive up to the church porch. See to it that nothing detains you. You will meet us at the porch and give her your hand with all the grace you can command. Thereafter I will take everything upon myself. Don't you worry! We shan't disgrace ourselves! And yes, don't forget to step on the carpets before the bride does! You may laugh, but it's an old superstition, brother, and you can't get away from it! Who first steps on the carpets will rule the roost! That's so! But I don't know why I am chatting to you and talking nonsense like this. I must be off upstairs to see about the catering arrangements.'

Vanya got up from the sofa, smoothed his waistcoat, arranged the buttonhole of orange blossom in his dress-coat, and blowing a kiss to Yasha, disappeared.

In the hall, long tables were set end to end and covered with a snow-white cloth. In the four corners of the room stood artificial palm trees planted in big tubs. Pyramids of bottles and immense dishes loaded with hams, jellied fowl, and delicacies both sweet and savoury, whetted the appetite. At separate tables there were various kinds of vodka accompanied by choice examples of Grandmother's home cooking, such as pickled mushrooms, truffles, various kinds of fish, salted cucumber, chopped cabbage, soused apples, and all the other savoury morsels of which the provincial Russian housewife had so great a store. The finishing touch was supplied by the two clean-shaven waiters in full evening dress, who were listening to the caterer, a tall man issuing orders in the manner of an army commander on the field of battle. Vanya surveyed the scene, sampled a mushroom, shifted the palm trees, and then, satisfied on all points, rushed off to act as escort to the bride.

Since early morning Olya had been dressing and she was now quite ready. In her white wedding dress, trimmed with orange blossom, and fitted with a veil which fell gracefully from the crown of her head to the floor, she stood in the middle of the room, to avoid creasing her dress, and chatted gaily with her friends.

Old Mlle de Muchel had honoured Olya by her personal attendance, and ensconced in a comfortable chair was now giving her a last lesson in *le bon ton*. 'It is most important, my little Olya, that you should bear yourself with dignity,' she repeated, speaking French for greater emphasis, but adding more affectionately in Russian, 'You always were a good little girl. And I—' But at this moment the carriage drove up in which two groomsmen wearing top hats at a rakish angle were to be seen sitting on the upholstered seat. There was a concerted rush to the window as the bridesmaids excitedly exclaimed, 'Thank Heavens we shall not be late!' Vanya, graceful as a young lion, ran up the steps of the porch, and having politely kissed the bride's hand, impressed upon all that there must be positively no delay, that everything was ready, and that it was time to make a start. This news was duly conveyed to old Okorokov, who came out with majestic austerity to bless his daughter with the family ikon. Olya sank to her knees before it, her dress falling around her in graceful folds, and shed unwonted tears; Mlle de Muchel started to sob in the corner; the brides-maids giggled nervously; Agafia, in a silk dress, was suffused with tears of happiness; even old Okorokov was trembling.

'And now, Olya,' he said in a choked voice, 'God grant you happiness,' and kissing her thrice upon the lips, he added, 'Well, now it's time to go. Come, come! Dry those tears! Why should you be crying? It's a wedding, not a funeral! Come along, Vanya,' he said turning to the groomsman, 'Let us be off!'

And so the procession headed for the gate, with Olya and Mlle de Muchel seated side by side, and opposite them Okor-okov, a groomsman, and a small boy carrying the ikon. Vanya, as befitted the chief master of ceremonies, graced the box-seat with the coachman.

The horses trotted along at a brisk pace, and within a minute drew up at the church porch where Vanya, to the amazement of the assembled crowd, in a single bound lightly leaped from the box, opened the carriage door, and received the bride with all the courtly grace of a Spanish grandee.

At the church porch stood Yasha, surrounded by more grooms-men and guests. In truly deafening tones the choir bawled out, 'Draw near, draw near, my bride,' as Olya, barely able to control her steps, advanced to the altar leaning on Yasha's arm, with Vanya clearing a path in front and the guests following in pairs behind.

After the wedding service the procession returned, and in a bunch crossed the road to Grandfather's house on foot, for as the house was situated only a few paces away on the opposite side, no carriages were necessary.

A crowd of gossips and tradesfolk audibly discussed the merits of the young couple as they passed by.

'The bride, there's a girl for you! Like an angel she looks!'

'That wedding dress was all pure silk, I managed to finger it as they were crossing the road!'

'Well, what of it? They're very wealthy folk!'

'See Okorokov there, all puffed up like a turkey-cock! He's a haughty old man.'

'There's not much amiss with the bridegroom.'

'He's painfully thin, though.'

'Yes, he's got legs like a bird.'

'Look at that groomsman, the tallest one, with the curly hair, he takes everybody's eye.'

'Yes, that's the one, like a real, full-chested lion. He could squeeze the life out of you!'

At the door of the hall Akim Ivanovich and Grandmother awaited the happy pair. Akim Ivanovich wore a new full frock coat and displayed a watch-chain across his middle, while Grandmother had an old-fashioned silk gown surmounted by a lace head-dress.

'And here comes our little Olya with her lawful wedded husband,' said Grandfather kindly, 'Come in, and welcome! Come to your home, my pretty one. And may God grant you and Yasha many years of happiness under this roof.'

With this he kissed Olya three times.

Grandmother, too, welcomed Olya with an embrace and wished her happiness. Then, turning to Yasha she exclaimed, 'Yasha, my first-born! And Olya as well! May God grant—' but without finishing her speech, she buried her face in her handkerchief.

Vanya now gave the waiters an order to serve the champagne, and raising aloft his glass, loudly proclaimed the toast 'To the health of the newly-weds!' Draining his glass at a draught, he dashed it to the floor, where with a tinkling sound it shivered to fragments. There was a babel of voices—

'To the health of the newly-weds.'

'Good counsel and love be theirs.'

'May they live to a hundred—'

As all, clinking their glasses, advanced towards the young

couple, beaming with happy smiles, Olya replied to each without hesitation and with never a trace of shyness. Yasha, however, was confused and abashed, but happy beyond all measure. Okorokov, glass in hand, surveyed his fellow-guests morosely, thinking 'What a rabble! What a bunch of specimens! How they fight for a place at the trough. It must be the first time that they have tasted champagne! Alas, for my own misery. What has tomorrow in store?'

Succeeding at last in shaking off his depression, he went across to the *zakuski* table, where Grandmother was dispensing home-made delicacies to her guests, amid a hum of conversation.

'What lovely mushrooms you have, Praskovia Feodorovna! They are simply delicious!'

'Have some more, little Father. I marinated them myself. They came as a present from Elets. I made three barrels.' 'And do try some of this pepper-brandy. It is like molten iron. It will warm your heart indeed, and send you into a sweat.'

'Hello, Gushchin. Why are you so quiet over there? Are you scared to death by your embezzlements? You'd best be dead!'

'For curiosity's sake I bought a bottle of zubrovka from Gushchin's firm. As a bottle it was as honest as the day. It had a label with medals, the factory trade-mark, and a wealth of high-flown language. But when I tasted it! It was a pure swindle. Torricelli's vacuum itself.'

'You'd better clear away from this table, Gushchin, before I get so annoyed that I shall have to kill you.'

'Now then, gentlemen, no quarrelling. A wedding is no occasion for knifing each other. It isn't polite.'

Vanya clapped his hands and summoned everyone to sit down. The bridesmaids, who had not taken part in the lively scenes at the side tables, promptly skipped to their places like young lambs. The happy pair occupied the place of honour in the centre opposite Okorokov, Grandfather, and Mlle de Muchel. A groomsman sat at the head and foot, and the rest disposed themselves as they wished.

At a further signal from Vanya, crayfish soup was served with little puff-pastry pies. The caterer occupied himself with a pie whose corners were decorated with different fish, and carved the colossal turkey, the glazed sucking-pig, the geese, and the ducks. As the waiters scurried by, he deftly put helpings on the plates.

When the soup—generally voted 'inimitable'—was finished and the meal was proceeding to various kinds of game, Vanya knocked on the table and, waiting until all had charged their glasses, addressed the company.

'Ladies and gentlemen. We are gathered together here on an occasion of much ceremony. For years we have all known Yasha. I must beg his pardon and say Yakov Akimovich. And for years we have been in love with Olya, now Olga Polun-ina—Now Gushchin, stop shuffling your feet,' he suddenly remarked to his friend, who was sitting quietly beside him. At this there was a roar of laughter, for all were well aware of Gushchin's luckless courtship.

'To proceed, ladies and gentlemen, we are gathered to-gether on an occasion of deep significance, to wit, the marriage of the lad Yakov to the maiden Olya. They are sitting before you, and when you look at them, does it not strike you that they were destined for one another?'

'Come to the point!' the audience demanded.

'So be it, ladies and gentlemen, we shall now come to the point. And the point is this. A feast for all to see! *Gorko!!*'

'*Gorko! Gorko!*' rang out from all sides.

In response to the call the young couple rose to their feet, and Yasha, blushing to the roots of his hair, put his arm round Olya and kissed her on the lips, while the assembled company beat a tattoo with their forks and shouted 'Encore' to express their enthusiasm.

Vanya meanwhile made a mental note of the fact that another wedding custom had been truly observed. It only remained now to tread warily until the end. He anxiously wondered whether he would be too tipsy.

Yasha, nineteen years old.

Olya, about seventeen years old.

It was after the roast that the ritual reached its climax. The waiters had dispensed all the champagne. Everyone was silent. At last a door was noisily flung open and the caterer, in person, appeared bearing a large dish, on which towered a marvellous confection whose base was an enormous cake. On the summit was a Greek temple, fashioned with great skill out of cardboard, and surmounted with sugar bells and embellishments of crystallized fruits and marzipan. From the temple porch, along the slopes of the enchanted cake, ran roads of sugar, spanned by bridges, along which horsemen were galloping. But what chiefly evoked the admiration of all beholders were the tiny sugar models of a bride and bridegroom, standing beneath a flowering bush and kissing like turtle doves.

'Well, Suslikov has produced a masterpiece!'

'Say what you like, he's an artist!'

Suslikov, flattered by the universal admiration, placed the edifice in front of the bride and bridegroom, and having armed himself with a large knife, cleft for them the lion's share of the sugary landscape with a single stroke. The temple reeled, the lovers staggered and collapsed, two or three bridges and part of the road vanished from the face of the earth, and in a quarter of an hour nothing remained on the dish save the mangled limbs of the unfortunate lovers and some shattered fragments of columns and capitals.

'So will it be in life,' thought Okorokov in his melancholy. 'Nothing will remain. There will be nothing for me nor for any of them. Look at Olya there in her youthful beauty. What lies ahead for her?'

They were now drinking sweet wines, cordials, and liqueurs and there was much noisy laughter and shouts of '*Gorko!*'

Akim Ivanovich, displaying interest in life in foreign parts, was engaged in a long conversation with Mlle de Muchel about the religion of France, its churches, its markets, and its fish. While the French lady did her best to satisfy his curiosity, she was all the time wishing that she could converse with Okorokov, who remained as dumb as an oyster.

K

Grandmother never stopped talking to Father Savatiy about parochial matters, the newly appointed arch-priest, and the charitable institutions. The priest, in his silk cassock adorned with a pectoral cross, held back his full sleeve with his left hand as he helped himself to liqueur and discoursed with dignity on the greatness of the Orthodox faith. Grandmother decided that she must send him a present of a goose. 'He really looks majestic,' she thought as she glanced up at him, 'Why shouldn't he indulge himself a little!'

On Grandmother's right Gushchin and Aksentiev were exchanging some sort of nonsense with the bridesmaids, who burst into shrieks of laughter, coyly thrusting their plump hands over their mouths, displaying their rings. They shook their heads, too, in protest, setting their ear-rings swaying. And good solid jewellery it all was! Vanya was everywhere at once, signalling to the waiters, restraining Gushchin when his jokes became too virile, smiling at the happy pair, adding fire where it seemed required, or damping it down where it threatened to become uncontrolled.

Yasha and Olya responded to every question with smiling faces, though they were evidently tired by all the commotion. Yasha's wish was to be alone with Olya. Olya's dress hurt under her arms, her shoes felt too tight, and she found the fumes of the wine almost intolerable. Nevertheless both had to continue to sit and look happy.

For nearly four hours they all sat at the table without getting up. At last they rose to their feet, some standing upright and others with a decided list. Okorokov was the first to make his adieu, pleading urgent business affairs. He was followed by Mlle de Muchel, while the young men drained their glasses. As a result of Grandmother's hospitable entreaty the rest stayed behind and drank tea.

Grandfather soon departed to his own room. His eyes were smarting and his ears ringing. 'They've smoked too much and created as much fog as a crowd of real Turks! God forgive me! I am off to rest, Párochka, and you can tell me when you've managed to get rid of them all.'

The guests who stayed crossed over to the drawing-room and sat down before the round tables, sipping tea. Two samovars of boiling water were in constant use, and around the warmth of their gigantic bodies were arrayed jars of every conceivable sort of jam and plates of cake. Tea-cups, saucers, and glasses guarded the hostesses like ranks of soldiers, as Grandmother poured out at one table and Olya, in the role of a young house-wife, at the other. From behind the door a servant peeped in : Agafia, unblinking, watched her young mistress, and more than once went to her aid to show her, without her mother-in-law noticing, how to make tea properly, or to correct the mistakes of her inexperience.

With tea and conversation three hours slipped by imperceptibly. Outside brooded the peace of a summer evening. The cockchafers were droning and beating against the walls; around the candles moths were fluttering. As far as he could, Yasha saved them from inevitable destruction, and grieved whenever he was too late. Olya smilingly watched his efforts, thinking, 'Darling, darling Yasha! My faithful husband! He even grieves over moths!'

When Father Savatiy got up, the young people, under the leadership of Gushchin, departed in a bunch, with the evident intention of continuing the evening somewhere else. Vanya said goodbye, clasping the happy couple to him in a single embrace.

Olya and Yasha were left alone, sitting close together on a sofa before the open window. Yasha was silent, thinking how lovely was Olya, how happy himself, asking himself why God had thus blessed him in sending him such an one to share his life.

The candles guttered, the room was faintly lit by the glare of the street lamps. It was quiet and close. To Yasha the little Russian provincial town became a fairy-land. Over yonder he could discern a knight on a white steed brandishing his sword. The gates of Paradise were flung open, and a woman of miraculous beauty, having the features of Olya, and swathed in white raiment from head to foot, stood before the enchanted gaze of this horseman. And the maiden with Olya's eyes advanced to meet her knight. And the knight was none other than Yasha himself.

'Olya, Olya! Do you know what has happened? Do you realize? You are my Dulcinea.'

Olya did not understand, for she had only just summoned back her thoughts from memories of the past, and to her it seemed that Lieutenant Pereverziev of the polished manners and parade uniform was tightly pressing her hand and asking, 'Olya, Olya, do you know what has happened?' Then she realized that it was Yasha, her dear Yasha, and she pressed closer to her husband's side. Pereverziev slowly sank from her imagination, never to rise again. For Yasha lived. Her dear Yasha was hers for ever, for all her life. The clock in the tower of the Town Hall struck ten. Olya gave a little shudder, and shaking away her dreams of the past, gave herself up to the present.

Grandmother, in a quilted dressing-gown and a night-cap, cautiously tip-toed up to the door and then, seeing them silhouetted against the light of the window, involuntarily crossed herself and exclaimed, 'Why are you sitting there in the dark? It's bed time. I've been searching and searching for where my children could have disappeared, and there they are, sitting and cooing like turtle-doves!' The old woman therewith warmly embraced them and, making the sign of the cross three times over them, went off to her own room. It was dark in there, and Akim Ivanovich had long been snoring on his great-grandfather's spacious bed.

XVII

MANY years have passed since Olya spent her last night in her father's house.

Old Okorokov has long since died, after having lived to see himself completely ruined. The house has long since been sold and pulled down, and its garden uprooted. On its site now stands the ugly brick yeast factory and distillery owned by Petchke Brothers.

The whimpering old mother, too, has passed to another land, with her habitual plaint upon her lips, 'How will you all get on without me?'

It was now that Grandfather, Akim Ivanovich, fell ill, the disease starting in his legs.

'Why must you always be scratching, Akim Ivanovich, as though some rash troubled you?' asked Grandmother.

'I don't know what misfortune has befallen me, Párochka,' he replied, looking up guiltily at his wife, and rubbing his thin legs, 'But I've an everlasting irritation as though someone were digging pins into me.'

Grandmother thereupon proceeded to rub in some pork fat, causing the old man to give a blink of satisfaction, for it seemed that this homely treatment was giving him some relief. Such, however, was not the case. His legs began to swell and turn a bluish black, and finally to break out in eruptions. Thoroughly alarmed, Grandmother talked about sending for a doctor, but Grandfather flatly refused to see one. 'Send them to Jericho! They are only an expense. The thing will pass of its own accord. Why worry?'

Grandmother, quite unconvinced, refrained from contradiction, and directed her consuming energy along other channels.

She had heard that in Elets lived a 'wise woman' who could work miracles. To Elets, therefore, she set off as though to visit relatives, and repaired straight to this healer, to whom she related all the circumstances, telling how there was an old man whose legs had become swollen and blue-looking, and so painful as to render walking difficult.

The beldame pondered and pondered, and after investigating a store, emerged with two boxes of ointment and a bunch of dried medicinal herbs, which she deposited on the table.

'This, Matushka, is my word to you. The disease is difficult, and it is catching. A hundred roubles and your man will be cured of it. Refuse, and there will be no offence taken. First employ this box which, as you see, contains a black ointment. When the blueness of the legs turns to white, start using the other ointment, that is, the white. You understand? First the black, and then the white. See that you make no mistake lest the disease spread inward, in which case nothing can avail. When you start to rub in the white ointment, take this bunch of herbs, grind it to powder with mortar and pestle, and boil the powder in rain-water three times. Mind that you use rain-water and not water from a well. When you have boiled it for the third time, then filter off the liquor and give it to your man to drink immediately after food. You understand? As soon as he feels himself again, take you this herb. It is, little mother, like the elixir of life, and would even make a dead man rise to his feet. A rare herb indeed, culled from the sea. Place it just as it is in a bottle of spirit and make, as it were, an infusion of it. Then hide it in some dark place for eight weeks, and thereafter give it to your husband to drink, one small glass at a time. Do you understand? Well, then, now repeat what I have told you.'

Like an obedient pupil, Grandmother repeated all word for word.

'Good!' concluded the beldame encouragingly, 'You have brains in your head! Pay your money, take the ingredients, and go back to your husband. He will recover. That I warrant you!'

To Grandmother's astonishment Akim Ivanovich displayed

instant faith in this folk-medicine. He obediently fulfilled all the
instructions, and praised the wise woman, asserting that he
felt much better. And indeed within a few months the disease
had entirely disappeared and he was going down to the shop
again, shouting at the assistants and making a great to-do.
Everything had turned out well, and in the house all was happiness again.

The young folk, Yasha and Olya, billed and cooed on the
first storey from morning to night, like a pair of turtle-doves
under the eaves, or spent their time gazing at each other. Grandfather, walking below in the court, looked up at the window
above, and smiled into his beard as his thoughts turned to
planting poplars for his grandchildren. In the sky, as in their
hearts, there was no cloud. All was quiet, peaceful, and good.

Suddenly a blow fell. News came that Pospolitáki had died
unexpectedly. The result was confusion. The majority of
Grandfather's creditors refused payment, on the pretext that
their guarantor had died.

'Now reason it out for yourself,' Akim Ivanovich would say
to some obstinate debtor. 'You had the goods from me. Well,
what then? It follows that you must pay me.'

'How can I pay when Pospolitáki has been called away by
God? Whom can I pay?'

Grandfather again did his best to explain.

'Stupid! You had the goods from me?'

'I did.'

'And I had to answer for them to Pospolitáki. You pay me and
I pay Pospolitáki.'

'How can you pay him when he's dead?'

'Well, if not him, his heirs. It comes to the same thing.'

The debtor would not give in. The man was dead and that
settled everything—'Whom should he pay and why should he
pay?'

Other more exceptional creditors flatly refused. 'Akim
Ivanovich, we have absolutely no intention of paying you.
What's the use of it? And we advise you not to pay either. The

heirs will only waste all the money, and in any case there's plenty for them. You, old friend, had best cease payment and stop applying to us. Just go bankrupt. There's nothing novel in it! It can all be done with a bit of jiggery-pokery. You'll not be the first! And we shall then all have our fill and be satisfied. Look at Yermolaev in Elets—bankrupt three times, and now worth a million! On the other hand, suppose there's a lawsuit. You go to court and a fine hubbub starts. You've not got a single document in evidence, because you rely on us. Who'll be the loser? Ha, ha, ha!'

Grandfather, worried, advanced proofs and swore, but the fishmongers stood their ground. Wipe off the debts, or bankruptcy. As for the heirs, not a penny piece should go to them 'He had his knife in us often enough!'

Notwithstanding the crying injustice of it, Grandfather did not take his case to court, but made a clean sweep of all his savings, and paid Pospolitáki's heirs down to the last farthing. It was difficult to do, as it demanded practically all the savings of his lifetime, and when the account was closed, he was left with his house and only a very trifling sum besides. But to the old man it was preferable to walk about with his head held high, rather than indulge in a fraudulent bankruptcy. The merchants in Traders' Row laughed at the simplicity of Akim Ivanovich, but, speaking generally, they respected him even more than before.

There followed further misfortune. Grandfather fell ill again of an obscure and complicated disease. As before he refused to call in a doctor and resolved to be cured by folk-medicine. But even the wise woman of Elets was powerless this time, and gave him up. After a long and painful illness he died.

Thenceforth the whole life of the household underwent revolution. Yasha entered the tea trade as a salesman, and Pasha accepted a position as second assistant in a fish business. Olya, with three children on her hands, busied herself about the house, and was often plunged into despair after sleepless nights with the baby. For her there now began a period of continual shortage of money, coupled with anxiety for the children, and she had to do everything herself, since there was no longer any servant. Grandmother alone did not apparently change one iota, but, as always, energetically ran around doing her housework and shopping, nursing or making garments for her grandchildren. It was she who tended Grandfather as he lay dying, and she who carefully prepared him for his last journey. And when at last Akim Ivanovich, feeble and wasted beyond all recognition, came to the close of his life upon earth, she never so much as trembled. Gently she closed his eyes, laying upon them two copper coins, then crossing herself before the ikon, she took down the family Bible and wrote in her clear hand the date and time of the passing of her devoted husband, friend, and master, Akim Ivanovich. In the bulky volume, with its thick binding, secured by silver hasps, was inscribed all the family history of her house. She read again the previous entries.

'January 25, 1845. My son Yacov was born.

'May 21, 1865, at noon. The wedding of my son Yakov to the maiden Olya Okorokova, in the church of St. Savatiy on the Yamskaia.

'January 2, 1867, at midnight. My grandson Victor was born.

'April 10, 1870. My grand-daughter Nadya was born.

'September 29, 1874. My grandson Nikolai was born. He was suckled by Agraphena, a foster-mother, owing to the weakness of his mother Olya.'

As she read the final entry the whole of her life, with its joys and anxieties, rose plain before her. And now 'He' was no longer with her, sadly mused the old woman, gazing up at the ikon of Our Saviour, before Whom, as ever, the amber-coloured flame was warmly glowing.

'My God! My God! Why hast thou forsaken me?' But the wheel of life stops not for a minute, and Grandmother's presence was needed at every turn. The grandchildren pulled her this way and that; to their mother she was essential; upon her depended the whole household. No time was left for grief or meditation, and thus was she saved from despair.

Nowadays Yasha left home for work with a certain feeling of pleasure, for the house seemed cheerless. His every impulse was towards realms unknown. He still clung to his belief in the joy of life. He had apparently all that he wanted in a beloved wife and beautiful children. Why, then, was he so heavy at heart? An unaccountable yearning benumbed him. He would return to his companions only to find that even the ever-cheerful Vanya Puzanov could not attune him to the old pitch. Sitting with his friends, he would start thinking of his family and wish to return to them as quickly as possible; but arrived home, the familiar yearning would again descend upon him and, finding no peace for himself, he would wander restlessly from room to room.

When, therefore, it was proposed that he should take over an administrative post in the tea business of Perlov Brothers, entailing a move to Moscow and a new start in life, he seized the offer as a drowning man clutches a straw. It was, he thought, well worth while to move anywhere in order to escape from a provincial town which was becoming repugnant to him. He would plan his life on new lines, his joy in it would return, and all would again be well. Full of animation and fired by new hope, he set off to Moscow as soon as he could, leaving his wife and the three children in Grandmother's keeping.

Olya's life without him was monotonous but busy. He frequently wrote to her in his firm hand, and she replied with rare letters which by reason of their rarity were the more beautiful. Though he longed for his family and yearned for Olya, he had necessarily to prepare his road with patience, and to better his position, before he could again think of family life. Olya was dejected, but somehow the days passed surprisingly quickly. Her eldest son, Victor, was already attending the gymnasium, an institution whose severity in those days was reminiscent of the Spanish Inquisition. The Minister of Public Instruction, the well-known Delyanov, was a firm admirer of classical times, and, to the fullest extent of his power, crammed the youth of Russia with Greek and Latin. Countless Czech teachers and other

Slav brethren did their fell duty and squeezed out from small first-form boys all the classical juices. In this they were helped by a priest, who loaded his hapless victims with whole volumes of Holy Writ, besides catechism, psalter, and liturgy. The teachers seized hold of their pupils on the public walks and confiscated their cigarettes, or raided their rooms in search of forbidden novels. The cries of the oppressed never ceased, and for the most trifling reasons boys were expelled and given 'Outlaws' Passports'. Truly the youth of Russia will never forget the beauty of the classics! Even to this day they jump up in the night at the memory of it.

It was astonishing that this classical regimen had no sub-jugating effect upon Victor. He diligently learned Latin by rote, translated Greek, and managed to get on quite well with the Czechs and their other Slav relations, as gradually he ad-vanced further and further along the path of scholarship. Grandmother could find no words of sufficient praise for him. In her letters to Yasha she depicted in glowing colours her eldest grandson's excellent behaviour, obedience to his elders, and outstanding success.

'He even does his hair in Latin! And he thrives on Greek,' she wrote in one of her long, lively letters to Yasha.

'A funny thing happened today—Here's education for you!— We suddenly discovered that our little Kolya had completely vanished. We looked everywhere for him, until we found him on the Moscow road with some books under his arm. When we stopped him and asked where he was going, he said that he was off to the gymnasium. "Why, you can't go to the gymnasium," I said. "A little five-year-old like you, whom people can hardly see!" And he started to cry, saying, "Victor goes to the gymnasium, so why can't I?" We quieted him as best we could. But what clever children they have become! There were none like them in my time,' concluded Grandmother.

At last arrived the time when Yasha's position on the ladder of advancement was such as to envisage the possibility of mov-ing his family to Moscow. Grandmother, however, tearfully implored him to leave her grandchildren with her—'For what should I do, all by myself in an empty house?' It was decided that the children should, for the present, remain behind, and that Olya should join her husband. Yasha thereupon took a little wooden house in Kiselniy Lane, near the church of Nicholas the Bellringer, and having transported thither his furniture from Grandmother's house, settled down with Olya to enjoy the more cheerful life of a capital city.

More children arrived, Peter and Vera—a Moscow-born family. The last arrival, a son, christened in the neighbouring church of Nicholas the Bellringer, was Vladimir, or Volodya, and his godmother, for want of a better, was a maiden lady named Malyard, the owner of the wooden house, and by profession a midwife.

1880-1890

XVIII

IF you were ever in Moscow in the old days, you must have noticed, as you approached the magnificent edifice of the Bolshoi Theatre, a large, curiously wedge-shaped empty space jutting out almost up to the side entrances of the Palace of Arts.

Overgrown with grass, nettles, and weeds, as though it were not actually a part of Moscow, this space was in fact within five minutes' walk from the centre of the city, where any vacant plot is worth its weight in gold. For over half a century it impeded traffic and the approach to no less than three theatres.

It would have appeared quite easy to have abolished this crying anachronism and done away with the wilderness by levelling and paving it and throwing it open to traffic. But nothing was ever done. Its owner, Count Noztitz, an Austrian emigrant, turned down all offers for it, however tempting, and refused to make any concessions. In short, he stood his ground with the obstinacy of a mule. And so the derelict space remained, unkempt, forsaken, and hemmed in on all sides by immense stone buildings.

The waste plot sloped up from the Bolshoi Theatre, and at its highest point came to a melancholy conclusion against a blind, windowless wall of the Count's great house which was approached through a wide arch with shabby gates.

Devoid of style, and many storeys high, the great house enclosed a courtyard paved with rounded cobbles. Once upon a time, the Count had the house painted a pale blue, but this must have been many years before, because its colour was now that dirty grey which Russian house-painters call 'wild'. It was now entirely split up into flats which were reached by creaking and invariably untidy wooden staircases.

In the centre of the courtyard—'neither in the village nor yet in the town'—stood a squat outhouse with rows of numbered doors which served as cellars and lumber-rooms for the tenants of the flats. If you had come to see us you would always have been annoyed at the impossibility of reaching our door without circumnavigating this unshapely encumbrance, which spoilt the general look of the Count's house and destroyed its proportions.

We never tired of watching from the upstairs windows any manifestation of activity in the court—and by 'we' is meant that little band of descendants of a legendary grandfather, Akim Ivanovich, whom we knew only from hearsay.

Our windows were large and the view from them excellent. Below lay the rusty roof of the outhouse and the round cobble-stones of the court; above, a square of clear sky. In the court sparrows hopped cheekily about and now and then an old acquaintance of ours, a piebald rat, poked a sly nose from a drain-pipe to satisfy himself that there was no one near before darting across like a streak of lightning and diving beneath the outhouse. Meanwhile at no great distance lay a cat, curled up and fast asleep, obviously quite unaware of what was going on in its domain. Of human beings there was no sign. The court was as empty as a desert.

Every now and again, however, a Tartar pedlar might wander in with a neat, tidily stocked pack on his shoulders. Before he came in sight we used to recognize his cry, for to us he was always a novel and interesting visitor. His funny 'Shuroom Buroom'—'buy and sell'—would reach our ears before we caught sight of his grey burnous and inevitable pack. On seeing us he would politely doff his fur cap and bare his gleaming teeth in a smile. Then he would beckon to us and start undoing his pack on the cobbles.

All we could see from above was his skull-cap embroidered in Eastern fashion, his blue-shaven forehead, and his lively black eyes with bluish whites to them. Frightened by his oriental splendour we waved to him and quickly concealed ourselves at the back of the room well away from the window. Finding that

Москва — Зимою. Театральная площадь.
Moscou en hiver. Place des théâtres.

Old postcard view in Moscow: left centre, the Bolshoi Theatre and beside it (left) block where Polunins lived (Chap. XVIII), and off left, the State Theatre. Behind the fountain, the English Stores and the Marly Theatre.

Vera and Volodya, in 1883 and in 1889.

we had gone, he would stop smiling, carefully re-arrange his pack, sling his wares over his shoulders and slowly make off, but his 'Shuroom Buroom' would re-echo round the court for some time before eventually fading away beyond the gates.

For what reason it is difficult to say, but these orientals somehow frightened us. We knew that now-a-days the Tartar peoples lived quite peacefully and quietly in the neighbourhood of Trubniy Square and committed no crimes. On Mohammedan feast-days one could see them out walking on the boulevards with their families, the wives all dressed up and wearing their hair in thin plaits, accompanied by hordes of healthy looking children in national costume.

Our elders used to tell us that they were an inoffensive people who earned a living by selling oriental toys and Kazan soap, and made a speciality of buying up for a mere song all manner of odds and ends. They harmed nobody, but lived happily enough wandering through all the streets of the town and calling in at every courtyard in Moscow.

Certainly we got to know that there was no limit to the good-natured patience of the Tartars. One could bargain with them by the hour together, and then finish up by buying nothing. Often they only provoked laughter and as often they were rudely kicked from the premises. None the less they kept on flashing their white teeth in a smile and importuning with 'Gentleman! Look! Buy. Good stuff. Listen!' Though we knew all this and had indeed seen it for ourselves we nevertheless had an instinctive dread of 'the Tartar invasion'.

Other visitors to our court were less interesting. On rare occasions the *dvornik* lazily sallied forth and proceeded to do some sweeping in the court. Clouds of dust floated upwards and the tenants slammed their windows in annoyance. The *dvornik* would go on working for about ten minutes and then give up, evidently deciding that it was not worth while to put tenants to inconvenience over such a trifling matter.

Sometimes chimney-sweeps would come round with long canes and a regular battery of curious round brushes. Covered from head to foot in soot they balefully blinked their gleaming white eyes at us, and remained hidden in the doorway for hours. We invariably imagined them to be evil negroes, white negroes of a special kind, who were bloodthirsty tiger-hunters, and so forth; in short, a dangerous race from whom it was best for us to keep at a distance.

But when a strawberry-seller came all our fears would vanish and we would rush back to our watch-tower.

From above it seemed that a big tray, laden with little heaped rows of appetizing berries, was walking of its own volition around the court, for the vendor himself was invisible beneath his wares. We knew that he must be there, however, for no one else could have shouted 'Ripe Strawberries' in such penetrating tones. Even to look at his fresh strawberries from the height of a second storey was a joy to us.

But it was no less a joy to watch with a certain sinking of heart the pigeons wheeling on high in the open air. The sun gilded them with its gold or tinted them with all the colours of the rainbow, making them creatures of unrivalled beauty. The ecstatic loveliness of that sight was generally voted not inferior even to strawberries.

Once a week without fail came an organ-grinder. With a grunt he would unsling the broad strap which bore the weight of the heavy instrument, fix up a home-made wooden support, and flood the court with wheezy dissonant chords. He would start his programme with the rousing Boulanger March, and afterwards proceed to the mournful aria from *Traviata* 'Oh, Alfred I am dying', which used to reduce us to tears.

'Poor Alfred and poor Traviata', we thought as we sat above the organ, until, by the time the last notes faded away, we would be in the grip of such remorseless sorrow that we would want to sob. Then all of a sudden the organ would strike up a jolly dance and the strains of 'Ah, you birch tree, you are my birch tree' would resound through our room, causing us to forget both the dying Traviata and her poor Alfred as our hands and feet mechanically beat time to the merry tune. Finally, the

organ-grinder would doff his cap, look up at us be-
seechingly, and picking up the coppers which we flung from the
window, quickly disappear through the entrance gate. But 'Ah,
you birch tree' rang in our ears for a long time afterwards.

One of the treats we most looked forward to was the appearance of the Bulgarian with his monkey. This was a very rare
event which always created a deep impression upon us. As
usual, master and monkey had the same pathetic appearance.
In the eyes of both there was something mournful and appealing.
When they begged for some small offering the monkey held out
its wrinkled hand in just the same way as its master did.

At first the wizened little creature—so human in appearance
—hid itself in its master's ragged bosom and seemed only
reluctantly to come into the open. It was always kept on a
short length of chain so that its freedom of movement was
limited to only a few feet. These two beings thus chained to
each other gave an impression of sadness and indescribable
loneliness. Mournfully the master gave his orders.

'Show how a little boy steals peas—ah, la, la, la.'

'Show how a peasant comes home drunk—ah, la, la, la',
and as mournfully did the monkey perform its tricks, turn its
somersaults, and swing on its chain, before leaping with a
single bound on to its master's shoulders and holding out an
invariably supplicating hand.

When, for a joke, anyone gave it a ball of paper or a nutshell
instead of money or sugar, it wrinkled its angry little face,
swore, and danced up and down shaking its clattering chain in
rage at the insult.

The Bulgarian with his neglected monkey, trembling from
fear and cold, always evoked our sorrowful interest. They seemed
to have no means of escape from their relentless poverty, bon-
dage, and misery. The monkey especially aroused our deepest
sympathy. It had been snatched away from its father and mother,
transported from the blazing sun of Africa to the cold of Russia,
there to be chained like a galley slave for the amusement of
cruel children!

When the miserable beast had taken its sweets from us and picked up the last of the coppers, it sprang with relief into its master's bosom, closed its little eyes in weariness, and relaxed.

Its master, 'Misery walking upon two feet', thereupon counted the coppers, gave us a sad smile, and followed by a crowd of children, servant-girls and workmen, went slowly through the gates, and for a long time was seen no more.

Thus in one way or another gazing from the window became one of the most important pastimes of the descendants of Akim Ivanovich.

From here we had, as it were, a bird's-eye view of life and awaited solution of its problems, explanation of its mysterious phenomena, and a working of miracles.

Though it was never our good fortune to find this solution nor to see any miracles, our faith in such possibility long survived and only disappeared imperceptibly with the passage of time. Only the window, our watch-tower over life, remained in our memory, associated with resounding footsteps in the court and the joy with which we shouted, 'The students! Here come the students!'

Through the court, making straight for our door, marched a little band headed by our brother Victor, of the College of Medicine. With his smooth face he looked little more than a boy. He was followed by the burly 'Cachalot' Puzanov, a powerful engineering student with a bushy beard, Vanya's young brother. Trotting behind with little mincing steps, came Kholodkov, also of the medical school, but looking rather clerical. Lastly, bringing up the rear, marched Venediktov, the eldest student of all, with bushy beard and blue spectacles, wearing a capacious ulster cloak with a plaid across his shoulders, and a broad-brimmed robber's hat. In his hand he carried a ponderous knotty cudgel.

Seeing us they halted for a moment and blew kisses to us. Kholodkov pulled faces. Cachalot glared at us fiercely and thrust out his lower lip. Venediktov brandished his cudgel and shouted, 'I'm coming to give you a good hiding!'

The front-door bell pealed abruptly and we ran to let them in. Even in the entrance they starting romping, joking, and playing the fool. Now was the time for indulging that irresponsible gaiety of youth with which a visit from 'our' students was always associated.

Kholodkov bowed on all sides like a Chinese idol and chanted through his nose his eternal

> *Rakki, Kikki, Boom,*
> *Rakki, Kikki, Boom,*
> *Allah, Dallah, Rishah, Bim!*

before making a sudden pounce on one of us. With laughter and terror we would bolt into the hall, wherupon he became subdued and, squatting on his heels, mournfully sang in a high-pitched quavering voice, 'Peeckuly, Packuly, Pockuly.' This made us feel sorry for him, and conquering our fear we climbed on his knees.

While tea was being got ready Cachalot juggled with the spoons, or played leap-frog over five chairs disposed around the room. In the manner of a showman he performed feats of strength or demonstrated 'the accomplishment of the impossible'. In the best fair-ground tradition he would announce: 'Here we have the spotted hyena', and forthwith Kholodkov, lifting up his coat-tails and exposing his pitiful backside in its threadbare student's trousers, would start crawling about the floor.

'The spotted hyena! He hunts *only* in the moonlight, except when there's no moon and he hunts without it! He feeds *exclusively* on rabbit—or anything else he can get. Step up, children! This is very instructive!' With a tiger-like roar Kholodkov lashed about on all sides.

Afterwards he imitated different animals in turn, to our delight; though none of us laughed louder than the 'old student' who, without his ulster and knotted stick, proved homely and jolly. Indeed, one had only to point a finger at him to set him off laughing again with his little trembling laugh. It was like having a crowd of colts burst in from the street.

When Father came home things became even livelier. Despite the difference in years, outlook, and position, he served as the connecting link between all these young people of different character. With them he was again the Yasha of old surrounded by his contemporaries. The students loved him for his unaffected manner, his good nature, and his hospitality.

Kholodkov was small, of indefinite age, and of rather Tartar appearance, with lively black eyes. He had an inexhaustible fund of jokes and amusing anecdotes, and made a speciality of imitating the habits and mannerisms of priests, of which he had a profound knowledge. When he tossed off a glass of vodka he would hold back the narrow sleeve of his short coat so realistically that one could fully believe that he was preventing the deep sleeve of an imaginary cassock from getting wet.

> *The Priest has a sleeve—*
> > *Oh, my fathers!*
> *So deep and so broad—*
> > *Oh, my mothers!*

Sometimes, in jest, he would solemnly intone in a nasal tenor voice for his host, as founder of the house, the blessing of 'Long life'. And when his improvised choir took up the refrain 'Long life! Long life!' it was just like being in a crowded church during a festival. The choir harmonized church music accurately and with feeling, and, doubtless as a contrast to their care-free students' songs, would with the utmost gravity and every appearance of inconsolable grief, suddenly embark upon a requiem.

Although in all this performance there was an element of fun, it was without offence, and never exceeded the bounds of a deep-rooted sense of decency.

Father was passionately fond of choral singing. He would listen raptly, and often, when no one was watching, would

himself join in at some specially loud passage. He had no ear and
was afraid that his poor efforts would ruin the harmony. Sometimes however the choir would break off unexpectedly and his
quavering note, quite half a tone lower, would become a
resounding solo. Though everyone laughed good-humouredly, he
was as abashed as a child.

Kholodkov was irrepressible and enlivened everything by
his jokes and his wit. He gave wonderful impersonations illus-
trating life in out-of-the-way parts, and the tales of his adventures were so funny that it was difficult to distinguish fact
from artistic embellishment. He read Gogol excellently, his
voice portraying every delicate shade between the 'tears and
laughter' of that great author.

His studies at the University were spasmodic, being dependent
upon his finances. When hard times came he would leave the
University for years and wander the by-ways of Russia taking
jobs in the Excise, the Post Office, or the Customs. When he
had saved enough he would come back and resume work until
he passed his next examination, after which he would again
disappear into the provinces. In short, he was a living example
of perpetual motion.

His University course had in this way extended over about
ten years, but his constant wanderings over the length and
breadth of Mother Russia had brought him into contact with all
types of people and his knowledge of conditions and customs,
and of the most intimate details of Russian life, was drawn from
the fountain-head. There were apparently no limits to his
patience, misfortunes, or surprising adventures, but his unruffled good temper and his harmless way of laughing at himself
and his bad luck, as well as at everyone around him, saved him
from despondency and from any kind of excess. 'An unlucky
man would drown in a tea-cup,' he would say of himself with
a laugh.

He found success in the end, and having taken his medical
degree settled in the depths of the country.

His absence was always felt whenever the students gathered

together. Father cherished a special weakness for him and more than once helped him out of financial difficulties.

We very much liked the 'stylish' student, too—he of the robber's hat—and christened him 'First Jester'. He had a favourite song with a slightly political flavour, and he would always sing it as a solo regardless of his audience. He was deeply concerned by the state of the country and there was something quite impressive about the way his beady eyes flashed behind his glasses as with obvious delight he listened to the words of his own song:

> *A council school was standing*
> *A council school was standing*
> *But down it fell!*

Sometimes too he would recite from Nekrasov's poems, 'Show me the dwelling where no peasant suffers'.

When the choir took up a mournful song, and waves of harmony spread like the ripples of a pool in which a stone has been cast, Venediktov would fall into a melancholy reverie and, sitting at a distance, muse on the sadness of a student's fate.

> *Swift as the waves are the days of our living,*
> *Shorter, still shorter, our road to the grave.*
> *Then pour out the Wassail Bowl, Comrade, now pour,*
> *God knows what awaits us, what lurks at our door.*
> *You will die and be buried as though you had lived not,*
> *From corruption you'll rise not to feast with good friends.*
> *Then pour out the Wassail Bowl, Comrade, now pour,*
> *God knows what awaits us, what lurks at our door.*

With moving chords the grand, sad melody faded away to pianissimo. The company was hushed, each thinking of his own fate, no one any longer feeling quite at ease. Then Kholodkov jumped up from his chair and jokingly pronounced the blessing of 'Many years' upon his host. The glasses were charged again, depression vanished like snow beneath the rays of the sun, and jollity returned.

At midnight the party broke up. In the entrance hall Kholodkov bade us good-bye with his 'Rakki, Kikki, Boom—Adah, Lalaridah, Dim,' as he was putting on his threadbare summer overcoat which, in his own words, was 'made of fish fur.'

Outside a snowstorm was raging.

XIX

THE night nursery of the younger generation was a long room screened off from Father's study. It had no windows and so even in day-time was always semi-dark. One length of wall was entirely taken up by a collection of cupboards, drawers, and bric-a-brac in which we imagined all the terrors of night to be concealed. From here, when all else was quiet, there always came mysterious muffled sounds of struggling. With a numbing fear one would try to pierce the impenetrable darkness to catch sight of unseen monsters! Every nerve would be alive to the presence of something invisible, quite near and yet far away beyond the limit of things known—something alive, intangible, and terribly repulsive. At last it would begin scraping along the floor. Terror would then reach such a pitch that one's courage quailed at the thought of resisting alone, surrounded only by the sleeping forms of one's brothers, a manifestation of subterranean powers.

Little Volodya would rouse his brother Nicholas, who, only half awake, would say that it was nothing to worry about, as in a state of semi-stupor he fumbled under his bed and sent a thick boot hurtling into the mysterious corner with a thud. Immediately the invisible world would be silent and still, and the little boy would close his heavy lids and fall into a gentle sleep.

A welcome sunny Sunday morning! True the sun itself was not visible, but its warm rays found a way through the web of thick material forming the screen. Everyone was up already, and from the hall came the subdued sound of voices and the clatter of crockery. The terrors of the night had vanished away, and even the mysterious corner was now calm and peaceful and no longer frightening. The subterranean powers had been finally placated and allowed one to dress in peace and go to breakfast.

The joyful sun was peeping in at all the windows of the main hall. A copy of Makovski's 'Dear Guest' in a deep gold frame hung on the wall and, as usual, the 'dear guest' himself was unable to make up his mind whether to drain his flagon. Alexander the Second, as sad as ever, gazed down upon the roof of the outhouse. A boiling samovar and some rolls from Philipov's were set on the table and, except for Mother, the whole family was assembled. Father, not wearing his spectacles and dressed in a soft grey dressing-gown with a blue silk cord, was drinking his glass of incredibly strong tea. Apparently he was not in good spirits for he took no notice of any of us.

There was always a feeling of restraint about the house after a visit from the students.

Sitting opposite Father was Victor, our eldest brother, wearing a short jacket. He was deep in some pamphlet or other, and sipped his weak tea without zest as though in performance of a duty.

Between him and Father there was constant friction, and though at the moment all might be quiet, a quarrel would flare up on the least provocation, for when Victor thought himself in the right he never hesitated to state his views with the utmost candour, regardless alike of his method of presentation and the feelings of his listeners. This often hurt Father who was horrified at his son's callousness and surprised by his lack of understanding of life, which however he attributed to his youth and didactic nature. He himself was never able to cope with Victor's logic and was always overwhelmed by the sheer weight of his arguments.

So it was now. Angered by some brusque remark, Father roused himself from reverie and a quarrel started.

'Why do you lecture me?' he said angrily, at the same time concealing his beautiful eyes behind smoked glasses. 'I have forgotten more than you ever knew!'

Victor at once jumped on this expression, remarking that he was sorry to know that his father had forgotten more than he, albeit the fact was most painfully obvious—and so forth. Father made an angry gesture and, thoroughly vexed, retired to his bedroom.

Victor buried himself again in his pamphlet quite unperturbed, though he was secretly reproaching himself for his unbridled tongue, his fiery temper, and his inability to assert himself without show of feeling. Father, while recognizing the logical force of his son's observations, was annoyed by his manner and by a certain studied heartlessness with which he approached life's problems.

With such melancholy reflections his Sunday morning began.

And now in his untidy bedroom he was brought face to face with the bitterest tragedy of his life.

On a large bed, unkempt, all engrossed in her own thoughts, the merest shadow of her old bright self, lay Mother. She had greatly aged. Her hair was grey, her features obscured by wrinkles, and in this weak-minded though good-natured woman it was difficult to recognize the Olya of timepast.

'Olya, aren't you up? It's nearly twelve o'clock,' said Father, a trifle petulantly.

'Just a moment, just a moment, Yasha, and I'll get up'— there was almost a note of pleading in Mother's voice.

Father went from the room. Mother settled down again in the bed.

Thoughtfully pacing across the hall from one corner to another, Father recalled his life's history from the day of his leaving his parents' home. In the beginning, he and Olya had made a happy enough start. She had come to Moscow full of energy and sympathy, bravely enduring hard times, shortage of money, and reverses of all kinds. At every turn she had helped him, indifferent alike to poverty and sacrifice. At last conditions had improved and it looked as though henceforth life would run smoothly for them.

Even Grandmother Praskovia Feodorovna, educating Victor at the local gymnasium, was now easy concerning her Yasha's fate. In her rare but affectionate letters insinuations against Olya became ever less frequent. Though the feeling remained, however much she glossed it over in letters, that she had no real love for her daughter-in-law, there was no longer that open hostility which had been patent to all in the early days of her son's married life. Now that Father's affairs prospered her fears for the children's future gradually diminished, as the family gradually increased with more and more children, strong and healthy.

Suddenly, from a sky in which was no visible cloud, fell a thunderbolt.

With horror Father recalled every detail of the awful day which marked the turning point of his life. Though it had all happened seven or eight years ago it seemed like yesterday.

We were all living at the time in a country cottage on the outskirts of Moscow. It was getting on for evening. Father was reading an amusing sketch of merchant life in the city. Olya was feeding at her breast the bonny little boy she adored. Some strangers appeared in the garden. Father got up to meet them, wondering why they had come, failing to realize what they wanted.

They all made way for him. On a light stretcher he saw the mutilated body of a child. It was Peter, his son.

The little fellow had strayed some distance along the railway line and had been run over by an engine. Both his legs were severed, his chest crushed to fragments, his features disfigured.

Never, never until Yasha died, would he forget that inhuman cry which rang through the garden before Olya, her face twisted in agony, fell forward as though dead among the flowers. Her baby rolled down upon the grass.

By nightfall the young mother was in a high fever. 'Her milk has got to her head' was the neighbours' verdict.

There followed complete collapse and loss of reason. The shock of that terrible accident had been too much for her, and she had to go away for treatment. In three years, haggard and changed almost beyond recognition, she came back home—the ghost of the Olya he had known. Her interest in her home and children had gone, and for hours together she sat motionless or lay on the sofa lost in her own thoughts.

The home seemed to fall to ruins. It was no longer anyone's duty to attend to the house-keeping or to look after the children. The servant-girl managed everything alone. Prostrate with grief and fully occupied by his business, Father had neither the time nor the skill to manage a household.

The younger generation ran wild. Their clothes were in rags. They became unused to any form of discipline. Mother was conscious of this and indeed it caused her suffering, but, as a result of her illness, her will had been undermined and her energies paralysed so that life pursued its disorderly course from day to day without her playing any active part in it.

So two years passed.

Suddenly, for no apparent reason, her malady re-asserted itself in full force. She went away, this time for about three years, and returned only to lie on the sofa again in apathy.

From then onward there came recurrences of her illness, with alternating periods of good health during which she lived with us happily and at times normally. Father suffered more than any of us, and to the end of his life was unable to reconcile himself to this misfortune.

And now as he paced diagonally across the hall he was calling to mind all the details of the years that had gone.

The ikon of Our Saviour, so revered by Grandmother, that same ikon before which she had herself so passionately prayed, gazed down benignly. The soft red glow of its lamp, lit for the feast-day, barely illumined its gilded tracery.

'Such, it seems, is the cross I must bear,' sighed Father, and with a face less clouded he went into his study.

Here surrounded by his familiar books and papers he felt less care-worn. Life's daily worries and problems here demanded instant attention. Even though his ever-present sorrow still pressed down upon his shoulders, the sword of Damocles was to some extent shrouded by the business of every day.

As he went through his papers a feeling of annoyance at his quarrel with Victor returned. He was a good lad; indeed, but for him, the whole household would have fallen into chaos. Father readily confessed this, being aware of his own power-lessness.

For Victor had found time not only to attend his lectures but also to see to the ordering, check the linen, deal out indiscriminate punishment, and generally correct the younger generation. While Father knew that there was no love lost between ourselves and Victor, he also knew that it was Victor who had seen to all our needs. And so, as he sat in his study alone, he forgave for the hundredth time Victor's unbridled bitter tongue and his unseemly outbursts, attributing them only to his youth.

Yet deep in his heart he felt his eldest son's character to be opposed to his own, and in some way to fall short. 'Man does not live by reason alone,' he reflected as he rejoined us in the hall.

We all sided with Father instinctively, for his gentle affec-tionate nature won the sympathy of us all. Sometimes we even hated Victor, not so much for his dictatorial authority over us as for his antagonism to Father.

After spending a few minutes with us, Father, evidently tired, changed to his coat and smart hat, picked up his ivory-handled cane, and went off, trying to avoid meeting Victor again.

We knew that he was seeking escape from the disagreeable atmosphere at home because he had not the strength to face family discord. When engrossed in business at the warehouse he was different, more self-assured, confident that he was master; and when we young people made one of our rare calls upon him he would greet us warmly, as a friend, and as soon as he caught sight of us would invariably take some cash from the office and distribute it between us for buying sweets.

The warehouse, a small building on the junction of two busy thoroughfares, had once been part of a monastery. Its walls were incredibly thick, and light was admitted through windows so small that they looked more like embrasures in a fortress than windows of a trading concern on a crowded street. The office was a little room all spick-and-span with white paint and a blue border at the ceiling level. Its furniture consisted of a desk fronted by a most comfortable chair with a high round back, and two chairs for visitors.

Father felt at his ease here. He whisked the beads across the abacus just as in Grandfather's time, jotted down notes in a ledger, and beamed at us from behind his gold-rimmed spectacles.

As he sat in his office he would survey through an arch-like opening all that was going on in the warehouse. The walls of the warehouse were decked with trading licences. Within was a long counter at which Boris, the young assistant, officiated and one could hear how he attended to his employer's interests as he chinked money, packed cases, and persuaded customers. Business went smoothly, and gradually became more and more lively as the day wore on.

Somewhere about noon friends or hangers-on would drop in to see Father.

Whistling and imparting the inevitable flourish to his cane came his old friend and one-time rival, Paul Alexeivich Gushchin, in the best of spirits. He had aged much, and wore a shabby suit whose fit proclaimed a previous owner. For many months he had been strenuously engaged in looking for employment, for he had long ago been discharged from the municipal *abattoir* owing to some misdemeanour or other of which no one knew the true facts.

At the present time, while awaiting some other post, he frequented the Zamoskvorechie suburb and its convents. He attended church services and thereafter in the warehouse alluded to the beauty of the liturgy or talked scandal about the Novo-Dievitchy Monastery. He had quite gone to seed and

Father, thirty-five years old.

Volodya as a schoolboy.

Volodya as a student in Moscow.

endeavoured to curry favour with everybody by suiting dirty stories to the particular taste of his audience.

He visited the warehouse every day, treating it like the *bourse* and imagining that something might possibly be picked up there in the way of a trifling commission or small business deal. All the time he was revelling in talk about arch-priests or mothers superior he was looking up impatiently at the hands of the clock on the wall. His heart grew cold as he figured the chances of Father's asking him to lunch, and wondered when the magic hour would come for him to be taken off to a neighbouring restaurant.

Father was fully aware of what was in his mind, but deliberately closed his eyes to the deceits of his fellow men. He had a feeling that people of Gushchin's type stood in special need of his help, and he forgave in them traits from which he would have turned away in disgust had he met them in well-ordered lives.

The clock struck half-past twelve. Closing his ledgers and locking the drawer of his desk, Father winked at Gushchin and called through the door, 'Boris! I'm off. If anyone calls, tell them I'll be at Moisev's. And don't forget to despatch forty pounds to Klyagin!'

'All right, Yakov Akimovich,' Boris replied cheerfully from behind his counter.

Shameless Gushchin, tripping left and right, was delighted beyond all measure. He called to memory his best stories of monastic life and anticipated the blessings in store.

In the small restaurant quite near the warehouse Father was so well known that he was received with open arms. All the waiters flocked round him in a crowd, bowing obsequiously, and reckoning it an honour to serve at his table. His quiet, good-natured, easy-going manner, coupled with his generous tips, had made him a welcome patron. He in turn was flattered by this popularity and often when ordering a meal would say to the waiter, 'Surely you don't know me?'

'Of course I know you, Yakov Akimovich,' the old waiter

would reply, with difficulty concealing a grin as he held out the menu card. 'Why we all of us know you.' And Father would answer with a pleasant smile.

Gushchin sat at his side, throwing a friendly nod to the waiter, looking in a servile way into Father's face.

They discussed the menu with feeling, knowledge, and deliberation, paying due regard to the waiter's opinion and to his confidential information regarding the ingredients of each dish. To Gushchin this programme of good things was enchanting. He tendered instructive comments and observations on every course. This was the chief event of his day.

'Mushrooms! They should be delicious just now. I tried some at the Arch-Priest's place. They would have made your mouth water. Salt cabbage, too! The very best kind. And what a choice of fish! There's no end to them! They're just giving them away!'

When the discussion was over and the meal ordered, just as the waiter was darting off the more quickly to execute his commission, it was one of Father's favourite jokes to stop him and say, 'While they are landing the fish, and going to the shop for the roast beef, you go and bring us two portions of mushrooms and smetana. And don't forget a carafe of vodka.'

Gushchin winked affably, and chuckled at Father's jest. He seemed the embodiment of good nature and contentment. Over his *zakuski* he related some of his pungent anecdotes, for notwithstanding his very humble status, and the periodic buffetings of fate he still retained his old interest in the fair sex and was proud of his success in that direction.

Father listened while he ate and laughed good-humouredly at Gushchin's prevarications, for he always adhered to that wise popular rule: 'If you don't like it, don't listen; if I lie, don't interrupt.'

They would spend about an hour and a half in thus quietly chatting over their meal before Gushchin lazily rose from the table and furtively slipped into his waistcoat pocket the three-rouble note he had succeeded in begging. He would then plead 'business affairs' and depart, leaving Father to stroll back leisurely to the warehouse.

After lunch the activity invariably seemed to have become keener than·ever. Carters were now arriving with goods from the station. A constant stream of retailers in wretched carts jolted indolently along. Chance clients looked in. Boris was as agile as a monkey in dealing with everybody's wants.

By tea-time quite a crowd had gathered in the shop; in addition to the regular clients, friends and so forth had dropped in either to exchange bits of news or simply to crack a jest or two.

A small boy was dispatched at the run for boiling water and a 'bite' consisting of a currant loaf. To the accompaniment of laughter, oaths, and complaints about bad times and rotten trade, business would follow its normal routine, orders be taken, and accounts produced.

When the confusion and argument reached a climax and Boris was too exhausted any longer to cope with the welter of demands and accusations, when, in fact, there was every prospect of a violent storm, Father quietly emerged from his office. His gentle manner, his smart clothes, and his never-failing readiness to come to a compromise at once threw him out into sharp relief against this rude, slovenly, and hard-fisted crowd and where but a minute ago Boris had failed, he found some solution quietly and without fuss. His opponent's anger gradually subsided. Father's integrity, his gentle reproof, his kind child-like eyes had done their work.

'Discuss this reasonably,' he said to Agaphon, a little dwarf of a man, a customer of long standing, who had not yet recovered from the excitement of a tussle with Boris. Agaphon was silent; the fire in his eyes died down; he shifted from one leg to another.

In his face could be seen evidence of the struggle that was going on within him, on the one hand his obstinacy and unwillingness to give in to Boris, and on the other his honest desire to oblige Father. And Father's 'discuss this reasonably' won the day. He undid his purse, and took out his money. Agaphon was tamed again.

'Take it, Yakov Akimovich. God knows it's all I've got. I swear on the cross that if it hadn't been you I'd not have parted with a kopeck,' he blustered as he emptied the coins on the counter and smoothed out the dirty notes.

Father ordered some fresh tea. Agaphon drank it out of the saucer, and after a long and heart-felt speech about his love and respect for Father, gave fresh orders, and discussed the question of enlarging his business. Completely mollified, he held Father's hand in a long grip.

'You're an awfully good fellow, Yakov Akimich,' he repeated over and over again looking affectionately into his eyes. 'It's because of my respect for you that I pay.' And off he went with his chests.

Klyagin arrived on his starveling horse. Father retired to his office again. Boris nervously put himself to rights in anticipation of a battle. The lookers-on, full of curiosity, got together in a corner to await a scene.

Klyagin was tall and as thin as a skeleton. Prematurely old, he was now in the last stage of consumption. Foaming at the mouth he burst into the shop, flung on the floor a case of goods, and shouted, 'Look what muck your firm lands me with!' The small boy locked the door. Boris strode forward and started to reply. Klyagin worked himself up into a frenzy. The audience chuckled and taunted both sides alike.

Despite his humble rank, his wild character, and his exhausting disease, Klyagin carried on a comparatively large business. He was known to be honest and he counted for something in his dealings with Father.

Father returned to the shop and in a minute Klyagin's feverish energy had departed. He was quiet, and even bared his almost toothless gums in a smile, hanging on Father's words as he brought the conversation round to his favourite topic. For

Klyagin was a patriot. He cursed the Jews and was full of hatred for any manner of living which did not conform to the Russian.

Whereas it had looked as though no force could have arrested his wild imprecations and frenzied cursing, Father managed not only to arrest them but also to touch in the man a vein of calm sincerity. Tortured as he was by his disease and his recurrent fits of passion he spoke about his family, his children, and fishing.

In the end he was completely mollified. He not only settled his account quietly and without excitement, but also ordered more goods on credit and as he went away invited Father to come and see him. 'Bring all your family, too. You'll be welcome.'

Once we all went with Father to visit Klyagin and were amazed at the unexpected contrast—the clean, fresh little house on the outskirts of Moscow in a district of seemingly endless market-gardens, the kind, stout wife, and the happy children, Klyagin himself, too, in his best clothes, quiet, hospitable, and somehow childishly gentle.

After a number of years of suffering from consumption Klyagin died, but not before he had settled his account with Father down to the last kopeck.

But business relationships did not always terminate thus happily.

Fur coats, watches, divers silver articles and knick-knacks of all kinds were frequently deposited with Father as tokens for payment by bankrupt purchasers. These were all kept in the warehouse and occasionally an article would disappear for a while only to turn up again unexpectedly on the top of the file. Everything which had thus been left 'as a mark of special friendship' had its own story which when the time suited Father could always remember.

Often he would make a display of his 'museum' whose historical and financial significance was unique. Common silver watches represented fifteen hundred roubles, sheepskin coats had been valued by their owners at hundreds, and accordions at ten roubles apiece.

Years later there was to be added to the 'museum' a sack full of counterfeit silver money. Even this was brought as a friendly gesture to 'that kind fellow Yakov Akimich.'

But in addition to his business dealings and business anxieties Father took upon himself an enormous amount of work, worry, and trouble which had no connexion with his life in the warehouse.

He had an everlasting passion for rehabilitating people. He advised them, proposed new plans for them, loaned them money while they were looking for work, and gave them comfort and exhortation.

Sometimes he went to absurd lengths in the care and trouble he took over all these friends of his—the Gushchins, the Bielikovs, the unrecognized authors, and the luckless artists who repaired to him as though to the *bourse*. Often those who found easy access to his good nature were nothing more than brazen swindlers, but he shut his eyes to the obvious worthlessness of any unrecognized genius, and pleaded, persuaded, and even demanded on the man's behalf until in the end he managed to get his grateful but unfortunate subject somehow established.

When for some discreditable cause this same subject was shot out with a bang Father would run off again to persuade and explain and would quite often succeed in getting the poor disgraced fellow taken back again.

For it was hard to resist Father's disinterested, touching, and childlike enthusiasm. For Yakov Akimich people did their best.

But there was something incomprehensible and otherworldly about his extraordinary partiality and sympathetic love for all these unfortunate, and as often as not unclean and brazen people. For such, and only for such, he was prepared to endure any humiliation, evidently because he felt that of all unfortunates in the world those who had fallen stood most in need of his mediation.

It gave him the greatest satisfaction to cherish and to set on his feet some 'has been', and when that 'has been', established and prosperous, failed to recognize him on the street, or even spread malicious rumours about him, he was in no way put out, knowing that the time would come when his mediation would again be required. The repentant protégé, once more on his uppers, would come back a little diffidently to the warehouse, and Father would re-enact the whole scene from beginning to end.

It was extraordinary that towards people of deservedly good repute he behaved with a certain coldness, as though he could see in them something which was hidden from others. Their merits, though universally recognized, did not seem to him so crystal-clear and he was always influenced by the assured 'facts' revealed by his own clairvoyance.

'All is not gold that glitters,' he would assert on such occasions. Even on the sun he would see stains; in inky darkness he could discern flashes of colour.

'Be quiet!' he would exclaim to Victor as he angrily dismissed his energetic protests against any new friends of doubtful character who were looming on the horizon. 'We are all good! The egg can't teach the hen!'

And with the obstinacy of a child he would abandon his work and intercede for yet another of those 'unfortunates' of his.

His face would light up with happiness and his beautiful, brown-flecked blue eyes would gleam joyfully over the top of his spectacles as he remarked, 'Well, what did I tell you? Beryukov has been to me on bended knees saying "Forgive me! I repent, Yakov Akimich. My conscience tortures me when I recall how I have betrayed your confidence by stealing my employers' money. I have thrown up everything and come to obtain your forgiveness".'

'And according to you Beryukov was a rogue who should have been swept off with a filthy broom,' he exclaimed to the astonished Victor. 'Ah, you doctors, you doctors! You can never see beyond your noses.'

Victor would boil over with indignation and argue for hours with skill and conviction. His emotion knew no bounds for he looked upon helping scoundrels as both dangerous and anti-social. He even branded it as criminal—almost as bad as making counterfeit money.

Father was silent and not in the least perturbed. It was evident to him that he and his son spoke different languages. He installed Beryukov temporarily in his warehouse and afterwards found him a job with some respectable folk in the provinces.

From time to time Beryukov wrote him letters of gratitude. Then his correspondence ceased pending his next lapse. He was shameless, brazen, and entirely unscrupulous but nevertheless knew how to play on the heart-strings of his fellows. Occasionally his impudence transcended all bounds.

Once, after a long period of silence, when Beryukov was comfortably established in the provinces, he sent a long letter written in an affected and laborious style in which he described his mode of life. He continued: 'The recompense which I have received has enabled me still to live a well-ordered life, but the satisfaction of my physical needs still requires the best that can be procured. You will yourself agree, most deeply respected Yakov Akimich, that to visit "unfortunate but charming creatures" but once a month at most is insufficient for the health of a normal well-educated man.' The letter ended with a half-entreaty, half-demand, for the remission of a sum of money 'for the assuagement of physical irritation.'

Victor stalked along the hall with the letter in his hand angered to the depth of his heart. Father for his part refused to read into it the cynicism, the veiled blackmail, the humiliation, and the basely insulting innuendo which were quite apparent to Victor.

Such manifestations as this never caused Father to stumble on the difficult road of life, and his blind, all-embracing sympathy together with his unshakable faith in human nature continued to prevent his recognizing the most blatant extortion. It was as though he knew for certain that in the end the most flagrant scoundrel must be pulled up by the sheer strength of virtue. For all these brazen, depraved, and worthless characters sooner or later confessed their lapses to him, laying bare before him their begrimed souls, in the knowledge that so far from condemning them Father would stretch out his hand and gather them to the warmth of his all-forgiving heart.

As the moth flies to the flame so all this beggarly throng flew to him. It was as if on his brow were inscribed that noble message, 'Come unto me all ye that travail and are heavy laden and I will refresh you.'

XX

WE generally spent the summer in a country cottage near Moscow in the direction of Sokolniki. Here the suburbs came to an end and the State Forests began, and along the line of the road detached cottages surrounded by gardens nestled against the edge of the forest.

The road, furrowed by deep ruts, lost itself far away in this forest of tall pines. There was a smell of resin in the air and from early dawn the birds held concert. After sunset great flocks of rooks flew homewards cawing in their good-humoured bass as they wheeled lazily round and round the tops of the swaying pines before settling down in silence on their nests.

The season would be early May. The nights were still cold and there were draughts from the windows. The smell of resin penetrated into our cottage, where it was blended with the smell of the new oil paint on the balcony.

From the balcony we could see the tops of young trees— birch, maple, and ash—and whenever the wanton breezes ran through them causing them graciously to incline their obedient heads and raise them again with a little shudder and a rhythmic sigh, one could imagine that one was looking down upon some boundless expanse of water, on which green waves were tossing.

Early every morning the herdsman's song was borne in from far away as he rounded up his cattle. The beasts plodded slowly on their way and one could hear the sturdy breathing of the milk-laden cows, the irritable snort of the horses, and the bleating of sheep.

Then from the wooden church would come a jangle of bells and from our balcony we would see our neighbours breakfasting on their terrace and the priest, Father Peter, our landlord, donning his cassock before hurrying down the winding garden path to morning service.

The keen morning air gave one's nose a little tweak and sent a shiver running down the whole of one's body, although the sun was already gradually banishing the dew from the meadows and the leaves of the trees. The new paint on the balcony grew soft to the touch and gave out its own peculiar smell with greater intensity than ever. Soon the heat would become so oppressive as to make one welcome a secluded place in the shade.

The household gradually bestirred itself. Windows were flung open. There were sounds of splashing water in the wash-basins. A door banged in the kitchen whence came a clatter of crockery. The birds had long been singing their morning song and from the pine-tops the rooks, ponderously and at long intervals, took up their bass refrain.

After a long winter sojourn in a town, what joy it was to hear all these different sounds, to see the green of the fields, and to feel the life-giving heat of the sun! There was something strange, albeit longed for, in all of it. It was like an unexpected meeting with an old friend.

On the balcony at breakfast everyone was cheerful, lively, and inconsequently happy.

Even Victor refrained from admonishing anybody, and from starting any arguments at table. Father was in good spirits and drank his tea with zest. We younger folk were anxious to see the end of the meal so that we could scatter in different directions like chaff in the wind and set about our own business, seeing that each of us had preconceived notions about putting a long May day to the most strenuous use.

Father decided that it would be a sin to go up to the stuffy town on such a day, and so putting on waders took his rod and line and went off fishing.

This was his favourite pastime and he could spend hours at the water's edge without catching a single fish.

The silence, unbroken save by the soothing gurgle of the water and the muffled call of a distant cuckoo; the float bobbing up and down to the gentle ripples on the stream while all beside was motionless; the solitude; the warmth of the caressing sun on a May morning—all this combined to make him forget life's worries.

'There'll be flour when the grain is ground,' he reflected and took courage from the wise old country saying. After all, he mused, there were those whose lives were sadder than his own, and, thus consoled, he shook his head and abandoned himself to the enchantment of a quiet morning.

Victor took an interesting book and stayed in the fields until dinner time. We youngsters scampered through the forest each on his own highly important business.

There seemed to be no end to the State-owned forest of beautiful upright pines alternating with riotous undergrowth. Its atmosphere of mystery was almost oppressive and yet at the same time lovely beyond words.

Where the cluster of cottages ended there stood a lonely police-hut. The custodian of law and order had not much to do in a district populated solely by cottage tenants, and so rarely vouchsafed any sign of his existence beyond the boundary of his kitchen garden, which in consequence was a model of its kind. For even though the cottagers had no real use for him in his capacity of policeman they made brisk demands on the fruits of his agricultural labours.

We used to have dinner on the balcony or, on specially fine days, in the garden under the open sky. Father made the salad and told us about the Frenchman, Oliver, the chef at the famous Hermitage Restaurant, who won a world-wide reputation and a fortune from his 'Salad Oliver'. As Father talked, his gun, 'Monte Cristo', lay already loaded at his side and if a sparrow came in sight he would pick it up, take aim and fire in the middle of his story. Whereupon the scared bird would fly off into the bushes and the tale would be continued.

Even Mother on such days as these seemed brighter and more sociable. She took note of any untidiness in the dress of us young folk, quietly reproved us, and generally displayed an interest in what was going on around her.

Towards evening when the setting sun was throwing its last beautiful purple rays on the tops of the pines and the forest was wrapped in blue violet shadow there was so deep a hush that it seemed as though the thread of life had run to its end. Mother then went in to rest while Father would doze in his chair with a newspaper across his knees.

The shadows grew heavier until the forest became a thick impenetrable mass and the luminous blue-green sky gave place to the early stars. We would run along the darkening groves to an empty closely shuttered cottage whose desolate silence produced an eerie sensation. There we played leap-frog while the elders walked about in pairs whispering.

When it was quite dark we went home to bed, stumbling drowsily against the stones in the path and laden with impressions of the past day which a light refreshing sleep seemed only momentarily to interrupt.

As yet not many cottages were tenanted, but gradually shutters began to open here and there, loads of furniture were delivered, and housemaids were heard arguing with carters. In the evening cabs carrying tenants and their hand luggage rolled up, and thereupon another empty cottage awoke to new life. Flowers were planted in the garden, the flowerbeds were set about with big silver balls, and children scampered about the grounds.

In one of the big outlying cottages not far from the police-hut a German family always took up residence at the end of May. In the strict sense it was not a family at all since it consisted of one Ivan Ivanovich Scheffel and José, his light of love, a beautiful sportive woman with a most strikingly well-developed bust.

Outside this cottage coachmen and grooms would stand for hours at a time, while inside could be seen dandified gentlemen and free-and-easy ladies wearing gay-coloured risqué gowns. The place echoed with foreign talk, drunken laughter, the crash of breaking crockery, and voices raised to a pitch which betokened an impending brawl. It was as though the whole German colony with complete contempt for decency and disregard of Russian tradition were intent upon giving an exhibition of its own innate vulgarity.

José was a temperamental Polish lady and her friends visited her simply to have a good time and meet young men who were friends of Scheffel. Cupid, naked and unashamed, was incessantly engaged in finding temporary accommodation for some of his devotees and leading others to the altar. José for sheer love of her art was the moving spirit behind every intrigue, for it was she who brought the parties together, conducted the strategy, encompassed the enemy, and often brought the immoral campaign to a successful conclusion. But while she supervised the happiness of others she in no way neglected her own and thus gave rise to frequent quarrels with Jan, as she called her lover.

Often at about midnight the German colony resounded to the sound of shrieking and cursing in three languages at once. Sometimes these led to brawls, and José sent for Father, who alone seemed to possess sufficient authority to pacify a civilized German suffering from jealous pangs.

Something surprising was always happening in this establishment.

On one occasion, maddened by jealousy, the head of the house, his eyes bloodshot, intoxicated alike by wine and passion, brutally flogged his paramour who grovelled half naked at his feet bellowing at the top of her voice and making frantic efforts to tear herself from the vice-like grip of her lord and master.

Terrified dishevelled women and their escorts in crumpled dress-shirts crowded round the door while the cause of this jealous outburst, a bearded Don Juan, made good his escape by jumping out of a window without a care for the fate of his deep-bosomed Dulcinea.

Father on this occasion boldly went up to the half-demented Scheffel and wrested an empty champagne bottle from his hand while José seized the opportunity to get away to her bedroom behind a screen of frightened women. Scheffel, worn out by his frenzy, was gradually subdued and with much laborious panting finally came to his senses. Not before then did he realize the full depth of horror from which Father had rescued him.

On the morrow, however, life followed its normal course as though nothing at all had happened.

After these orgies and drunken brawls Ivan Ivanovich would keep quiet for a while and rolling his beautiful calf-like eyes betake himself to his violin. In the evening a quartette would be arranged and the majestic strains of Beethoven and Brahms would steal across the forest. For 'Vanka Shtrik', as Father used to call Scheffel, cleansed his heart from shame in crystal streams of classical music and knew the realms of melody like some well-trodden road.

Every one of his many nephews, cousins, and relations of all sorts had his same stocky build, his calf-like eyes, and his weakness for music. Every day from the corners of each room they could all be heard rehearsing on different instruments for the trios, quartettes, quintettes, and so forth which took place in the evening. For us, these evenings were incredibly boring.

During his periods of sobriety 'Vanka Shtrik' affected to look down on Father and indeed barely deigned to notice him since everything Russian was not only opposed to his beloved Germany but was altogether beneath contempt. The half-German, half-Russian town of Libau, that mighty birth-place of the great family of Scheffel, with its luxury and magnificence put sleepy Moscow and tawdry Petersburg in the shade.

Quite shamelessly these Russo-Germans drank to their German Kaiser, railed against Russia's backwardness and prophesied her speedy downfall. For notwithstanding the fact that the majority of them were German only in name and had been born and bred in Russia, the force of gravitation drew them to the land of their origin with such attraction as to make them avowed traitors to the country of their birth. Evidently the German heart lacked those generous qualities with which the heart of 'that uncultured Russian, Yakov Akimovitch' was so liberally endowed.

Yet whenever there was a scandal or mishap of any kind they shed their vaunted German *Kultur* like a husk and stood revealed as a rude, heartless, and empty people, totally incapable of ordering their own lives aright.

Once Scheffel, hatless and excited, came over to our cottage to see Father. He stayed a long time closeted in the study talking and at last went off somewhere with Father, downcast and dishevelled, with a dull gleam in his calf-like eyes, and betraying by his unsteady gait the stress of emotion through which he had just passed. For two or three days afterwards Father abandoned his own affairs and spent all his time at the Scheffel's house, only returning late in the evening.

All this secrecy looked highly suspicious to us. Though the Scheffels had no sense of shame it was evident that Vanka Shtrik was now deeply affected by something or other, and for a whole week José was not seen outside the house.

The conclusion of all this tragedy was worthy of a music-hall. It had happened that Vanka Shtrik returning from the city somewhat earlier than his wont had caught his lady-love in the embrace of one of the relations. Whereas the relation had escaped down the road in terror, bearing a couple of black eyes, José had been almost beaten to death and was lying all bruised and bleeding in her boudoir threatening open scandal, final rupture, and legal proceedings.

Father managed to convince both sides that the only way in which they could extricate themselves from the position in which they were now was by means of matrimony. To José he said that Ivan Ivanovitch as a married man would never accuse his own wife of infidelity and would not dare to insult a helpless woman. To Scheffel he suggested that after marriage José would come to her senses and would be deprived of the chance she now had to abuse her freedom. She would, in fact, be as obedient to his wishes as a dog on a chain.

He explained that in any other event there would always be quarrels which might either terminate fatally or result in José's running away with the first man she met. As Vanka Shtrik could not endure even the thought of the latter alternative, a legal marriage offered the only solution.

After long discussion for and against the project, the final decision was in favour of an abiding matrimonial yoke and Father was detailed as emissary of peace to the court of Madame José. She at first assumed an air of injured innocence but soon came to terms, having in the depth of her heart long desired permanent and legal fetters.

The marriage was celebrated twice—first in the Lutheran Church, since the groom was Lutheran, and then in the Catholic Church in deference to the express wishes of the sentimental José.

Arrayed in her wedding dress and wearing a white veil over her head, José, in the midst of a crowd of Polish relations from some place unknown, looked the picture of maidenly innocence. Hordes of calf-eyed Scheffels, including the Don Juan who had once been surprised in the bride's arms, solemnly congratulated the happy groom. Father, who was also present, was quite overjoyed.

On so auspicious an occasion Vanka Shtrik had to arrange 'a feast for all the world,' and so by special delivery from his native Libau came his favourite brand of sausage, and from Munich a hogshead of beer from the Imperial brewery.

The guests drank to the health of the young people and to Wilhelm the Second. They shouted 'Hoch' and patriotic German songs. Father was all smiles as he ate sausages from his fingers in German fashion and praised the excellence of the beer. He gave no indication that he thought it neither prudent nor tactful to exalt the might of Germany on Russian soil in the presence of a Russian.

After the wedding Scheffel's family life proceeded quite smoothly. José became circumspect and Shtrik settled down and was blind to the flirtations of his better half. Father's phrase—'like a dog on a chain'—afforded him consolation. She could never get away from him.

Luckily the German element at the Scheffels' cottage had its direct antithesis in the violent pan-Slavism at the Karnaliks'.

On the opposite side of the road from us, half hidden by the verge of the forest, stood a cottage which had probably once been a forest-warden's hut but was now tumble-down owing to age and lack of repair. In it, no one knew how, was installed the immense family of Karnaliks, of Slav origin, either Czech or Serbian.

Papa Karnalik, a little fellow with a tousled head and orange-tinted spectacles on his nose, was chiefly remarkable for boundless effrontery and liveliness. He was a patriot of patriots, a deeply religious philosopher, a potential genius, and an outstanding inventor whose inventiveness embraced everything from flying machines to patent shoe-cleaners. He had a firm belief in his star but at present was never free from debt, harried by the police, and dragging out a merely pitiful existence.

Madame Karnalik, a prematurely old little woman, was for ever bearing children, sewing, cooking, patching up quarrels, and giving advice.

The countless poorly clad children of the pair wandered in droves among the neighbouring cottages picking up a meal where best they could.

There was never any money in the house nor did it boast a single sound fork or unbroken plate. The children went about in rags, were unbaptized, learned nothing and knew nothing, for Karnalik considered himself and his offspring all to be geniuses and was undeterred by any fear of poverty, illness, or misfortune. Children were born and died seemingly without being noticed. Such trifles had no interest for Karnalik. They were just part of a normal day's happenings.

Yet he permitted no one to take any liberties with him, and millions of arguments and proofs quoted from texts in all languages protected him from insult.

His fondest dream was 'the union of all countries'. 'We

Slavs,' he would say in his country brogue in which could be heard traces of every Slavonic tongue, 'We Slavs', he would repeat more loudly, pointing an emphatic finger to the skies, 'are a mighty nation!' Nothing was more abhorrent to him than the German ideal. He could smell out a Teuton way of thought in anything, and Scheffel for his part loathed with all his might this turbulent trouble-monger whom he could not possibly suppress.

Karnalik when passing Scheffel's would purposely burst forth into his favourite song

> *You Slavs will be free*
> *When your heart beats for your nation.*

Scheffel would slam down his window and shout after the retreating figure in German or plain Russian: 'Pig! Scoundrel!'

To bring them to any kind of agreement was clearly impossible and all Father's efforts in this direction produced no result.

But Karnalik never once suspected that in the very heart of the German territory he had an ally who hated German ideals in every shape and form.

In a small cottage situated in the German domain and surrounded by a garden there lived all alone one Fedor Fedorovich Deme, an almost entirely bed-ridden invalid. He lay with his head on a pillow, above which hung an immense picture in a deep gold frame, and was slowly fading away with consumption.

Although he was fully aware of his rapidly approaching end, he refused to give in or confess himself a beaten man, but devoted every vestige of his feverish energy to a fanatical hatred of all things German. He seemed to be steeped in a corrosive rancour towards all that part of the world which is renowned for Junkers and sausages.

Bathed in sweat, he would in the interval between his terrible spasms of coughing, explain what he called 'the significance of the hegemony of Libau' and poke malicious fun at Vanka

Shtrik and his pan-German aspirations. For hours Father would sit at his bed-side and listen to the sick man's ravings, smooth his pillow, and bring him food before stealing out on tiptoe, leaving him pacified and ready to drop off to sleep.

However Deme and Karnalik might detest the Teuton monster, Scheffel remained safely ensconced behind his *Kultur*, fortified with heaps of Libau sausage, and unyielding as any alpine bullock.

In the autumn Deme felt better and even sat in an armchair on his verandah dressed in an embroidered fez and a dressing gown, with a long pipe in his hand. But when the warm days of St. Luke's summer came, he died quite suddenly while in the act of putting on his beaded slippers.

Father kept for a long time the picture in the deep frame which Deme left him. It depicted a Turk in a white dolman cloak on a galloping horse, slashing with his curved scimitar at a Cossack, who, mounted on a black horse, was engaged in warding off his adversary's blows with a lance. When showing it to his guests and praising its merits Father invariably narrated the sad fate of Deme the German with the Russian soul.

The troubles of the truculent Karnalik, Deme, and the German colony occupied a considerable proportion of Father's time and energy, and, as if they were not enough, some one or other of his unfortunates was invariably receiving free board and lodging in our little cottage.

Once an abject creature with hair so long that is reached his shoulders came to stay with us, and for days at a time occupied himself in the attic, hardly ever going out of doors. Father informed us with much sympathy at breakfast that the guest who had installed himself upstairs was an artist—a portrait painter— and that in general artists were a race apart. 'It is not given to every one to be an artist,' he added with a glance towards Victor.

Victor looked up from his pamphlet for a second and made some curt remark about the distinction between 'artist' and 'artful' and immediately became engrossed again in his reading.

Father retaliated with a sarcastic reference to doctors to which Victor made no reply.

To Father at this time Kratchkof, the artist concerned, was a rising star and a genius of the highest order. For his part the rising star quietly agreed with everyone's opinions and feelingly applied himself to his glass before disappearing upstairs to his room until the next meal-time.

In the evening, when Father went up to visit his artist, Kratchkof completely unbent and told him the most highly improbable yarns.

When on the morrow he retold 'Kratchkof's stories' we could never believe that so quiet a fellow would tell anything like them.

Bursting with laughter Father would start: 'Just listen to what Kratchkof told me yesterday! In the Academy of Art there is such an endless maze of corridors that, if you don't look out, you come back to where you started from. They're simply amazing. And the studios where the competitors—meaning the young artists—do their diploma work are positively enormous. In one corner will be an artist working on some immense picture in which repose all his hopes and in the others are hammocks where his homeless fellows live. Sometimes a whole family will come up from the country for a holiday and there'll be room for all of them. However, that's nothing to do with the tale.

'Kratchkof was telling me what fellows they are! There was a caricaturist among them, Sherbov by name. He was squint-eyed, a regular giant of a man, and no fool when it came to drinking. And when he started drinking and got up to his tricks there was no holding him. About the time we're talking of there was a dye which was much in vogue—aniline they call it—and if you were to dissolve a tiny crystal of it in water you could colour the side of a street! It is incredibly strong. Well, once they went out sketching, and worked and worked and Sherbov's landscapes were so gay that they seemed to dance, for there was a ludicrous element of caricature in everything he did. When they were tired they adjourned to a tavern, which was a favourite thing for them to do after a serious day's work. They found a clean spot where they deposited their easels and set themselves to drinking.

'While they were sitting drinking, joking, and so forth, a cart drew up and a big jovial bagman came in and sat down with them.

'Well, they went on drinking and from under the window came the jingle of harness-bells which meant that the merchant's nag was standing outside.

'The bagman soon bored them—he was terribly purse-proud —and so Sherbov winked and said in a whisper, "You just go on chatting to this fat fellow here while I go and turn his horse into a zebra for him!"

'In about ten minutes he was back again whispering, "I've done a really good job on that nag. Now let him go to the deuce! Up the working-class!"

'They all bade adieu to the bagman and quickly crossed the road where they concealed themselves in the hedge to watch the fun.

'The bagman came out and gave one gasp, for his horse had completely disappeared and there in the shafts was a striped zebra with zig-zag markings of blue on a background of green. How they laughed!'

'Then there was the time when Sherbov threw some red crystals onto a roof and, when it rained, red water trickled down into the street. The police rushed to the spot convinced that a most appalling murder had been committed! The passers-by laughed and said that the young rips were smashing barrels of red wine and that it was raining crimson blessings.'

Father smiled as he went on. 'But all this was small beer to what happened next. They got completely covered in dye and wanted to wash. So off they went to the public bath, Sherbov, the wag, taking his crystals with him wrapped up in paper, for he never went anywhere without them.

'Well, they had a good steam and then went to the bath for a wash. While they were waiting their turn Sherbov took out a crystal for he'd seen in the bath an old man who had been washing for hours refusing to make way for anyone else. So he chucked some blue at him. In a second his bath had turned blue and the old boy was so terrified that he started to get out. But either because he was terribly old or frightened or something he only succeeded in raising himself a couple of inches before sitting down again. When finally the old josser did manage to scramble out he looked exactly as if he'd got his bathing suit on, for his whole body was blue and white stripes! The gang shouted with laughter and made for the exit. There was a scandal and so forth—but what scamps they must have been, to be sure!'

Weeks passed, and though on our walls appeared some second-rate pencil sketches of Father, Mother, and us youngsters the genius of the first water himself came downstairs less and less often and finally disappeared completely.

In the autumn when we were moving from the cottage the maid discovered in the attic a startling collection of empty vodka bottles. Victor burst out laughing and exclaimed, 'What did I tell you, Papa? And you kept saying that he was a rising star—a second Aivazovski.'

Father pulled a wry face, and made excuses for Kratchkof, putting down his weakness for the bottle to the non-recognition of his talent, but for a long time Victor used to give him sly digs on the subject of Kratchkof's genius.

Twice during the summer the extraordinarily noisy but keenly intriguing Doctor Chekh descended upon us like a bolt from the blue. He spoke broken Russian chopping his words and jumbling up hugger-mugger all the languages he knew in a torrent of speech. Moreover his enthusiasm and genius never allowed him to remain seated in one place, so that in the middle of dinner while talking about one of his 'projects' he would leap up from the table and run round the room balancing his cutlet on his fork and relating the most amazing and incredible tales.

For apparently he was omniscient; no problems or secrets of nature had escaped dissection by his keen intellect. It was he who found petroleum in Baku, and without him Nansen would never have been Nansen. The great ones of the world, kings, ministers, and renowned geniuses of every country on the globe were, according to his story, his bosom friends profiting by his advice, arranging constitutions according to his plans, and falling over one another to crave his attention.

He had only to express a wish and he could promote anyone he liked to the heights, making him a general or something of the sort, or conferring upon him a foreign order or even a star. The doors of every court in Europe stood open to him, he knew the hidden springs of international intrigue, and in his person was the key to the solution of the most complex international crises.

This is what one deduced, although at present he was selling patent medicines of his own invention which were guaranteed to cure the sick of any complaint. He also dealt in veterinary surgical instruments and roof-coverings.

Father would listen to him with rapt attention, innocently believing in his powers, and buying his medicines and loaning him money.

It was impossible, he thought, to deny help to such a man for even if only a millionth of the rewards he had been promised were realized, before him in the person of Doctor Chekh was sitting a really great man.

After loud harangues, accompanied by much gesticulation and unexpected digressions into the unattainable heights of human ambition, Doctor Chekh would imperceptibly get round to the underlying object of his visit to Father's humble cottage. For all these grandiloquent discussions were only the prelude— the song of the siren, as it were.

The truth was that Doctor Chekh was secretly negotiating sales of foreign orders and diplomas of different ranks and associations.

For a mere hundred roubles he undertook to obtain letters

patent for an order together with all the seals, titles, and signatures affixed thereto. Operating principally among petty merchants he met with considerable success, since everyone was flattered to keep in an ornate golden frame the letters patent of some high-sounding rank or to wear in his buttonhole the glittering order of an impoverished court.

Father used to snap at Vanka Shtrik when the latter remarked, 'That doctor of yours—Chekh—he's not a doctor at all. He's just a scurvy Czech—a swindler and a rogue!'

When, some time after the doctor's departure, shoddily made medals and unknown diplomas began to arrive, Victor with solemnity read aloud the foreign texts and produced a great impression with the high-sounding titles of dukes, reigning princes, and 'Marshals of the Army of Monaco'. He congratulated Father on his new title, 'Acting member of the French Fire Brigade'!

Father was annoyed at first, but afterwards entered into the fun of it all. In the end the diplomas in their frames with orders affixed to them vanished from the walls and were left to harbour dust behind a cupboard door.

XXI

MOTHER, as usual, spent her time in her room. The forest had no charm for her, nor was she interested in the drama of the Scheffels, the hopeless state of the Karnaliks, nor in our own well-being.

She was everlastingly smoking cigarettes, lighting one from another as she gazed out absently over the green sea of leaves beneath her, immersed in those compelling thoughts which we could never share. Apparently nothing could interest or rouse her. Her days passed monotonously, each resembling the other. She took hardly any notice of us. It was only when father handed her a letter from her brother Vasily Nikolaevich that a semblance of life returned to her, her dear tired eyes began to sparkle and her face, until then apathetic, grew radiant with a long-forgotten happiness. She discussed in detail with father where to accommodate this dear 'little' brother, and even what to cook for dinner.

She had not seen brother Vasily, now a full Colonel, since that visit of his to the old Okorokov house, and while she welcomed the impending meeting she felt a little fearful of herself as well as of the limited accommodation offered by the cottage, and the complete disorder of the household which only in this moment of self-revelation did she appreciate to the full.

Uncle Vasily Nikolaevich arrived late by the night train and the morning of the following day found us acting sentry before his room in anticipation of the triumphal appearance of a Colonel of the Guards.

We knew every detail about him. We felt pride in him, regarding him as some legendary being whose existence lay only in a beautiful dreamlike fantasy.

When at last he appeared at the door, still tall and upright, and came forward reverently to kiss Mother's hand with all the courtly grace of an eighteenth-century grandee, our astonishment knew no bounds.

When we approached nearer, however, Vasily did not look so young; it was obvious that his hair and close-cropped moustache were not their natural colour, and beneath the powder which he had applied after shaving a mass of wrinkles was discernible. His cheeks too were lightly tinged with rouge. But, for all that, he was still handsome and won our hearts by his quiet gentlemanly bearing, his affectionate manner, and his open countenance.

Mother, too, looked younger as she sat in an affected pose on the divan wearing a silk dress and with her hair carefully coiffured. As soon as her brother had seated himself in the arm-chair she devoted herself to him, recalling memories of the past, the old home and their childhood.

Father, meanwhile, tactfully took us off into the garden and in a few hours Vasily Nikolaevich got ready to take his leave. As he put on his resplendent cloak he distributed some new rouble pieces among us, gave our sisters a little pat on the cheek and exchanged a few words with Victor. Then with a gracious bow to all of us he set off in his phaeton.

This was our first and last meeting with the ornament and favourite of our Mother's family.

Vasily Nikolaevich in due course became a general, but some years afterwards retired on grounds of ill health. He died in poverty leaving scarcely anything at all, and of the 'twelve bold bad brothers' only Platon then remained. And Platon waxed rich as a clandestine money-lender, as great a miser as Gogol's Plyushkin.

After Uncle Vasily's departure Mother displayed an interest in all that was going on. She recalled the past and told us about Mlle de Muchel's school, even giving a demonstration of how the Irish jig was performed in that Institute for Young Girls of Noble Birth.

Gradually, however, this interest in us faded and more than ever she remained alone in her room and even began not to come down for dinner.

But once, in the early morning while we were all still asleep, she awoke in a state of perturbation as though she had been forcibly roused. Putting on her silk dress with a morbid air of coquetry, and not forgetting to arrange her hair carefully with its central parting as of old, she went downstairs.

It was still dark in the hall, but on the window-sill she could see the pots of withered geraniums whose flowers, since no one ever bothered to water them, hung from their parched stalks like blood-drenched rags.

The dining table was still uncleared of the remains of last night's supper. A grey shroud of dust lay on the arm-chairs, on the sideboard and on the newspapers thrown carelessly aside on the divan.

A spider was hurriedly putting the finishing touches to his night's labours, and an immense, mathematically constructed web stretched from the ceiling to the back of the broad divan. The sight of this frightened her and she stopped at the door only to be dumbfounded by the picture which presented itself.

It was as if some unknown hand had opened her eyes so that she could take in at a glance the abomination of desolation in every room, the carelessness and the utter collapse of her home-life.

When now, in a flash, it was revealed to her, she set to work with an unnatural energy to put it all to rights.

She cleared the table of its dirty plates, swept up the dust, watered the geraniums, and fearlessly demolished with her broom the spider's nocturnal task.

Bravely surveying the terrified spider, Mother rolled up her sleeves, tucked up the skirt of her silk dress, and fetching a bucket set herself to wash the floor with undaunted energy. It was evident that it had not been washed since the days of Adam, for our slut of a maid never troubled about anything.

The kitchen presented a scene of sheer horror with its piles of unwashed dishes, its floor greasy with dirt, its scraps of food, its walls swarming with cockroaches busily intent upon carrying off a meal to their holes. Here again Mother busied herself with feverish energy in inducing some sort of order.

Hearing a noise in the kitchen, Masha, our housemaid, descended the stairs, half dressed and yawning her head off, to see before her astonished eyes the picture of her mistress—that mistress who was for ever resting in her room upstairs—with her lovely silk dress all crumpled and wet to the knees, crawling on the slippery kitchen floor in a mess of soapy water, while cockroaches crept around her skirts and swarms of flies circled above her head.

Someone knocked nervously at our door. 'Mama is ill! Get up!' We jumped out of bed in an instant but could hardly pull on our stockings for the trembling of our hands. Drowsy as we were we could still remember how some years ago, on just such a morning as this, the whole household had been plunged into confusion. Everyone gathered in the dining room. Mother in her silk dress, ruined by dirty soapy water, was wearing a coquettish little mob-cap and busily pouring out tea. She fumbled about with the cups, kept sending the maid away on trifling errands, and dispensing orders to left and right.

Father was reprimanded on account of his dressing gown, Victor because of his ignorance of table manners!

It was quite clear to us that some spiteful magician had during the passing of a single night transformed our Mother into that unknown cruelly beautiful creature now sitting in front of us and bearing Mother's name.

Though we gave no sign of it we were all frightened as we embraced her, and with hidden dread listened to her nervous, hesitant, talk.

Her keenly glistening eyes, the unco-ordinated movements of her hands, the outbursts of temper alternating for no comprehensive reason with trembling little manifestations of love, petrified and benumbed us. Instinctively noticing this she looked at us in wonder, realizing that something had happened to us and that we were behaving uncertainly and unnaturally towards her.

She laughed good-naturedly and tried to cheer us up. She was glad that at last she saw a possibility of helping us. Without her we had all been in confusion and there was no one to look after us. 'My Mother, poor soul, became an invalid,' she began, crossing herself devoutly, and then there followed unrestrained chatter of the past, as old friends and familiar scenes appeared in her mind.

Reality and life changed places with imagination. People long dead came out onto the stage again and started to live their former lives anew in the unintelligible environment of the present day. She began to get excited and complained about our unresponsiveness. Father, gloomy and as yet unable to believe in the return of her malady, endeavoured to calm her with rational argument.

His intervention, however, only succeeded in adding fuel to the flames. Mother returned to reality only to hurl accusations at the whole of the Scheffel contingent, for some unknown reason addressing herself in particular to the deep-bosomed José.

We were unable to sleep all that night. We went round to each other with a feeling of dread in our hearts. We thought of the accident that some of us remembered, and the terror of the day when Peter was brought home mangled and dead. If only that had not happened, Mother would have been well and everything would have continued happily.

On the morrow a carriage came round and under the pretext of going out for a drive Mother was taken away just as she had been before.

In the cottage all was quiet again and a tolerable sort of order was established. Mother's absence was hardly noticeable save for the fact that Father looked sadder and roamed aimlessly from room to room with nothing to do and obviously without the energy to apply himself to anything. Sometimes he was overcome by a desire to visit the hospital. Victor warned him against it and phlegmatically quoted the opinions of medical experts as though one could survey all the tragedies of life from a medical point of view.

Father looked reproachfully at us and taunted us with our heartlessness. He hazarded his opinion that it was not really necessary to remove Mother to hospital. 'It would have all come right in the end,' he affirmed with obstinacy and conviction.

Victor brought along lectures by psychiatrists and backed himself up with the highest authorities on the subject, but none of them succeeded in moving Father from his conviction.

Without saying a word to anyone he went to the hospital. He returned after his visit more than ever exhausted and bowed down by sorrow and for hours paced the long garden paths lost in thought. At last, however, he pulled himself together and became calmer and more firmly resigned. His own striving for constant harmony induced in him a wonderful capacity for withstanding grief and despair.

'You see I can laugh and be gay albeit a cat is scratching at my heart,' he would say to Karnalik, and Karnalik, for all his narrowness of mind, was able to perceive that the heavier Father's heart the more generous his behaviour towards others, the more welcoming his smile, and the more readily would he change the conversation to trifling topics.

After having carefully tested his ground and watched us with a barely perceptible air of reproach as though to say, 'It is because of you that I keep Mother in hospital,' Father little by little won us round to paying a visit to Mother. Victor, however, refused point-blank on account of his convictions, and so we the younger ones, as being less likely to be harmful to and more in sympathy with the patient, were equipped for our diplomatic mission.

The journey to the hospital was a high adventure. We were ready early in the morning and having bought little presents for Mother such as she loved, drove off in a cab under the supervision of a maid, traversing the length of Moscow on our way to the distant K—— estate.

Our hearts were heavy, for there was something frightening about it all. We wanted to see Mother and yet were full of misgivings. The thought that she was shut up was loathsome to us. If only nothing had happened to little Peter!

When the landscape began to open out into meadows and seemingly endless orchards with houses standing in their own gardens our journey neared its end, and far away in the distance we discerned the huge settlement of the K—— estate. Isolated completely from the surrounding suburbs, ringed round by high walls like a jail, and spread out over an enormous area, this morbid capital of the kingdom of the mentally unbalanced gave us a bitter sensation of fear. In the iron-barred windows and in the closely confined gardens, were sitting and walking and standing its white-garbed citizens. Here the frontiers of our normal world came to an end and here began that mysterious kingdom given over to those with mental troubles in their abnormal world.

In the spacious reception room, once the ballroom of the former owner, Count V., amid the lavish decorations of a bygone era, Mother somehow looked old and pathetic. She had forced herself to be completely calm and only a barely perceptible muscular movement of her eyelids betrayed her inward excitement.

Somewhere deep down under the blouse of institutional material there was beating a restless heart charged with timid love, perpetual yearning, and unhappiness. With intense inward excitement she received us and clasped us to her withered breast. She stroked our faces with her beautiful nervous hands. She asked us rational questions and showed an interest in every detail of our daily life.

The presents we had brought—her favourite almonds, raisins, and prunes—filled her with delight. She crammed us with sweets which we had intended for herself, she pressed us to stay for tea, and led us off to show us her room.

Nurses with their eternal keys at their waists unlocked doors and we found ourselves in Count V.'s magnificent drawing-room where walking, standing, dancing, and singing were white-clad women of every age and condition. Some of them ignored us altogether, others ran up to us as old friends or dear relations— their long-awaited deliverers. Mother majestically walked on and her presence guaranteed our safety. All made way for her, for hers was a privileged position and it was dangerous to play jokes with her.

More doors were locked and unlocked. There was more grating of keys. A strong good-natured nurse saw us and smiled at us with merry kindly eyes. When with Mother it was not so terrible to be among all these helpless but cruel folk. Passing through quiet corridors and on through a portrait gallery, we finally came to the dormitories, large rooms with big windows and very light. Everywhere could be seen again the same white figures. At last came Mother's room, clean and light and spacious. Sitting on a chair, as for the past fourteen years, uttering no word but swaying gently from side to side, was a white wizened creature like an Egyptian mummy. This was the old Countess V.

Neither our entry nor Mother's formal presentation of each of us in turn made the least impression on her. She remained silent, and to us looked like the wife of some Rameses of thousands of years ago, devoid of sight and hearing, a museum piece kept for the edification and amusement of the curious. But we learned from Mother's conversation that it was her pride which forbade the Countess either to see or hear. She only conversed with people of title.

Her last conversation had been with a distant relative and was such that this poor prince had fled from her presence as though he had been scalded. Reaching his gig he had galloped back to Moscow expectorating all the way. Since then the Countess had become more than ever reserved and now never pronounced a single word.

A nurse went up to her to straighten her cushion and set her little cap to one side. She remained silent.

At the end of the room, in an embrasure in the Italian window, a beautiful young girl in a white hospital dress was sitting deeply engrossed in a book. She got up on seeing us, patted her hair and gave us a smile of welcome. Mother introduced us and we had an interesting talk. She behaved as though she were in a drawing-room and gave no sign of her condition.

Yet we were more frightened by her than we had been by the Countess. It was impossible to believe that this sweet kind creature suffered from some malady that required her to be kept here.

As she accompanied us to the door she kissed each one of us and quietly went back to her book. Incidentally, as after events were to prove, she was one of the most difficult and dangerous patients on the K—— estate.

In the reception room over tea, Mother's conversation turned to memories of her home and of the long bygone past which for her had now returned again. She asked after the health of people who had long been dead and was especially interested in the success of our brother Peter, whose death ten years before had been the cause of her breakdown. When we tried to explain that Peter had died long ago she refused to believe us, affirming that she had herself seen him alive a couple of days before, and that she had had tea with him and found him well and happy.

It was clear that our incoherent replies were annoying her. She burst into a torrent of anxious words.

The matron came up to us, a tall woman with severe eyes, and sat down as though by chance at our table. Nurses imperceptibly approached and took their stand behind Mother's chair.

Soothing arms encircled Mother's shoulders. The matron gently clasped her round the waist and in procession they moved to the door behind whose deft closure our mother was lost again to our world. We were deeply moved. Only to get away! To get away, as quickly as possible from this place!

On our way home we realized how much our hearts had been torn and our nerves harassed. We felt terribly tired. The future

seemed devoid of the least vestige of hope. We arrived back
late, exhausted and depressed. It looked as though Victor had
been right after all and that we should never have consented to
visit the poor sufferer.

The days grew shorter. The wind blew through every chink.
Autumn was advancing with rapid strides. The grey clouds
clustered low over the deserted forest. The gales crashed through
the attic and oblique torrents of rain beat a tattoo upon the
windows. Our hearts were now filled with melancholy and
loneliness and we longed for the town and its people, its cosiness and comfort. We made farewell pilgrimages to our favourite haunts, we went on mushrooming expeditions in the
depths of the bare forest, and summer was coming to an end.

Father spent all his time in town. His business was flourishing
and he had taken a new and more commodious flat.

While the Karnalik children, still in their summer clothes
despite the cold, were playing with the frogs jumping on the
garden paths and dressing them up in little costumes of Karnalik manufacture, wagons came from the town to collect our
luggage.

After tea with the priest we set off townwards in cabs taking
our hand-baggage with us. The wagons with the luggage and furniture lumbered down the road in procession. The cottagers
were moving to winter quarters!

We reached the market-gardens on the outskirts of Moscow
with the housemaid sitting atop the luggage nursing some glass-
ware in her arms while the driver marched along on the side of
the road holding the reins. It was novel and strange to see our
well-known belongings under the open sky silhouetted against
a background of yellowing gardens.

By the evening we were already installed in a new and unknown neighbourhood.

XXII

TSIPLAKOVSKI Yard was an immense enclosed area on all sides of which rose two-storied buildings, and although it contained the inevitable cellars and storehouses it was so spacious that we young people never even noticed their existence, seeing that around them plenty of space was left for running and skipping. All things considered, we were well satisfied, and the presence of lumber-rooms there seemed both desirable and unavoidable.

When tired of racing about the main court we used to run into the yard at the back. This consisted of a long passage along whose length had been built coach-houses and stables which had now fallen into a state of dilapidation. Grass sprouted among its cobble-stones; moss covered its doorways and stable-walls with an emerald carpet; and the roofs were adorned by young saplings. This was where Peter the coachman had his own snug abode and kept his old grey mare Savraska.

A solitary cock crowed lustily upon a dunghill and on seeing us fixed us with an angry eye and beat defiance with his wings against his ribs. Nervously pacing his domain and bristling his vari-coloured feathers he moved off side-ways and hid within a cranny in a coach-house. Standing in front of the dunghill we would recite:

> *A cock on a dung-heap was scratching around*
> *When all of a sudden a pearl he found.*
> *'What's the use of this?' crowed he.*

However, to our universal regret we were never able to find the pearl in the dung-heap and off we would go in search of new adventure.

Where the yard came to a dead end it was frightening and full of mystery. We were firmly convinced that here in a half tumbled-down coach-house lived that kindly but bad-tempered creature the hobgoblin, for, as we were aware, hobgoblins always lived near horses, tending them, protecting them, plaiting the manes of their favourites at night, and curing all their ills. In their old age hobgoblins hide in some untenanted stall where in their decrepitude they live sadly on, remembering their favourite horses' beauty and characteristic ways.

To meet a goblin in the flesh was dangerous indeed and few would be so foolhardy as to seek such a meeting.

Although the coachman, Peter, who had spent all his life among horses used to laugh at us, we knew our hobgoblin was there well enough. How otherwise could one explain away the thumping of one's heart, the keen presentiment one had even when ever so far away, and one's readiness for instant flight when approaching this haunt of mystery?

We ran off to the main court which was always full of people. Girls, apprentices from the ladies' tailoring workshops, with their hair plaited in thin pig-tails, flitted about in white smocks.

Along the wood-paved covered gallery there was a clatter of heavy workmen's boots. A Tartar pedlar with his inevitable bag would amiably doff his fur cap to us.

From the windows of an adjoining block came a chatter of young voices, a ringing of bells, and sounds of singing in unison. Every morning a noisy young mob arrived bearing satchels and haversacks and other accoutrements of learning. Here on low forms children sat and imbibed the sum of human wisdom.

Passing through a little ante-room, cluttered up with tiny coats, fur jackets, and all sorts of headgear, one went through a study to the class-room—in actual fact, the drawing-room—which between the hours of ten and three was allocated to use as a school.

The most interesting place in this school was the study of Papa Irmish, a terrible fellow with horn-rimmed glasses and a remarkable likeness to Karl Marx. Papa Irmish was a veterinary surgeon by profession and, as he was generally away, his study usually served as a place of detention for delinquents. Under its windows stood a big table, heaped high with cases, leather-covered boxes, and ponderous books. In a glass cupboard surgical instruments of hideous appearance could be discerned —huge forceps, saws, and knives—as well as embryos in bottles of spirit, and the skeletons of antediluvian animals. On the walls were hung contraptions of leather, rope, and chain and all sorts of instruments of torture.

Papa Irmish was not unsuccessful at curing horses, cows, dogs and, in our imagination, even elephants if such ever chanced to fall sick on the Moscow streets. Hanging from the ceiling was a complicated contraption of cord of the thickness of marine cable which was evidently intended for no less an animal than a pachyderm.

In this abode of black magic or torture-chamber of the mediaeval inquisition youthful delinquents had to stand for hours at a time with fear in their hearts. Finally one lonely criminal, having passed from terror to despair, almost succeeded in committing suicide by poking his scrawny neck to satisfy his curiosity into a leather contraption which promptly went off with a click and caught the young dare-devil in an embrace of death, from which he was only just rescued in time. After this a dark lumber room was assigned to purposes of detention and Papa Irmish's study was redesignated the 'Museum of Natural Science'.

Papa Irmish's practice did not flourish—a fact which we ascribed to the rarity of sickness among the local elephants—but luckily the savant possessed in addition to his own scientific knowledge a trio of distinguished daughters who readily came to his aid when he found himself in financial difficulties.

Mary, Anna, and the radiantly healthy Minna Irmish had taken the reigns of government in their firm hands and formed a triumvirate. Above the front door they had hung a small sign: 'School for little boys and girls. M. A. M. Irmish'; and the ancestral name was thereby saved. So now Papa Irmish with an untroubled heart and a flagon of beer spent his evenings at the nearby 'Gambrinus' and even the elephant problem no longer troubled him.

In the drawing-room/class-room the three sisters performed miracles. The young pupils rolled up in such crowds that entries had to be refused. The secret of success lay in the fact that there were no formal lessons—just a little German, less Russian, some singing, dancing, games, music, natural science, and a dark cupboard for delinquents!

Father, considering us, said to Victor 'Let them go to school in the court. It's no distance.'

So to this palace of learning in the court nearby we daily went, and to the question 'Where do you go to school?' replied, 'In the yard!'

'What do you mean by "in the yard"?' we would be asked.

'To the Irmishs' school in the yard,' we explained.

'That's something quite different,' our inquisitive interlocutor would assert.

Minna Irmish, a kind, full-blooded German, was the most popular of the sisters. She was exceedingly temperamental and radiated health, and she blushed every time she took a natural history lesson. We soon guessed this weakness of hers and arranged embarrassing discussions just to see the confusion betrayed by carmine cheeks and downcast eyes.

Mary, the eldest sister, was chiefly notable for a complete lack of humour and her control over us was stricter. The fact that she taught arithmetic was not calculated to make her blush.

Anna was a pleasant-looking woman who was often absent altogether or else late for her lessons to which she came armed with her sewing consisting of little jackets and shirts. She was invariably distrait and as often as not curtailed her lessons and departed.

The school was largely attended by children from German families who were taking firm root in what to them was hateful and savage Russia. These young Germans chattered like jays and interlarded the Russian language with German words. They made short work of the appetizing lunches which they brought from their homes, and they shed tears over Russian grammar.

When the joyous and long-awaited bell sounded the pupils jumped from their forms and flung their books into the air. There was a concerted rush for the ante-room and everyone endeavoured to get away as quickly as possible.

In the spacious hall at home the sunshine poured down on the bare walls and on the table which had been already set for our meal. Dazzling shafts of light glanced from the cut-glass water jug. The cook came in with a soup-tureen and we children fell upon our food like a pack of beasts, for the lessons of the Irmish sisters gave us the appetites of wolves!

Father's study had been partitioned off from his bedroom by a heavy curtain and had in it a writing desk and a display cupboard with his collection of old coins. The familiar portrait of Alexander the Second occupied a place of honour on the wall.

In the bedroom stood Mother's bed looking empty and forlorn.

Victor's little room was tucked away in a corner and reminded one of a burial vault. It was always incredibly cold and was cluttered up with human bones, piles of manuscript, and lecture notes. The powerful jaws of a skull from a dismembered skeleton leered ludicrously; blackened bones served for ash-trays; and the walls were hung with brightly coloured anatomical charts.

Sitting at his table engrossed in a massive folio, Victor resembled the mediaeval Faust seeking the Philosopher's Stone and the Elixir of Life. We children were forbidden to enter this study—or ice-box as Father used to call it—and indeed we trembled before its doors no less than before the mysterious abode of the Goblin.

Father alone used to go in whenever he liked. The door would shut and for a long time we would hear muffled exclamations and the sounds of argument before, agitated and restless, he came out into the corridor flinging back his familiar

'Ah! You doctors! You never see beyond your own noses!'
For the old disputes with Victor still persisted.

Although we now had a real live housekeeper, Victor kept
control of all the household management as before and the
house still revolved round him.

'Shishiga' or 'Kutsiga', as we called this housekeeper behind
her back, was not the sort to make our family life more easy.
She was tall and had a face like a horse, and, being a coquettish
maiden of about sixty wearing a bunch of false curls, she preferred to spend her time more agreeably than in poking her
nose into dirty linen or harrying the cook.

Her spritely reminiscences and her sentimental sighs over
'The Maiden's Prayer' rendered on an out-of-tune piano afforded
the genuine pleasure of a good joke to the laughter-loving
students who used to make fun of her even to the bounds of
indecency. The old coquette, however, took everything
seriously and with a simplicity which only added to the students'
mirth. They wrote her anonymous love-letters, sent her boxes
of sweets stuffed with pepper, mustard, or purgatives; and even
put into her virgin bed cleverly carved representations of the
god of love and fertility.

But Father, jolly and good-natured as he was, tolerated her
failings and said nothing at all. Victor indulged in sarcastic
innuendo at her expense and was rude to her face but Shishiga
failed to understand the language of innuendo, and pouting
coquettishly murmured that everything was always exaggerated
and continued to enjoy her comfortable parasitic existence
completely unruffled.

'We must get rid of her at the end of a broom!' said Victor
angrily, whereat Father went into long peals of laughter at his
son's powerlessness to deal with her. And when the students
came in the evening there was Shishiga again occupying a
conspicuous place as 'Queen of the Ball'.

Now that Father's business was flourishing and our flat larger,
the band of young students had been reinforced by new members
who noisily filled every room.

Among their number was Dora, an engineer, who wore his hair brushed back from his forehead in imitation of Gogol, and Berezantsev, a medical student, a handsome lad with an excellent opinion of himself; Doctor Nazarov, too, who aped the fashions of England, and many more besides whose names God alone knew.

Kholodkov 'leaping and dancing with nimble feet' created a furore and always evoked thunderous applause.

Dora, for all he was a student of engineering, would strike a pose like a love-sick poet and rolling his Grecian eyes sing in a sugary voice the sentimental ballad then enjoying a great vogue, 'Gazing at the sunset's purple ray', which sent the ladies into raptures. Father, too, genuinely enjoyed the performance and hung upon its every note.

The choir sang much and did well being accompanied by Nicholas or Cachalot who frequently had to change places since each knew only his own pieces. Invariably when an item was concluded Father's thin *tremolo* would linger on the air. Although he was about half a tone higher or lower than the rest, his pleasure in his performance was childlike and made his eyes sparkle with joy. 'There's Papa—spoilt it again!' one of the singers would remark though more for conscience's sake and the love of art than with any suggestion of reproof. Father would look crestfallen but despite all his determination not to err again could never resist the temptation of emitting his false note.

After supper—'What God has sent us'—Cachalot either recited something tragic and gloomy or else told funny Armenian anecdotes. Then, after considerable persuasion Berezantsev would go to the piano and running his hands through his hair wait for silence, before flooding the room with Rubinstein's 'Valse Caprice' or Tchaikovski's 'Barcarolle'. This student of medicine was a real artist and the whole company kept silence.

'Ah,' said Father, 'You have missed your true vocation. You should have been a second Rubinstein.' He then persuaded him to play something simpler and easier to understand whereupon a joyful Russian song, transposed to order by the skilful pianist, would trip merrily over the keyboard to our utter enchantment.

At midnight the party broke up, only to foregather again, another day without the least warning. One of these merry gatherings, incidentally, was responsible for a lawsuit. Stout brewed by the Kalinkinski brewery was much esteemed by the students and it happened on one occasion that in some bottles of a new dozen a suspicious reddish watery deposit with a strong smell of santonin was discovered. The matter was taken to court and the whole party attended in force at the local Bench. Venediktov made a passionate oration on the obnoxious effects of poisonous liquids in general and of santonin in particular. The assembled company interrupted clamorously and in unison, whereupon the judge threatened to clear the court and the case proceeded with all seriousness. To everyone's satisfaction a peaceful settlement was effected and the brewery, only too thankful that no account of the proceedings reached the newspapers, sent several dozen bottles of fresh stout addressed to Tsiplakovski Yard.

The whole party came direct from the proceedings to our flat and commemorated the great day with much uncorking of bottles.

Father often used to make Venediktov, as representing chief counsel for prosecution and defence, relate in detail the court proceedings. After mirthful interruptions he would take his stand before an imaginary Bench and re-enact the scene.

'I testify, Your Worship, that following my habitual custom I visited the dwelling of Yakov Akimovich there to spend an evening over a glass. Well, Your Worship, as soon as the first bottle of stout was uncorked we found in place of stout plain and unadulterated santonin.'

The gathering roared with laughter and drank good health to the brewery.

José, accompanied by her Jan, came in one evening and Victor joined issue with her in a passionate wordy battle over something or other. Shtrik, having filled himself with Teutonic courage, warned his wife against excitement, imploring her to remember her weak heart, and inviting her to come out into the open air and go for a drive in a *troika*.

José yielded to the persuasion of her passionately devoted husband, although it was no secret that her real inclinations lay not so much in *troikas* as in consequent carousing in distant taverns. Everyone in fact was aware that the excursion would end in a first-class debauch at 'Yar's'.

They were whirled off over the snowdrifts in the deserted streets where arguments were forgotten. José drank the fresh air into her lungs and dreamed of the champagne and palm trees of the famous restaurant. At last the *troikas* drew up before the blazing lamps at the entrance to Yar's and a gigantic porter in princely livery helped her alight from the sledge as though she had been thistledown.

In the huge dining room, decorated with enormous palms and tropical plants, it was as warm and dazzlingly bright as a May day on the promenade of Monte Carlo. Charming young gentlemen, ravishing demi-mondaines, and whole families of merchants drank in the scent of warm foliage, warmed themselves beneath an electric sun, and gulped down oysters. Corks from champagne bottles went popping off into the air; sweet smiles flickered on eloquent lips.

Shtrik pulled down his waistcoat, glared with his calf-like eyes, and loudly demanded champagne. On the stage gipsies sang 'Harness the *troika* for the snow is like powder, and around us the frost and the night', and at that instant the voluptuous José was prepared to give herself to every charming young man in the room. Visits to Yar's almost invariably ended in a scandal.

Shtrik observing José's ecstasy became jealous at every casual glance directed towards her and like an enraged lion was ready to rend in pieces anyone who looked on his mate with eyes of longing. Father diverted his attention by engaging him in conversation and ordering him a *langouste*.

By the time his *langouste* was finished Shtrik was at peace with the world and began yawning and suggesting to his wife that they ought to be getting home. José who had just succeeded in establishing wireless communication with a handsome colonel at a neighbouring table, had to terminate the intercourse without waiting for a definite response. They went home by *troika* again with Vanka Shtrik, tamed by champagne and lobster, slumbering peacefully on the broad bosom, not to mention the aching heart, of his wide-awake wife.

XXIII

ONCE a year, generally after Christmas, Father's partner, Fedor Ivanovich Petchke, the distillery-owner, used to come to Moscow.

His visits were always exacting and were for the most part associated with business. He would arrive from Father's native town at an extraordinarily early hour, which Father described as being 'neither daytime nor dawn', and would endeavour to transact all his dealings as early and as punctually as possible in the best German tradition.

'Halluph past eight without fail,' Father would say, imitating Petchke's comical way of speaking. 'It's all very fine for him to say half-past eight, but how does he expect to do business with everyone asleep and the whole place shut up?'

Petchke himself, a good-natured German with little short legs, was as round as a ball. His fat bloated body apparently moved without the aid of his legs, floating along like some enormous protoplasm. His square head, covered with coarse closely cropped hair, and his rubicund face were firmly set upon his round shoulders without the intervention of any neck. His small shrewd eyes glinted craftily from brows as beetling as Bismarck's. Twenty years previously he had bought for a song the old Okorokov house and the factory he had erected on its site so flourished that he was now worth a very substantial sum.

For a long while before his arrival there was much checking of accounts and balancing of totals. Buyers also began agitating about the poor quality of the goods supplied. Thus when at last Petchke arrived there was a crowd of disgruntled clients assembled to meet him. Gathering round him they complained that his wares were rotten and demonstrated embarrassing samples of his products while threatening to withdraw their custom and give it to his competitors.

The worthy German went red as beetroot, and blew and puffed, and made the wildest promises, after which he sent strongly worded telegrams to his factory. Father meanwhile retired, smiling, to his office, murmuring, 'You can write and go on writing to the fat devil but, God forgive me, you'll get nothing out of it. "I don't believe a word", he'll say, "My goods are the best in the world as you can see with your own eyes." But he's completely scared now.' Shaking with mirth, Father would survey from his fastness the ups and downs of the civil war being waged below.

Within a fortnight or three weeks a fresh stock would be dispatched; nevertheless, the business gradually declined. 'He'll send more cases which stink to heaven! He ought to have his nose rubbed in his stuff,' the loquacious Boris would complain when there were no buyers in the warehouse. But as soon as the door opened and a client appeared he would bow and scrape and praise those same cases to the skies.

In the evenings Petchke considered it his duty to visit Father at home and sometimes even there they would continue to settle accounts. Petchke was evidently not too satisfied with the state of the business—payments were coming in but slowly, there had been but little expansion of trade, and so on. Taking off his glasses he lit a fat cigar and fixed his gaze attentively upon father.

Father was quite evidently roused and several times tried to light a cigarette, breaking one match after another in the process before finally throwing the cigarette away and making his dignified protest.

'Look you here, Fedor Ivanovich! You talk and talk and I just listen! But in the past financial year, thanks be to God, I've guaranteed you twelve thousand roubles clear profit. And twelve thousand clear, after paying all overheads, is no sum to be sneezed at! And what was our initial capital? You remember— don't you? Yet you just talk.' And he in turn glared at Petchke.

Petchke stood his ground for a while though it was clear that in his heart he was not dissatisfied with the position of affairs. Accounts now began to weary him and he looked round for some pretext to bring the financial discussion to a close. Observing us he beckoned us to him with a playful glance and asked us various questions in his funny Russian.

We were shaking with laughter and the good German, imagining himself inordinately witty, laughed heartily at his own jokes and distributed some silver roubles among us along with some German moral precepts.

After he had talked philosophy with Victor, whom he greatly esteemed for his erudition, he ponderously heaved himself out of his chair and left with the inevitable 'Tomorrow, then! Halluph past eight!' whereat we went into fits of laughter and had to retreat into the corridor. When he had gone Father got ready to go to bed grumbling, 'Halluph past eight! Where can he be hurrying off to?' The bell rang and one of the students came in. Father stayed up, beer was produced, and we were packed off to bed right in the middle of a jolly talk.

After a few days Petchke returned to his factory and Father, able to breathe freely again, promptly disappeared somewhere into the country and came back full of energy and fun. He had an extraordinary affection for unusual people, for wild things, and for every sort of prank of nature. Strange or forgotten folk fascinated him.

He would tell us that he had met a marvellous author brought by grief and want to the doss-house or that he had come across some most promising inventor whom he described as a second Kulibin. In point of fact it would turn out that the outstanding author was a chronic drunkard who had once been on the staff of some rag of a newspaper, and had twenty years previously given to the light of day a meagre little volume of unsuccessful short stories. The inventor, too, for all his genius, had never got further than inventing some patent fastenings for galoshes and both in misfortune and circumstance proved a blood-relation of our 'pan-Slav' Karnalik.

The heroes of Jules Verne and Eugene Sue seemed to fall in with Father almost every day as he trod the road of life. His very appearance, the cut of his clothes, his flights of fancy, and his approach to life all bore witness to his boyish enthusiasm and his unrealizable dreams.

True, all his out-of-date heroism was bound up with a great sense of humour, a remarkable goodness, and a certain softness of heart. The slightly ludicrous side of his romanticism showed itself in pleasantly unexpected ways. It was like meeting in one's old age a childhood friend who had retained the spirit of childhood.

If the fashion were for long frock-coats then Father invariably ordered the tails of his to be cut a little shorter and vice versa. If he went out shooting it was not game that interested him so much as the possibility of divers adventures. No one else had the like of his different coloured cartridges, hunting coats with blue lapels, immense game-bags, and other sporting gear.

He was but a poor shot, and often if he were returning home empty-handed he would buy two or three ducks so as not to deprive himself or us of the pleasure of the chase. Occasionally there would be no wild ducks to be had, in which event he would buy the domestic variety. Then when he had enjoyed his triumph he would let us into the secret and laugh merrily at himself and at us.

He possessed an extraordinary revolver, round and flat like a big watch, which was carried in a chamois-leather wallet. It was especially designed for dealing with highwaymen intent on snatching one's purse on the road. Father would demonstrate the effect of this lethal weapon on evil violators of the criminal code.

'Now, for instance,' he would say, 'you or I are going along a road in the dusk. Suddenly under a bridge we see the mug of a highwayman'—here he would pull a terrible face—'and "Your money or your life," says he. So you or I,' he continued, pointing at each of us in turn, 'take out our purse—like this,' and he revealed the revolver in its chamois case, 'and when the villain

puts out his hand to take our gold, we just pull the trigger and
—Bang! Bang! Bang!—the robber is blown to pieces!'

We rushed to the door in terror while Victor burst out laughing and said it was all tommy-rot. Father was quite angry and
declared that he would give a good deal to prove how entirely
right he was. Victor replied that the days were past when on
the highways could be heard choruses of 'Your money or your
life!' and that in any case the revolver was only a toy and a good
deal more dangerous to its owner than to any imaginary highwayman. The pressure on the trigger would, according to his
way of thinking, materially affect the aim, and any diversion of
aim, however slight, would be reflected in the track of the
bullet, and so forth.

Father accepted this, but pointed out that the revolver was
only intended for use at point-blank range. Victor at once
became interested in making exact measurements of its range
and with much intricacy of detail calculated the trajectory of
the bullet. The range proved to be negligible, confirming
Victor in the opinion that a good stout club would prove more
effective for dealing with robbers and would be less dangerous
to the robbed!

Father's belief in Jules Vernesque situations coupled with the
vividness of the scene he had just described made him as fixed
and immovable as a mass of granite. He had a childlike belief
in the realization of the impossible and expected a kindred
enthusiasm from everyone else. It appeared to him that, if one
were to banish from life all that might suddenly and unexpectedly happen, the world would be empty and dull.

In addition to his collection of old coins, medals, and orders
Father had a strange passion for collecting watches, of which he
had more than a dozen, each possessing some peculiar feature.
One interesting specimen had a miniature landscape showing a
river with waterfalls and mountains in the far distance on its
face. At noon a train with carriages and trucks crossed over a
tiny bridge, while in two small circular apertures above the
centre were shown the earth in its orbit and the phases of the

moon. For us as well as for him this watch was a source of unflagging interest, being regarded as a miracle of nature and a tribute to man's inventive genius.

There was another plain gold watch which we were not even allowed to handle. According to Father it was an exact replica of one worn by the Tsar's brother and in the whole world there were only two of its kind, one belonging to the Grand Duke and the other now to Yakov Akimovich. When the cover was opened, to one's amazement there was revealed an exquisite piece of enamel-work depicting a very naughty subject. Whoever was responsible for it had evidently been a master, for so delicately and artistically was the subject treated that its naughtiness passed almost unnoticed, quite overshadowed by the astonishingly skilful craftsmanship. Victor's puritan soul could not abide the sight of this watch and he would take Father off into his study to tell him so with fervour.

But the pride and joy of the collection was a simple insignificant-looking watch of English make. 'You can't wear it out,' Father would proudly remark, 'It just goes on ticking out the minutes.' He used to take this watch to the General Post Office and check it against all the public clocks, and he even seriously contemplated making a trip to the Pulkov Observatory, there to verify the accuracy of this paragon.

He had, besides his love for watches, a love of silver toys and trinkets of all sorts and always carried on his long watch-chain a dangling assortment of silver match-boxes, penknives, scissors, cigarette-holders, and similar pretty little knick-knacks. On his finger he wore a silver ring skilfully fashioned in the shape of an owl's head, the ruby eyes of which opened and shut on the pressure of a hidden spring.

As soon as any new invention or pretty toy came on the market—'the next bit of hocus-pocus', Victor would call it—Father ran off to buy it and in praising its novelty prophesied a revolution in the industry. He bought us flying dragons, which refused to fly, parachutes which failed to open, and balloons which burst at the gentlest touch.

In his side pocket he always carried a massive silver cigarette case, engraved all over with autographs, verses, and quotations and ornamented with monograms and emblems set in precious stones. This smoker's anthology, the gift of friends in perpetuation of happy moments of his life, was full of meaning and memories for its owner. To offer a cigarette from this storehouse of reminiscence, after having first related step by step the story behind all its hieroglyphics, was one of Father's chief pleasures.

He greatly valued friendship, and although it caused a noticeable bulge in his coat pocket, he always kept on his person this 'Gallery of Happy Relationships', as he called his cigarette case. His old companion and childhood friend, Vanya Puzanov, who in all things shared his feelings, had just such another case with no less a number of emblems and hieroglyphics, many of which had been contributed by Father.

Whenever he felt depressed, Father would take out these treasures and go over them all one by one recalling events of interest in his life. It was on such an occasion when he was playing with his watch and waiting for the moment when the train would appear on the miniature landscape, that there was a ring at the door-bell and a telegram was handed to him.

Grandmother, that old lady whose whole life had been spent in restless activity, had died.

Great tears streamed from his eyes. We tiptoed away, not daring to break the silence.

XXIV

WHILE at the cottage we had noticed that our eldest
sister, Nadya, used to spend a great deal of time over
at the Scheffel's.

Father was not altogether pleased with these visits, for Nadya,
besides being a lovely creature with the clear-cut features of
some charming cameo, was developed beyond her years and
had the independence of character of a boy. His daughter's
contact with José, who stopped at nothing and was invariably
surrounded by 'beautiful' young men who looked like so many
hairdressers, seemed to Father to be both dangerous and unnatural. But to all his tactfully worded hints and guarded
warnings, Nadya replied with a complete lack of understanding,
and the round eyes and candid expression of a sixteen-year-old
girl belied any suggestion of danger or fear.

Father could not understand the friendship which he described as 'the devil hand in hand with an infant', and despite
his usual philosophy of 'Do as you know best, for to you things
are clearer', he had thoughts of exercising paternal despotism
and imposing his absolute veto.

Just at this time José was fully occupied in the noble task of
uniting the hearts of a man and woman and at the moment was
spreading her net in anticipation of a rich haul. She looked upon
Nadya as a mere child, of no consequence in herself, but essential
for the conduct of this scheme, seeing that her presence was a
sop to public opinion, kept Shtrik quiet, and was useful in a
number of ways.

The scheme in question envisaged the establishment in life
of a young friend of José's, named Alicia, who had the look of
a night-club singer and a past which was not above reproach.

Her case was one calling for immediate and determined treatment; it reduced José in her kindness of heart to tears, while she searched her mind for the man who would be the most appropriate cure.

In the German colony was an exceptionally good-looking, dark young fellow, with a certain resemblance to Peter the Great, named Arthur Makenrod. He was universally popular on account of his happy disposition, youth, and wealth. He had been entirely prodigal of life and to José's thinking would not prove averse to uniting himself in matrimony, 'or otherwise,' with her 'poor deceived Alicia'.

Consequently, disregarding Nadya's presence, she discussed with Alicia strategic moves, coached her in tactics, and made all preparations for a final assault in confident expectation of victory. Certain commissions were even entrusted to Nadya, such as the delivery of letters to Arthur, the conduct of negotiations, and getting into touch with Alicia. But just when everything seemed to point to satisfactory fulfilment of the scheme, an event occurred which completely wrecked it.

Arthur, who at the start had appeared as ready for the fray as a war-horse, now tended more and more to delay the final attack, and more often than ever to rely on Nadya's mediation. It was now apparently essential for him to spend hours with her discussing Alicia's charms, until during one of these conversations he definitely made up his mind and formally proposed, not to Alicia but to Nadya, that slip of a girl fresh from school who had only been employed as an emissary!

José's anger knew no bounds. She flounced around from room to room throwing things about and pouring out torrents of abuse on Arthur. Nadya, of all people! The injustice of humanity, its deceits and its intrigues completely overwhelmed her and left her aghast.

It was thus that all her loving care had been repaid! Why, on Alicia's low-cut gowns alone she had laid out a fortune, to say nothing of entertainment, organizing tête-à-têtes, and so forth. And all for nothing! Everything had been confounded by that 'chit of a girl'! A fine fish had wriggled off her hook and the poor lonely Alicia had been left without a protector! She wept from sorrow and indignation.

When the news was made known to Father he breathed freely again, and without going into any details, gave his unconditional consent.

To us Arthur was something of a hero and we had long marked him out among the Scheffels' guests. To begin with, it could be said of him that he was not a German at all, and then, being of Swiss descent, he was a sort of 'William Tell', while, of the most importance to us, he possessed an exceptionally happy disposition, shared our interests, and promised to be our 'comrade in arms'. Nadya in our eyes became extraordinarily grown-up.

Arthur came to see us every day, bringing sweets and flowers. He heaped bon-bons upon us, took part in all our games, and more than ever endeared himself to us. He would sit for hours, talking nonsense to Nadya in the drawing-room until, judging by the uninterrupted laughter and lively chatter, one would have thought that a whole company of young people was gathered there. Sometimes there would fall a mysterious silence, in which no sound could be heard save the beating of the flies against the window-panes. We were banished from the drawing-room so as to leave the lovers undisturbed.

There is something childlike and laughable about the cooings of two lovers, but the relationship between Nadya and Arthur was so pleasant and friendly and young, that it seemed full of promise for a lifetime of mutual happiness.

Arthur had now completely settled down. He gave up drinking and severed all his former ties. His old companions were sorry for him, although their farewells occasionally took the form of revenge. Former friends presented him with promissory notes, which he redeemed simply to relieve any doubts, though he well knew that their senders were all seizing the opportunity to live awhile at his expense. Some of his erstwhile sympathizers went even further and sent him anonymous letters or put about sensational rumours in their endeavour, by fair means or foul, to compromise his future.

Thus, on one occasion Nadya sat up late into the night in her party frock vainly waiting for him to come, as had been arranged, and escort her to a ball at the German Club. As he was invariably true to his word, his failure to appear was all the more alarming and she wept copiously imagining that all was finished between them, that he had jilted her, or that he was dead.

Father consoled her by pointing out that his absence was doubtless due to some 'unfortunate concatenation of unforeseen circumstances' but she refused to listen to any such assurances. In the end we all retired to bed at a late hour, fully expecting to hear of some catastrophe on the morrow.

Early next day Arthur rushed in as bright and radiantly happy as ever. Nadya threw herself into his arms and he laughingly told us what had happened.

Half an hour before the appointed time he had been quite ready and in top hat, dress-coat, and white tie had proceeded downstairs whistling like a nightingale. Suddenly on the third floor landing he found his way blocked by a muffled female form, but as it was quite dark at the time it was difficult to recognize who it could be.

'Are you Arthur Makenrod?' asked a laughing voice, while a pair of roguish eyes gleamed in the darkness.

'I am the man himself,' he replied, 'What's the matter?'

'Take that,' was the rejoinder and with that a whole bucket of paraffin was thrown at him, drenching him from his top hat to his shoes.

'Well, I just had to sit all the evening in a bath! My topper and dress suit had gone to the deuce. And that's all there is about it,' he concluded gaily. 'I stink of paraffin still!'

Who thus sought revenge, and why, remained a mystery. It was hazarded that the ambush was José's doing, but Arthur was confident that he would have recognized José even in Stygian darkness. It was someone a good deal livelier, judging by the fact that after the event a pair of nimble legs took the stairs three at a time.

After this his former friends left him in peace, so that he was able to devote his whole time to making Nadya happy. She, as though to avenge herself on José for the paraffin episode—being fully convinced that José had had recourse to a hireling in order to prevent her going to the ball at the German Club—used to derive great pleasure from disclosing all José's intrigues when she was endeavouring to ensnare Arthur in Alicia's embrace.

'They used to say all that quite shamelessly in front of me, without even noticing I was there,' she would relate.

Arthur again averred that José was not behind the plot and the mystery was never solved. Arthur alone knew that the roots of the matter went much deeper, and that the paraffin represented the 'parting gift' of a discarded mistress. But the past was over and done with and he devoted himself entirely to the future.

They discussed the wedding in all its details and Arthur poured out money in the purchase of expensive presents, apparently wanting to overwhelm Nadya in gowns, cloaks, necklaces, and boxes of chocolate.

Nadya trotted about the shops, visited her dressmaker, and did everything regardless of expense, a new and interesting experience.

They had taken a large flat in an expensive new building situated in a fashionable quarter of the town. They furnished it at the best shops on a lavish scale, Nadya having an eye for every detail and giving full rein to her taste. Arthur, moreover, had much of his own furniture brought from Switzerland— handsome arm-chairs in dark oak, massive cupboards, some quite good pictures, and of course the traditional cuckoo-clock.

But all this display of magnificence did no more than satisfy the bare necessities as far as our Nadya was concerned, though Arthur went out of his way to meet her whims, humouring her like a child, since it was clear that she wanted to compress the whole world within the four walls of her new flat.

The wedding, as a result of their earnest deliberations, was now promising to be a most luxurious affair. At this time it was regarded as smart to be married in a private chapel and so Nadya insisted that, in accordance with the dictates of fashion, they would be married in the chapel attached to the Municipal Riding School. In this building—which was generally associated with military parades, Shrovetide booths, merrymaking, and the rounding up of students arrested after their periodic strikes —were married members of the aristocracy and such others who could afford inordinate expense.

Arthur, not being a member of the Orthodox Church, was quite indifferent about where they were married, provided that they could get the business over as soon as possible. Nadya, on the other hand, regarded this question of place as of paramount importance. Indeed the whole ritual, as planned by Nadya, rose to such heights that there seemed some danger of our not being able to live up to it all and of our toppling down to earth at the most critical moment. A private chapel, footmen on the carriages, new clothes for us all, a black suit for Father, and, most emphatically, full evening dress for Victor, were among the immediate demands of the despotic bride, whose whims were apparently without end.

Victor at first flatly refused evening dress and only after much persuasion surrendered himself to a fashionable tailor. Father insisted that his coat-tails should be cut shorter than those shown on the latest fashion plates and was adamant even to Nadya's tears. For our part we made no protest, but rather found peculiar delight in the novel experience, carefully surveying our silk garments, patent leather shoes, white stockings and all the rest of the paraphernalia that Nadya's careful hand had ordained for us.

At last the long-awaited day arrived. We were all ready, attired in our new clothes, at early dawn. Our hair was curled by a barber, who had paid a special visit to our house for the purpose. We surveyed ourselves in the mirror, adjusted tapes, removed bits of fluff, and polished our shoes for the hundredth time although without any further polishing they shone like glass. Meanwhile the bride was being robed in her own room, to which entry was forbidden, save to the maid and a few intimate friends.

The maid kept rushing to and fro every minute; bells kept ringing on the main staircase; telegrams, parcels, and bouquets of flowers were delivered. All was excitement, hubbub, and confusion.

We were thoroughly weary and more than a little nervous with all this fuss. Breakfast was cancelled owing to lack of time and though the table was set with some cold hashed-up *zakuski* no one touched them.

Father in his new abbreviated tail coat and wearing a foreign order suspended from a chain in his lapel, walked through the hall every few minutes in order to ascertain the time, paying no regard to the general disorder. He expressed surprise that the groomsmen had not arrived and was afraid that the carriages would be late. Several times he sent to see whether Nadya was ready, although he must have been fully aware that there were still three hours before the appointed time and that there was no need to hurry—we were not going to a fire!

We ourselves had long been wanting to slip out into the court and find out at the gates whether the carriages were coming, but in our new clothes this was impossible and so we had to sit stock-still on the edges of our chairs, impatiently awaiting the appointed hour.

Victor spent the whole time in his room where he was almost in tears over his full evening dress. He felt quite different in this unaccustomed garb which seemed to have 'something missing in front' and 'something bobbing about behind'. He was ashamed to show himself in public lest he should be laughed at.

The groomsmen arrived. Cachalot with his beard trimmed and his hair left in its natural curl, was dressed in a tail coat with a buttonhole of *fleurs d'or*; Kholodkov was so dandified as to be unrecognizable. Everyone was now animated and happy and Victor was dragged out from his room. Not knowing what to do with his hands, he mechanically wound his coat-tails round his stomach as he cursed the stupidity of fashion and half in anger and half jokingly warded off the groomsmen.

Kholodkov pulled faces and gave impersonations of characters at a provincial wedding and the tension of the solemn occasion so gave way to the normal jollity associated with these gay friends that even the unusual apparition of carriages in Tsiplakovski Yard passed almost unnoticed.

The two smart carriages, with footmen in cockaded top hats and patent leather boots with yellow tops, made a graceful circuit of the yard before pulling up at our entrance.

Crowds of children from the whole building now rushed up to behold this marvellous sight. The horses snorted and pawed the ground, while we looked proudly down on the magnificent spectacle with a feeling that we were indeed the heroes of the hour. We suspected, too, that our prestige in the neighbourhood would rise considerably.

Father at once became serious and summoned the bride. Laughter and joking ceased abruptly. Nadya, as is the custom of brides, was not ready. Father's foreign orders jingled on their gold chain. Time seemed to stand still. We were all aware that now had come that touching moment when we were to speed the bride upon her way. There was an oppressive stillness, a complete silence.

Victor alone, now fully reconciled to his dress suit, still wanted energetically to play the fool, failing to catch the spirit of the moment. He even poked fun at Father, exclaiming, 'Hello! Here comes His Excellency, our French Fireman!'

Father's face clouded, but just as he was about to administer a reproof, Nadya entered surrounded by her radiant retinue of friends. The maids of the next-door flat came out into the corridor to catch a glimpse of her.

She stood there in all her bridal finery. A white veil enveloped her from head to foot, and she wore a white satin dress. She seemed taller and more important. Her eyes were smiling happily and her whole being radiated happiness, boundless and unconcealed. It was as if Spring with all its flowers and sunshine was standing in full view of us all, beckoning us with white hands.

Father took down from the wall the ikon of 'Our Saviour' and, calling Nadya to him, blessed her with it three times. Tears streamed down his face and his emotion prevented him from uttering a word. Nadya looked up at him with her dear, kind eyes in which were reflected her ignorance and failure to understand the reason for this emotion.

'So! May God send you happiness, my little girl,' he said at last, forcing the words from him, and therewith the whole company noisily and in disorder began to troop downstairs.

The court was an ocean of faces. All Tsiplakovski Yard from the basement upwards, together with the population of the neighbouring buildings, had come to see us. The footmen, with their experience in such matters, dispersed the crowd while we of the procession took our places in the carriages and moved off to murmurs of good cheer, the bystanders praising the loveliness of the bride, though finding her exceedingly young and thin.

Passers-by in the street looked on with faces wreathed in smiles. A policeman—we knew him well—so far forgot his dignity as to give a gaping drayman a dig in the ribs. The whole street, if not the whole town, seemed to know that our Nadya was being married to her Arthur.

At the main entrance to the Municipal Riding School, an immense building almost half a verst long, a considerable crowd of invited guests was already waiting. The first to descend from the carriage was the small ikon-bearer—Volodya. Then a groomsman helped the bride to alight. The ikon-bearer headed the procession with a large consciousness of his own importance written upon his round face. The bride followed, leaning on Father's arm, while the rest formed up in pairs to make a long procession.

The length of the Riding School seemed endless. Its earthen floor, hard-rolled, was not meant for thinly clad human feet. The roof loomed above in the dim distance. In all this immensity people were lost and of no account. The small private chapel was situated at the far end. Semi-circular in shape, it was an appendage to the main building and in its constricted space we regained our self-importance. Indeed, Arthur's stature was so imposing that he seemed to be supporting the low ceiling on his head.

The bridegroom was noticeably nervous, his customary indifference being undermined by the strange atmosphere of an Orthodox church and by his fear of falling into some error from ignorance. Father, standing a little distance apart, was wondering why there should be such a ridiculous craze for private chapels which were dark, offered no standing room, and charged an exorbitant fee.

The wedding service was over unexpectedly soon, and the witnesses were already signing the marriage lines in the bulky church register. The old priest in silk lilac-coloured vestments beamed serenely at the young couple.

With the conclusion of the service everyone felt a certain sense of relief as they marched without semblance of order down the immense length of the riding school, now shrouded in darkness. Any feelings of sadness were dissipated and everyone wanted to laugh and talk as they straggled along fooling like schoolboys on a Christmas holiday. In the backs of their minds were visions of the luxurious wedding dinner, which had been ordered in a private room at the Great Moscow Tavern nearby.

There, on the marble staircase were standing lackeys in snow-white shirts and trousers, bowing low as though in a temple. The young folk were silent, but when they entered the vast dining room to see rows of long tables, an ocean of *zakuski*, a galaxy of bottles, a mass of flowers, all brilliantly illuminated by crystal chandeliers, they were seized by such indescribable happiness that they wanted to scream, or dance the hornpipe, or even pull the beard of the sedate waiter, who stood like some high priest at the head of the table.

The newly married pair occupied a seat in the middle, and all eyes were on them, so handsome did they look. Nadya toyed with her bouquet of roses, while Arthur out of sheer pride exerted all his strength to avoid committing some folly in the sight of his friends.

Father sat near Nadya and made happy comments to an aunt Anna Fzansevna who was all decked up haphazardly in silks and satins. The groomsmen joked with all the young girls and Kholodkov amused the men with some exceptionally diverting anecdote. The *maître d'hôtel* in evening dress, like a black crow among white doves, made his preparations. At his signal, waiters with dishes on their arms helped the guests to food, while others poured champagne into slender glasses from bottles swathed in white table-napkins.

The first toast was to the happy pair, and each in his turn left his seat to touch glasses with them and give them congratulations and good wishes. Then they drank separately to each of them, to Nadya and to Arthur; then to their parents, whereat Father gallantly bowed again and again; then to the groomsmen which made Cachalot roar with delight; and finally to the assembled guests.

After the ices had been served the men lit their cigars and cigarettes, while Victor made a semi-humorous speech and read out the congratulatory telegrams, of which there were about a hundred, some coming from people no one quite remembered. He afterwards confessed that in order to add to the impressiveness of the occasion, he had written a number of these telegrams himself, thinking that in such a mass of greetings they would pass unrecognized as his handiwork.

The diners remained in their places for some hours before moving over to small tables at which they drank coffee and liqueurs at ease on soft cushioned divans. It was now late. The waiters were clearing away and removing from the debris on the table all that had been left over. Kholodkov was drinking sweet cordials with some other students and young girls and they were all chattering like magpies. The newly married couple seized the opportunity to get away.

Meanwhile the older people lingered over their liqueurs and, as they digested their dinner conversed amiably about the instability of Fortune.

'Yes!' Father said, 'You see that waiter over there, the one with the bald patch, as handsome as a saint on an ikon—there he is clearing away a lobster. You would say he was just a waiter. I address him as "Thou" and for twenty kopecks he will almost bow down to the ground before me. Yet he owns two stone-built houses in Moscow and has a son who is a Reader at the University and a daughter married to a Colonel!

'I say to him, "Hello, Simeon, what about retiring? You've had your fill of work. Maybe it's not convenient to retire just now?" "Well, Sir", says he, "I've tried to give up, but I'm always drawn back to it again. Fifty years I've been on my feet! Started as a boy, I did. I can't unlearn the job now!" '

'Yes, you meet cases like that,' agreed a guest, taking a sip at his liqueur.

Victor, no longer in the least embarrassed by his dress suit, sprawled on a divan and philosophized on citizenship. Kholodkov was now treating the ladies to his Armenian anecdotes. Only Cachalot, clutching a bottle of cognac, was desperately ill in a corner of the room, where he was drowning his grief and longing for Nadya.

He was left to his sufferings, as we all made our way home at cock-crow. Somewhere in the suburbs a bell was ringing for morning mass.

Nadya's flat was like a little treasure-house. Everything in it had been the subject of much thought; everything possessed its peculiar significance, radiated its own beauty and charm.

In the dining room a round hanging lamp covered by a crimson shade cast a warm circle of light on the embroidered tablecloth below. There was a large carved oak sideboard whose massive shelves were laden with Swiss crockery, Bavarian jugs in the bottoms of which, when held to the light, could be seen views of the Tyrol; silver tea-pots, sugar sifters, and trays. The drawers within contained table linen of needlework and crochet, each piece a marvel of ingenuity and labour.

Covers of padded velvet concealed an array of knives and forks and other silverware, and a silver tea service reposed within its own nest like a brood-hen—for silver cups, however difficult to drink from without burning one's lips, make a brave show.

Piles of plates, a flowered dinner service, with immense dishes for meat and fish, bore further testimony to the wealth and standing of the owners.

On the walls were displayed views of the Tyrol, but pride of place was given to an oil painting, depicting a young Bavarian girl poised on a barrel, holding foaming tankards of beer in her hands. This was the work of a German artist, a boyhood friend of Arthur's, who had painted it from life at one sitting in Arthur's presence in a Munich beer hall.

A tiny copper samovar for two, a row of solid chairs along the wall, and, hanging before the window, a round cage containing a green parrot, completed the splendours of the dining room.

It was here that Father loved to spend an evening, in the knowledge that at Arthur's house he was always assured of a kind word and some excellent wine.

The drawing-room had a more formal appearance. Its floor was completely covered with a carpet, whose rosy colour was matched by the sofa and satin-upholstered chairs. Facing the door hung the familiar picture of 'Turk and Cossack'—lent by Father—in its ornate gold frame, while a well-executed oval painting of the Madonna, evidently of the Italian school, gave softness to the formally disposed furniture.

From the drawing-room one could catch a glimpse of Arthur's study with its array of leather-bound foreign volumes in heavy bookcases and its collection of photographs of unknown men in Tyrolean costume and ladies in crinolines against a background of snow-covered mountains. Arthur, by the way, never used this study, preferring to spend all his free time with Nadya in one of her own little corners of the flat. For there could be no doubt that the greatest treasure of the place was our Nadya!

Yet only a few months ago she had been trotting off to school in a brown frock with a broad white collar. Only a few months ago she had been lisping in French, coming back in rapture from the ballet-school, and quite turning the heads of all the students. A longing for pleasure, for glitter, for conquest, had been the impulse of her life.

Among her own contemporaries, she had assumed command like a general on the field of battle. They had been a happy little band of young people, fluttering about like butterflies in summer. Sometimes, locked up in a room for days together, the girls had read novels or composed thrilling letters. Sometimes they had gone off further afield.

Victor, who regarded any form of excitement with the eye of suspicion, once laid a trap for them by intercepting a letter and confronting them with it. There had been strenuous denials, angry protests, and finally floods of tears. Following up his clues as though he were to give evidence in a court of law, Victor had brought to light a clandestine friendship with a handsome Italian boy in Avantso's picture shop and had intercepted correspondence with a fashionable young actor at the Little Theatre.

He had then used all his powers of persuasion to convince Father that such behaviour demanded ruthless measures and the girls were accordingly punished by being made to stay at home. In their enforced seclusion they had courted us, the younger brothers. They taught us monologues from Shakespeare and Schiller, made us up like their favourite actors, and forced us to learn all the tricks of the theatre. Five-year-old Hamlets, Don Carlo's, and Tchatskis performed their tasks laboriously, often with tears, but they never lacked applause with an audience composed entirely of enthusiasts.

All this had been but a few months ago! And now here was Nadya in her charming flat, an omnipotent mistress whom even the great Arthur obeyed, and in whose eyes Victor had lost all

semblance of authority. Here she was ordering a servant about
with all the assurance of an experienced housewife, arranging
soirées, buying expensive presents, and doing just as she pleased
without asking leave of anyone.

Often she would call round to take us out for a drive or
whisk us off with her to spend a few days in her new home with
its marvellous parrot! Arthur had completely cut himself
adrift from his old friends and would often engage a carriage,
so great was his impatience to get back from the office as soon
as possible and take Nadya in his arms.

Sometimes, too, Nadya would call at his office where it
would give him special joy to steal a kiss when none of his
staff were around. She would clamber up on a high stool in
front of a desk and, opening with an effort the heavy ledger
which lay before her, would marvel at its thousands of figures and
be at a loss to know how Arthur could decipher anything in
such a welter of symbols. In her presence Arthur would shed
his dignity and become a big child whose one desire was for a
romp. At last they would both agree to have supper somewhere
out of town, and she would skip happily out of the office leaving
as her parting gift the scent of her English perfume, while
Arthur would open the hateful ledger and endeavour to concentrate upon his work.

Father often spent the evening with them, and so for us at
home evenings became dull and lifeless. Victor was preparing
for his Final Examination and either never emerged from his
'ice-box' or else was on duty at a clinic. When he was with us
he was always worse tempered than the devil. Our second
brother, Nicholas, was now a boarder in a military academy.
The students no longer called, evidently because they too were
busy with examinations.

Father would wander through the empty rooms in silence,
and then would take his hat and gloves and go to spend an evening
with 'the children'.

With 'the children' he was always assured of a warm welcome.
Arthur would open a bottle of good red wine. Nadya would

bring him a *marron glacé*, being a connoisseur where they were concerned. Later *pâté de foi gras* in a dainty little pot would be produced, and the evening would pass quietly, in true family fashion.

The thought came to Father of how the carefree happy existence of this young couple would continue on its untrammelled course and be for ever blessed with love and plenty. Arthur was as strong as an ox and Nadya was young. Their home was full of happiness. What could be better?

Thus musing, he took an apple, the rosiest and ripest, and gazed in admiration at nature's wonderful handiwork, before cutting it with his dessert-knife. When he did so, he found that the inside was so completely worm-eaten that it looked like grey chaff.

This trifling incident plunged him at once into depths of depression and, without waiting for the close of the evening, he took his leave and set off hurriedly home.

Nadya was perplexed, but Arthur turned the whole thing into a joke. 'Papa's got the tummy-ache—that's all—and you're worrying about it' he said consolingly to his wife as he gathered her to him. Yet, unknown to her, that moment marked the entry of sorrow into Nadya's heart.

Thereafter Father's visits to 'the children' were less frequent, and sometimes, having set out to call upon them, he would turn aside and drop into a restaurant, where he would sit alone and kill time over a bottle of beer.

Victor wrote a long poem about this, beginning:

> *I meant to my son-in-law's house to repair*
> *To pass a quiet evening there.*
> *The 'Restaurant Rus', where I found I'd got,*
> *Is really such a delightful spot.*

Within ten months, Arthur had died of consumption.

XXV

ARTHUR burned away, wasting before our eyes like a candle. His illness originated in a trifling cold, caught early one morning, when returning from a restaurant in the outskirts of the town where both Nadya and he enjoyed spending 'bachelor evenings'. No one paid any attention at first to a cold, seeing that Arthur was known always to enjoy the most robust health. Then, morning sweats, with sudden rises of temperature, began to undermine even his hardy constitution.

His complexion grew ashen and his black curly hair seemed almost in a moment to become flecked with grey. Little rings of silver glinting in his hair at first contrived to lend him an original and even a younger look. But when the grey hairs began to spread more and more, and the black gave place to them and finally disappeared altogether, it was obvious that something was seriously amiss. Not that he ever gave in, indeed he seemed incapable of taking anything seriously. He laughingly turned his illness into a joke by alluding to his 'venerable' old age, the problems of married life, and his wife's obstinacy, before directing the conversation to more cheerful topics. Only his eyes which had now lost their habitual sparkle and become large and dull, betrayed an inner anxiety. There was something touching about his quiet trustfulness and delicacy, which reminded us much of Father.

His love for Nadya and his constant watchfulness over her, as over some small child, increased without abatement. All his thoughts were apparently concentrated upon her and he was always trying to perform for her some act of kindness.

Thus it happened that when, at an outlying restaurant which they frequented, they heard a zither-player whose outstanding skill Nadya greatly admired, Arthur without a word to anyone resolved to arrange a little surprise.

A few weeks later it was Nadya's birthday and on waking early and rousing Arthur, she heard echoing through the house the sounds of enchanting music as from a distant invisible harp. To her amazement song after song, all the favourites of her own repertoire, were being rendered by a master hand. She lay in bed spellbound and motionless, entralled by this ethereal harping. What could it be?

Though tortured by feminine curiosity she yet lacked the energy to get out of bed, slip on a kimono, and discover the secret. An inexplicable lethargy stole over her and her one desire was just to continue lying as she was for ever, listening to the streams of melody, following the delicate tracery of sound.

When at last she went into the hall in her kimono there was no one to be seen. The room was full of flowers, the sofa covered with presents, but no sign of zither or artist.

Arthur was sitting in his study pretending to be busy. He failed however to keep up the appearance and burst out into boyish laughter though not until the evening did he give away the trick. Nadya's beloved virtuoso had, it appeared, agreed to his request to come to the house and to play, upon receiving an agreed signal. At another signal he had slipped down the back stairs just as Nadya, a prey to her curiosity, had entered. This episode, so typical of Arthur's gentle charm, was long remembered by Nadya, to whom it revealed a new and enigmatic side of his character.

She had another opportunity of seeing him from an angle rarely vouchsafed to her sex. He always pretended that he felt in the best of health and would drag her off to entertainments of all kinds simply to please her, since he knew her passion for those amusements which had by now become wearisome and uninteresting to himself. He so disguised his feelings as to convince her that he personally could not stay quietly at home but must needs have musical comedies, restaurants, and joyful music.

When the warm weather came, therefore, he booked a table at an open-air music hall, where turns succeeded each other with the speed of a kaleidoscope. These consisted of a vaudeville show and a chorus attired in Boyar costume and accompanied on dulcimers, balalaikas, and other ingenious and old-fashioned instruments. The chief soloist was a stout Boyar lady with a head-dress studded with 'property' pearls who sang in so deep a contralto that one could have taken her for a man with a bass voice. A Hungarian chorus too, rendered a very good march and an even better *czardas* whose main attraction lay in flashing eyes, bare arms, and short skirts revealing pretty legs shod in dainty high boots. Somewhere in the sky above, acrobats performed such spectacular somersaults that members of the audience held their breath and convulsively clutched their neighbours without knowing it.

At last there was a roll on the drums and upon the stage stepped a man dressed in a costume composed entirely of glittering scales. He made a truly marvellous sight and Nadya read the flamboyant announcement in the programme: 'The Human Snake. First appearance in Moscow. Touring from Paris to London.' Indeed this man in the glittering scales was able to transform himself into a veritable snake and like some enormous boa constrictor climb a high tree, erected in the centre of the stage, with such sinuous writhing movements as had never before been seen in any human being. It looked indeed as though every bone beneath that glittering sheath must be broken into fragments and yet his body was as intact as the body of an enormous reptile.

The human snake then noiselessly descended the tree in spiral fashion and head-foremost crept along the stage whereon he coiled and uncoiled himself like a steel spring before finally curling up into a compact circle. The public was dumbfounded. As he raised his slender head with its eyes agleam and a tongue made of peacock feathers flickering between its sharp fangs, his resemblance to the crafty serpent was so amazing as to cause the audience to shudder before they testified to their admiration by round after round of frenzied applause. The next moment he was standing cool and collected in the centre of the stage bowing to left and right fully aware of his own perfection.

His beautiful unexpected movements and his snake-like grace produced a deep impression on Nadya, who continued to talk about him for the whole of the evening. On the morrow Arthur, spurred on by his wife, professed himself unable to live without again seeing the human snake and from that time forward they never missed a single performance. In fact the human snake became an *idée fixe* and his name was for ever on their tongues.

To Nadya he had become a demigod endowed with wonderful grace and agility. 'What a man! I would give anything just to be near such a man!' she exclaimed under the spell of some kind of mystic rapture, until by the time Arthur realized what was happening it was already too late and she had succumbed entirely to the human snake's fascination.

Quite quietly, therefore, he went to look for 'the reptile' and on the next day the human snake dined with them in front of the stage, only to reveal himself as an uncouth lout, wearing artificial diamond rings and a loud checked grey suit like the ideal vaudeville lover. His eyes were made up, his cheeks rouged, and his hair dyed. He had the insolent stare of a circus rider and taken all round was a 'masher' and cad of the first water, although, when all was said and done, only likely to be a source of danger to suburban housemaids.

He spoke with complete assurance solely about himself, his world-wide reputation, and his success with women. According to his story baronesses, countesses, ladies and so forth went crazy about him, gave him palaces, and shot themselves by the dozen. Scores of husbands and lovers had perished at the hand which he now ran through his dyed curls with a played-out theatrical gesture.

Five minutes after meeting him Nadya did not know which way to turn. When seen at close quarters his glamour was shown to be base and his manners those of a lackey. During all this time Arthur had remained silent, listening attentively, passing the wine, and behaving with the acme of politeness. He knew now that the game was his and by this one daring stroke in bringing about their meeting he had decapitated the snake before his wife's eyes. Nadya's fascination had vanished like smoke.

After this Nadya no longer liked the open-air theatre. Arthur also ceased to be interested in it and preferred not to go out at all. In fact nowadays he tended to stay at home altogether and send Nadya off 'to enjoy herself'. Father therefore escorted her to a musical comedy or to the circus, which they both enjoyed enormously. Salomonski, the then ring-master and proprietor, all decked out with foreign orders including Persian and Turkish stars, entered at the head of his troupe proudly cracking his long whip, at a flick of which he could send a team of seven horses rearing up on their haunches.

The trick-riders, the trained elephants, the comical clowns with their inevitable red noses, getting in each other's way and in everyone else's, were all simple well-tried friends whose performances had a tonic effect on Nadya. On her way home with Father in a cab she would hum the popular airs from a musical comedy, or discuss the training of animals. Arthur would be found waiting up for them in his dressing-gown and would be delighted at Nadya's excitement and youth, as if warming himself before her radiating energy.

He was now paying more serious regard to his health, taking creosote, drinking milk, and doing all that his doctors insisted upon.

Nadya was herself so entirely happy that she gave little heed to his rises in temperature and was only worried by his dry hacking cough which, especially in the early morning, interfered with her sleep. Somehow she had become resigned to her husband's invalidism, and in response to his continual encouragement she hastened to enjoy the pleasure of being alive.

She had a retinue of courtiers and admirers, and Arthur considered it only right and natural that she should have. Thus by mutual consent they both arranged their lives on different lines—Nadya draining her cup of happiness at balls, soirées, and theatres; Arthur sitting at home gulping down creosote in full consciousness of the fact that 'his song was ended'.

To everyone except himself, Nadya's unconcern seemed strange. She evidently did not realize the gravity of her husband's complaint and for his part he did all in his power to save her from trouble and anxiety.

Surrounded by phials, medicine bottles, and respirators he sat in his chair, clean-shaven and fresh-looking but always now in his dressing-gown.

He loved helping Nadya to get ready for a ball and would arrange the folds of her dress, pin fresh roses on her corsage, and survey her critically from head to foot like an anxious mother seeing her daughter off to her first dance.

There came a ring at the bell and her retinue of courtiers arrived to act as escort. Full of joy and anticipation she descended the stairs while Arthur stood at the top and listened to their departing footsteps.

As the sounds died away he inclined his head and quietly collected himself. The feminine garments thrown carelessly aside on the floor or over the chairs all reminded him of Nadya, so young, so full of life. It was as though she had come back again or not gone away at all.

Sadly he seated himself in his chair and began to muse. He had a pricking in his lungs as though needles were piercing him. A cough started in his throat. Now that he was alone there was no longer need for him to guard every movement so carefully to escape the vigilance of onlookers. Now he was free to drift along with the current, and notice how each successive day was whittling down a frame which not long ago had been so strong and active.

Sitting there in the semi-darkness his bent body reminded him of some stalwart oak in whose heart an invincible microscopic host was already engaged on a task of destruction, gnawing at its foundations, weakening its deepest roots, bowing to the earth its waving branches. Proud and strong to all outward seeming and still raising its head to the skies, it knew that at the first roll of thunder, the first lightning flash, it would fall to the ground and be dissipated in dust.

Late at night the bell rang imperiously to herald Nadya's return. Arthur gave a shudder as though to shake off his lethargy and went himself to open the door for her. Excited, happy, and tired she did not notice how dejected was his appearance, and he, gradually becoming infected by her animation, found happiness in her happiness and laughter in her laughter.

'Well, what was it like?' he asked as he sat down by her side.

'It was awfully jolly! I danced almost without a stop! People asked after you and were sorry you hadn't come. And do you know whom I met? You'll never guess,' as Arthur pulled a serious face and prepared to answer her riddle. 'Your Alicia! Yes, Alicia! She dances at Yar's in the Hungarian chorus! She's got thin and become quite impossible—quite a harridan. She tried to sneak Victor's watch! We didn't know how to get rid of her. Yes, she's come down to that! And she was pretty once, and once I was even quite sorry for her. Can you remember her low-cut dresses? And how furious José was that you chose me instead of her?'

Arthur bent his head as though calling back the past. How long ago it all seemed to his imagination. And yet it was not at all long ago in actual life measured in terms of flesh and blood. It was only difficult now to remember who was this Alicia whom Nadya so tantalizingly called 'his'.

'And how did you get on without me?' Nadya asked as though she had only just remembered her husband's health. 'What is your temperature?'

'It's normal,' he lied.

'And how's the cough?'

'Not got one,' he lied again.

'Well, thank God for that! And now we must get some sleep.' She got up wearily, trailing her ball dress behind her, as, limp with fatigue, she made her way to the bedroom.

For a long time Arthur could not sleep. For him now began that period of agonizing insomnia wherein all things—the light, his life, his thoughts—were alike grey. Only here and there were bright spots of colour, rainbows in the haze of memory.

He saw himself as a boy coming back from school, in his short trousers and braces, without a coat. A leather satchel holding his books was dangling on his back. He saw his Swiss canton with its little chalets and its old red-roofed church with a spire. In the distance were snow-covered mountains but here in the valley herds of cattle, always with melodious little bells, were grazing in green meadows. A silvery tinkling could be heard ever so faintly as it was borne along by the breeze. He was striding home hungry but happy.

In school that day the old teacher, Bauman, had been more than usually exacting and bad-tempered. Arthur remembered the school rhyme about him and smiled involuntarily as it came back to him.

> *Over the hills and far away,*
> *Old Bauman stands on his head all day,*
> *Along comes a chap with a big long snout*
> *And sees old Bauman and gives a shout,*
> *'Say, how do you bake your cakes up here?*
> *Ils ne sont pas awfully dear'.*

What dear nonsense it was, he thought, as he gazed into the grey light and longed to be transported back to his native haunts, and see whether the old church was still standing or whether the mountains had moved. Why, he might even meet the terrible Bauman as a friend where

> *Over the hills and far away*
> *Old Bauman stands on his head all day.*

He remembered his student years, when he wore a velvet
jacket, his corps cap with its gay narrow ribbon, and a pair of
jack-boots. With long pipe in mouth and tankard of beer before
him, he watched his fellows duelling with rapiers. What good
times those had been, times of great hopes and plans and
disappointments. In those days, 'over the hills and far away'
there was no Bauman standing on his head. No. Everything had
stood quite naturally on its feet.

The grey light in the window took on a rosy tint, his lungs
were no longer pricking as much as they had been, his cough
gradually released him from its rending talons. His whole body
was weary and for a time he found forgetfulness as he fell into
a doze.

Victor kept a penetrating eye on him and allowed no detail
to escape. He was more fully aware of the seriousness of Arthur's
condition than was the doctor who was treating him. From the
medical journals he had learned of the new discoveries of
Doctor Koch, which promised amazingly happy results. Ob-
sequious advertisements declaimed in fact that his brilliant
research had enabled him completely to conquer that scourge of
humanity—consumption. Though not entirely believing in
German miracles, Victor nevertheless considered that every
remedy should be essayed.

Arthur himself showed no enthusiasm but succumbed to
Victor's arguments; after much correspondence through the
medium of his foreign connexions, he prevailed upon the
world-famous medical luminary to undertake his case.

When it had once been decided to go away, Nadya busily
applied herself to the necessary preparations. New countries
were beckoning her with their offer of new opportunities for
enjoyment, and despite his small faith in his recovery, Arthur
was anxious to see the place where he was born and quietly
made his plans for the journey.

From abroad Nadya wrote long lively letters giving all the
news. In bulky epistles bearing foreign stamps she described
in her vivacious way the new places they had seen and the new

friends they had made. According to her accounts, Arthur was making a rapid recovery and was even putting on weight. Doctor Koch's marvellous treatment was working miracles. More than anyone else, Father believed in the omnipotence of science and in all his restaurants and among all his friends he sang the praises of the doctor-magician.

News of this wonder of wonders even penetrated the warehouse where they grieved that 'that bad-tempered consumptive fellow, Klyagin' had not lived to know 'this stupendous discovery'.

Father carried all Nadya's letters in his pockets together with newspaper cuttings marked in red pencil citing cures effected by Koch's treatment so that when he was talking about these miraculous happenings he could be supported by documentary evidence.

Victor alone kept silence and was disinclined to share his enthusiasm, a fact which never failed to rouse Father. 'Ah, you doctors, you doctors! You never see beyond your own noses!' he exclaimed, using his favourite words. 'A man comes along who's above all comparison with you, and you just sit, and go on sitting until you've worn your seats out, and you discover nothing at all!'

Victor maintained his air of scepticism, for his clever eyes could penetrate the distance. Sometimes, almost against his will, he would remark, ' "We shall see," said the blind man, and "we shall hear" answered his deaf fellow'; or else he would simply retire to his room and his books in silence. There remained but a few weeks to the end of his final examinations and he was paying special regard to the employment of his free time and to the maintenance of an emotional equilibrium.

Arthur returned from abroad noticeably better, while Nadya had bloomed like a tea-rose in all its beauty. She had brought back with her several trunks full of foreign coats and dresses and trinkets, as well as presents for all of us.

Father often went to sit 'with the children' while Nadya again abandoned herself to her carefree life.

And then one day, for no explicable reason, Arthur felt far worse and like the oak, fell crumbling to earth.

He never now left his bed for his disease, having returned amazingly suddenly and in all its virulence, was now advancing with a quickening pace towards its tragic end.

One evening when Nadya was sitting at his bedside—for she refused to leave him now—he announced that he felt much easier. He joked, recalled to mind funny episodes during their travels abroad, and remarked that on the morrow he would go to his office since he must get business moving again.

Then suddenly he relapsed into silence, as though he were listening for something. 'That's strange,' he murmured almost inaudibly in a tone of astonishment. 'Something funny's happening to my legs. I've no feeling in them. I might as well not have any!' and behind his kindly smile he tried to conceal his growing fear.

As Nadya drew down the quilt his wasted legs were sharply outlined against the white sheets and their bluish-purple colour, their distended veins, and their look of petrifaction filled her with the dread of death.

'You've got an ingrowing nail. I must cut it tomorrow,' she said calmly, stifling a cry of horror.

Within an hour Arthur was lying dead, and Nadya was frantically rushing about the room, helpless in her grief and fear in the presence of death.

We spent the whole night with her. Father stroked her hair and calmed her with quiet endearing words until at dawn she fell asleep in his arms like a child.

Arthur lay in the hall on the massive oak table he had brought from Switzerland and looked even larger than he had been in life. His powerful will seemed still to knit together his strong limbs and his stalwart figure looked so strong and quietly confident and even proud, that one could not believe that he was cold and lifeless. More than ever did he remind us of Peter the Great.

Far from his own country, in foreign surroundings, our kind and beloved 'comrade in arms' had come to his life's end, and standing on the threshold of a new life was Nadya, widowed at the age of twenty, and looking little more than a child in her mourning.

And when we thought of Arthur we would invariably remember

> *Over the hills and far away*
> *Old Bauman stands on his head all day.*

1890-1902

XXVI

VICTOR passed his final medical examinations with
honours when he had just turned twenty-three. His
youthful beardless face, his grey enquiring eyes that
mirrored an enquiring mind, his shyness with women as well
as the ruthless logic of his conversation, all gave him the
appearance of a first-year student rather than of a fully qualified
doctor.

While awaiting his provincial appointment, he stayed with
us in the country cottage, enjoying repose and freedom after
the exhausting examinations. Father was very proud of his
eldest son's erudition and had a plate hung on the gate: *Doctor
V.Y.P., Patients Received Daily from 10 a.m. to 4 p.m.*; and he
waited with childish excitement for the first patients.

For a long time no one appeared. But one day, when the
hope of a 'large' practice had almost expired, the first patient
suddenly presented herself. She became known as 'The Lady
with the Finger'. Fashionably dressed, in an ostrich-feather hat,
powdered and rouged, with eyes made up, and holding her
bandaged finger in front of her, she floated through the reception room like a peacock and disappeared into the doctor's
surgery.

This 'surgery' had been temporarily set up in the drawing-
room, where a low couch had been arranged and a small
glass-fronted cupboard for medical instruments installed.
Two or three armchairs and a writing desk completed the
furniture.

In an hour's time, the patient appeared in the doorway of
the surgery evidently eased and relieved, accompanied by her

flustered physician. Turning with a pleasant smile at the porch, the lady declared that she would return the next day. When she had gone, we all gathered round Victor:

'Well, and how was it? What's wrong with her finger?'

'The devil take her, she made me sweat!' said Victor wearily. 'I looked at the finger. It was an ordinary abscess. A trifle! One had only to lance it, clean it, and bandage it up. But she was afraid. I picked up the lancet and applied it. And she gave out a squeal. What the devil, I thought, the lancet isn't cutting. I made her sit down again and comforted her and began again— no result. Again I sat her down and quieted her; I gave her a glass of water. Then I began for the third time! I chanced to glance at the lancet. And then I guessed what was the matter: I was cutting with the blunt edge, out of excitement, I suppose! Well, I turned the lancet over, made an incision, and she didn't turn a hair. The operation was done. That's the sort of thing that may happen,' he finished, looking at us shyly with his enquiring eyes.

The lady called every day for a fortnight, complaining each time of a new ailment. Victor was angry and ready to call himself a quack, but he received her; he could not do otherwise. 'The Lady with the Finger' was followed by other patients: an old man with kidney trouble, an old woman, and some young ladies from a neighbouring cottage. The fame of the new 'luminary' began to spread. But his country practice did not last long, for in the autumn his appointment was confirmed. He had to close down his surgery, pack for the journey, and set himself up in a provincial town in the Moscow region.

'One bird has flown,' Father said with both joy and grief. 'Nadya flutters like a butterfly from one watering-place to another, but ever since her marriage she has been "adrift". Now Victor's turn has come; the house has become very empty——'.

But in the autumn Nicholas, who had led a busy life that had constantly taken him away from the family circle, appeared

again among us in the glittering uniform of a newly commis-
sioned officer, and he stayed with us for a long while. Within a
few days it was already clear that neither his officer's epaulettes,
nor his new rank, had affected his character. He was the
'eternal worker', a silent, exceptionally clear-headed and
adaptable man. He never quarrelled, or tried to convince
anyone, but went his way performing tasks he alone knew.
He almost never frequented society; he never drank or
smoked, and he spent his spare time in his room, studying
military science, the French language from a textbook, and
Esperanto.

Always punctual, correct, and polite in his relations with
others, he was never in anyone's way and was soon the general
favourite, as well as the champion and pride of the family.

With Victor's departure and Nicholas's arrival, all acute
misunderstanding and crises came to an end. All questions were
now discussed on another plane, without bad blood or disputes.
Nicholas's healthy humour and inoffensive laughter, though
directed sometimes at Father, did not offend him as Victor's
had always done. Father frequently consulted him about his
business affairs or confessed his transgressions to him as he
might to a priest. When confronted with a hostile atmosphere,
Nicholas tried to hear his opponent to the end, and only then,
without any hurry, would he declare his disagreement and
defend his positions strongly. But he never entered into senseless disputes. An honesty that was crystal-clear, a simplicity
and decency of character could be discerned in all his acts.
Even his thoughts seemed pure and animated as a bubbling
spring. He would take upon himself the modest and the difficult tasks, and he fulfilled them with love, keeping himself
as it were to the side or in the shadow. His approach to
even the most insignificant tasks was cautious, but once
engaged he spared neither himself nor his time, and did them
splendidly.

Very soon his patience, serious approach, and knowledge
had advanced him to the forefront of his comrades, and he was

showered as from the horn of plenty with the most responsible and difficult assignments. Now, an infantry officer, he would be sent to Kiev to take a course of engineering, now he would be elected to represent the regiment in supervising the arrival of supplies or in inspecting the commissariat. In the course of a short period, it appeared that there was not a single office in the regiment which was not offered to him at a time of crisis. He had been instructor of the learners' squad, 'our true national university', as he called it; he had been the paymaster, and the regimental adjutant; he had given a lecture in the Officers' Club on Napoleon's strategy; he had organized communal educational reading circles and had trained a full soldiers' choir.

In the officers' mess he was liked for his equable character and appreciated for his sober, reasonable mode of life and his clear quiet outlook on the world; and he was envied a little for his astonishing grasp of his duties and the regulations. He knew his business surprisingly well and to the least detail. Even the older staff officers, who had grown grey in card-table battles, were a little shy of the young 'know-all'. They called him jokingly The Child, and prophesied that he would soon tire of the details of service regulations, but in all doubtful cases they had recourse to his assistance.

Whenever Nicholas had his fill of unresolved problems, contradictory evidence and boring conversations, he would sit down at the piano and find relaxation in the lively tunes of military marches. They soothed and dispersed his doubts. Rising from the piano, he would go off quietly and study.

He used to get up early, and immediately go on duty. His battalion was quartered in the old Krutitsky barracks, almost on the edge of Moscow and not far from the Sparrow Hills. An ancient gateway, with living quarters dating from the time of Czar Alexey Mikhailovich, led one into a spacious quadrangle, closed in on all sides by enormous buildings of the days of Nicholas I. There was always a squad being trained in the square, words of command ringing out, a clicking of breech-blocks and a clatter of equipment.

In his new uniform, Nicholas would run down the steps to the quarters of his unit. The sergeant would shout 'Attention!' and would give his report. And so the day began, a long day of systematically apportioned labour.

Nicholas had a particular love for his unit. He spent most of his time with it, entered into all the details of the soldiers' lives and tried to ease the first steps of the very young recruits. Looking upon the regimental school as a 'national university' as he did, he was fond of pointing out 'how many thousands of illiterate peasants have passed through it'. The company kitchen produced tasty borsch and baked its own black bread, and each soldier also got a daily portion of meat, 'While in the villages meat is not to be seen for months on end,' he would add.

Nicholas's watchful eyes would spot any manoeuvre on the part of the quarter-master or any 'excessive economy'. He would show them all up. Nor was he afraid of sending in a report to the higher authorities if he noticed any abuse in the kitchen. 'The army marches on its belly,' he used to say, tasting a spoonful of borsch from the cauldron. And this care for his men did not escape the keen eyes of former peasants.

The soldiers were picked peasant lads, healthy and tall, and mainly from the Ukraine. Strong as horses, with accurately clipped beards, they made a fine impression in the ranks. Well turned out and selected for height, they marched with measured tread, tramping the ground with their strong metal-heeled army boots. It seemed as if a whole army of broad-chested young giants was clearing a path for itself through every obstacle, and that it was irresistible and unconquerable. And he, Nicholas, a beardless lieutenant, a boy almost, held this whole mass in his hands with only a word of command.

But it was not mere power that Nicholas enjoyed: in his mind he was ever conscious of the duty and responsibility that were his when confronted with this mass of youngsters. 'For shall we not die together,' was the inner thought that rose from the depths of his soul.

'And in the meantime live a life. Live honestly, well and boldly!'

So, at the end of an exhausting round of duties, Nicholas would call the soldier-singers forward. The young soldiers would squat down on the floor in a circle, exchanging jokes and resting from the mechanics of discipline. The song-leader, a well-built lad of roguish appearance, came forward, tilted his peakless cap on the back of his head and, advancing his right foot, sang out in a high ringing tenor voice: 'And they whistled, the Cossacks—'.

'The Cossacks!'— a mighty chorus picked him up, as if a giant slice of bread had been cut off with a huge knife. And the melodious disconsolate anguish of the Cossack, leaving behind him his home and his Marussenka, resounded in low octaves through all the barrack buildings.

The eyes of that crowd of men reflected a sort of sorrow, the remembrance of the home they had left behind, and their beloved and dear ones. The sergeant pulled at his belt and demanded something more jolly. They sang 'That happened at Poltava', and then about 'the dashing commander, who slept not, nor dreamed, but saved his battalion'. Then it was the turn of the tambourines, the cymbals clashing in a wild roar as soldier-dancers flung themselves into a dashing *gopak*— it was difficult to sit still in the midst of this wild dance, redolent of the black-earth steppes and ungreased carts. It seemed as if a number of giant balls were leaping up into the air, striking down upon the floor at an angle and then bouncing off again.

At nine o'clock in the evening the company formed up and the roll-call was taken. The first name was that of Arkhip Ossipov, who many years before had blown up a powder magazine rather than surrender it to the enemy. Ossipov had been blown up with it, too.

'Arkhip Ossipov,' the sergeant called out in a deep voice.

'He died for the glory of Russian arms!' one of the soldiers answered.

'Ivan Schur.'

'He died for the glory of Russian arms—.'

There was something serious and inexplicably touching in the roll-call of the long-perished heroes of the regiment.

'Ivan Doroshenko,' the deep-voiced sergeant continued.

'Present.'

'Peter Goose.'

'Present.'

And so it went on until the last common soldier of the company was reached. Then came the command, 'To prayers. Off with your caps!'

There was a flutter of peakless caps in the air, and right arms dropped 'to attention'. The melodious, peacefully joyful sounds of prayer broke the silence and swam through the endless corridors of the barracks, coming to rest somewhere in the corners under the ceiling.

The working day was over. Nicholas set off home and again pored over his military lore, his French textbook, and his Esperanto. Occasionally, on Sundays, some of his fellow-officers looked in to see him. They would arrive, one after another, take off their swords and belts in the hall and sit down primly on the Viennese chairs in the drawing room. The conversation turned mainly on regimental news, passed lightly over non-controversial politics and lingered on the opera, Khokhov, and various ballerinas.

As with the students, Father soon found common ground and became the centre of attention when talking of the army in the days of Nicholas I, demonstrating outmoded rifle-drill and remembering incidents and anecdotes. They drank tea with a dash of cognac in it, while the *zakuski* would appear later, towards midnight, accompanied by vodka, liqueurs, *zubrovka*, and rowan-berry brandy, and other varieties of drink.

Tongues were loosened. Father would pour out a third round, repeating the while: 'God loves the Trinity.' And then he would say, 'A hut is not built without four corners!' And so he would go on until the proverbs, and the contents of the bottles, were exhausted.

Nicholas, who did not touch a drop, talked about military affairs, but he listened even more to what others were saying. He had no light to throw on ballerinas. When the anecdotes dealt a little freely with the more animal appetites, he would go up to the piano and drown the immodesties of human flesh in the bravura notes of military marches. It would be late already when the officers, slightly unsteady on their feet, bade their farewells and gallantly clicked their spurred heels. Father would escort them all to the hall, finish off his anecdotes there, call a young lieutenant a colonel, prophesy to them the rank of Generalissimo and, having seen them off, return to his unfinished glass of tea.

In his room, Nicholas was finishing reading about fortification. He would then do his gymnastic exercises 'in the style of Muller', and soon the whole house would be soundly asleep.

After the departure of Victor and Nadya, the household passed into the hands of the fifteen-year-old Vera. Vera did not attend school, but was studying at home to become a house tutor, and her learning was limited mainly to 'domestic problems'. With the help of her confidante, counsellor, and friend, the cook Tatyana, Vera gained unlimited authority over the household and reigned over it like a monarch in her own right.

In the mornings, when father was finishing his glass of strong tea and was hiding his fine blue eyes behind the tinted glass of his gold-rimmed spectacles, Vera would broach a difficult subject:

'Papa, will you please give me three roubles!'

'Again three roubles. What for?'

'For the household expenses, Papa, I must have them,' Vera said slowly, trying to make her kind eyes look severe. Father showed signs of irritation.

'Three roubles, indeed, you spendthrift; I gave you three roubles yesterday, and here you want another three today! I don't mint money, do I?' he asked the now frightened Vera.

'But, Papa, I must have them for household expenses!'

Meanwhile Tatyana would tactfully open the kitchen door and make as much noise as she could with the plates, moving saucepans about and displaying an incredible activity in her department. That helped.

Father would then pull out his old wallet, pick out a three-rouble note and hand it reluctantly to Vera.

'There, take it! You'll be the death of me! Let this be the last time!'

With the note in her possession, Vera would vanish into the depths of Tatyana's domain. And taking off his dressing-gown, Father would proceed to the warehouse tranquilly and as if all were in the day's work. Father's perplexity at Vera's daily demands for household money was a recurrent morning act in the comedy of life. By evening he would stop up all the gaps with generous hand and spend without regard on pleasures, purchases, and renewals. No one interfered with Vera's conduct of domestic affairs. All the problems were discussed with Tatyana in the kitchen. And there Vera spent the greater portion of her spare time.

Without a moment's rest, Tatyana busied herself with the oven-forks, cleaned potatoes, added logs of wood to the blazing oven, while Vera, settling comfortably on Tatyana's bed and pulling aside the variegated cotton curtain, unfolded to the cook a plan of earthly existence.

Here in quietude, to the restful noise of a boiling kettle, the problems of life, of body and soul, were resolved. Advice on how to salt cucumbers, pickle mushrooms, preserve plums, pickle herrings, was interlarded with injunctions about Christian life and lessons of 'love sinful and sinless'—the Fathers of the Church and Christian deeds were mingled with dreams of princes and young officers. Tatyana, it seemed, was a kitchen philosopher and with her peasant astuteness sometimes hit the nail on the head. To a woman of her healthy and sensuous temperament everything seemed interesting and 'wonderful'.

A long time ago, in the first year of Nadya's marriage, she had picked up Tatyana by chance in the street. She had observed a young and pretty peasant woman with a child in her arms sitting on the pavement as if waiting for something. Involuntarily, Nadya started up a conversation with her. This sitting about in a crowded street had struck her as strange. It emerged that the peasant woman had just become a widow and had arrived from her village to look for her uncle, 'a *dvornik* in Stoleshnikov street', but she could find no trace of him.

'And what did your husband die of?' Nadya had enquired.

'He didn't die. He drowned himself.'

'What? Did he do it himself?'

'No, he was swimming with the lads and was drowned.'

'Then he didn't drown himself, but was drowned—.'

'No, lady, he did not end his own life, but I tell he drowned himself.'

Nadya took on the woman and the child. And Tatyana turned out to be a good cook, and a nice person; and ever since that day she had been part of our family. When Nadya's home broke up, Tatyana came to us. Soon it was impossible to imagine the house without her. She did the cooking and sewing, and looked after the 'younger generation'. When the younger generation grew up, Tatyana became Vera's confidante and irreplaceable friend, and took the place of a mother for Volodya, the youngest.

Possessed of peasant wit and natural tact, she knew her place. She was supreme in the kitchen and shy in the drawing-room. When teased, she was not offended; but hiding her face in her apron, eyes twinkling roguishly, she floated away to the kitchen barely holding her laughter. Once in the midst of her andirons and saucepans she relieved herself in guffaws of infectious laughter.

'And the things they say, the jokers!'

Gradually her peasant tan and the awkwardness of her naïve mind gave place to a city shrewdness; her figure became rounded, and her spontaneous temperament found its level in city life. She became known in the shops of the Ohotny Ryad; the shop assistants bowed to her and the shop-owners cast more than a passing glance at this pretty woman, with well-developed breasts and lively eyes. There were romances, profitable offers, attractions, all warmly discussed in the kitchen with Vera and even the still youthful Volodya; but none led to positive results.

For half a year she was in love with a local policeman, but he was transferred to another beat and the love came to an end. Later a 'dark one' came on the scene, but no one ever saw him, although there was endless talk about him. Storms, squalls, collisions, dead calm, all succeeded one another in her dreamy, homely heart.

'Again too much salt in the soup.'

'What's happened? Tatyana must be spooning again—'

But Vera would pacify Father and would not allow him to ask the cook awkward questions.

Sometimes a mood of depression would creep over Tatyana. She would pack her belongings and say that she was going back to the village, never to return. But the anguished mood would pass, her belongings would find their way back to the familiar red-painted chest decorated with iron-work, and Tatyana would postpone departure till the spring. And so, until her death, she did not succeed in reaching her village.

It would have been difficult to find a more faithful person than Tatyana, one with so naïve and childlike a soul.

When, many years later, at the time of the general strike, the life of the city had been entirely upset and it was dangerous to move about in the streets, Tatyana made her way at her own risk through the pickets of soldiers, chattering on the way with sergeants, smiling at the strikers, and returning home loaded with provisions, milk, and vegetables. She did not explain how she managed to get all these things, but she brought back many curious impressions from dangerous quarters.

When, some years earlier, Alexander III was expected to arrive in Moscow, Tatyana could not sit still. All dressed up from early morning, with her hair pomaded, in a new mantle and silk kerchief, she left home earlier than she needed to, all joyful and excited. By lunch-time she was back home already, looking depressed and disappointed.

'Well, and did you see the Czar, Tatyana?'

'Yes, I did.'

'Was he handsome? Did you like him?'

But Tatyana turned her face away. It was clear that she was not keen on questions. We were all puzzled.

'Did anything happen?'

'What's the use of talking?' Tatyana suddenly burst out. 'I, fool that I am, thought that our Sovereign was all in gold, like a phoenix with fiery feathers. They shouted "Hurrah"—I looked but saw nothing—"There," they said, "there he is in the carriage, with a beard and in general's uniform—" I looked and it might have been sergeant Yedrenov himself—just an ordinary man—not a Czar at all. And I was expecting to see the Czar— "Burning like the sun"—but there—!' And thereupon, with her face in her apron, she burst into scalding tears.

Afterwards we laughed long at Tatyana's disillusionment and wasted patriotic idealism.

One day Tatyana was particularly out of sorts, her nerves were on edge and she was preparing to leave us for ever and go to her village. Tousle-haired Volodya was gadding about in the kitchen and was treading on Tatyana's corns.

'Why art thou clinging to my skirt like a bath-broom leaf, the Lord preserve us?' she exclaimed. 'Why can't thou go and read a book? You haven't got much brains, you gents, so you borrow them from others,' she growled, trying to get rid of the importunate boy.

This offended Volodya very much.

'How dare you "thou" me? Don't you dare, I'm not an Ivan Kuzmich!'

Tatyana was dumbfounded. Volodya, her modest Volodya,

her best friend and counsellor, and suddenly to use such words.
Tatyana's heart seethed with anger. Her peasant soul was
indignant.

'Ah, you bow-legged scamp. An inch off the ground and
that's where he's flying! Manners of a cockroach! Pfu! He
talks like a grown-up. I don't want to see the shadow of you
here!'

Volodya flew out of the kitchen like a bomb. All was lost, he
thought. His best feelings had been outraged. His human and
his 'master's' dignity had gone. All was at an end. He would
not put his foot into the kitchen again.

A week passed. Volodya was solitary, serious, and resolved.
He deigned no 'reply or greeting' to all the overtures and
advances of the cook. After a fortnight Tatyana was walking
about with tearful eyes, and at the end of the third week she
asked him with tears to forgive her, a stupid and presuming
servant. Grudgingly, Volodya forgave her. He allowed himself
to be tempted with a caramel in a gold wrapping, but for a
long time he could not forget the 'manners of a cockroach'.
Tatyana sensed this and remarked sometimes:

'How ill-natured you are and quarrelsome! But I'm a stupid
too!'

She never had any misunderstandings with Vera. Sixteen-
year-old Vera, tiny and with beaming eyes, had somehow
established a community of spirit with the deft and playful
woman of forty.

'What are you doing all the time in the kitchen?' Father
would ask Vera. 'Or haven't you finished talking everything
over?'

But Vera did not answer, and within half an hour she was in
the kitchen again with Tatyana. And there, besides the daily
chores, secret soul-to-soul talks went on about life, happiness,
and love.

Once Tatyana gave herself up seriously to the task of matching
her confidante. The owner of a grocery store had very much liked
Vera's looks, and so he decided to act through the intermediary

of the loquacious cook. To Vera, Tatyana described in bright colours the beauty, the noble lineage, the riches, and the love of the young merchant. The splendour of it: a private house, 'all divans and holy images!' And as for 'Himself', one couldn't describe him. He topped them all. Vera listened smiling. Even Volodya was initiated into all the details, and secretly supported Tatyana. But Father put a swift end to these 'grocery dreams' of the cook.

'What is all this foolishness? Stop it. It's not your business.' The match-making was broken off; and Tatyana changed her grocer.

But mysterious consultations took place frequently, and sometimes did not end till after midnight in Vera's quarters. For Vera had acquired admirers and suitors, she had her own friends, and all this served as an endless theme for conversations in the kitchen. Tatyana heard all the confessions with thrilling heart, weighed up all the 'honours' of the suitors and gave advice.

'Mighty thin, he is—' or 'There's no fun in him', or 'That one, he's got real force—A lion, not a man!'

On Sundays, regularly at tea-time, Yankovsky, an aspirant to Vera, tall, fair-haired, and bespectacled, made an appearance. In a strained attitude and smart uniform, he would sit for a long while in the drawing-room awaiting the coming of his 'object'. In the meantime Vera was hiding in the kitchen with Tatyana.

'He's come again, that nasty Pole!' she would say.

'He comes and comes, and what does he want?' Tatyana would express her surprise. 'He's not the right sort of tobacco. An ensign's no officer, and his wife is no lady. Yes! Our young lady will take a rich and handsome husband, but this Yankovsky, if you please—' Thus Tatyana comforted the abashed Vera.

But in the end she had to go and receive the guest; it would not have been polite to hide for long. As Vera entered the drawing-room, Yankovsky would leap up from his chair, click his heels, tenderly kiss her outstretched hand, ask after her health, and praise the weather. In two minutes the theme was exhausted, and there was nothing left to talk about.

The suitor sat on, sipped tea, sighed deeply, and cast stealthy glances at Vera. The time passed heavily and tediously. Vera felt like jumping up and driving out of the house this silent, brightly buttoned, giftless person, but she was obliged to sit on and answer 'Yes' and 'No' to the infrequent and flat queries of her visitor.

Tea was over. Yankovsky was still glued to his seat. Pleading things to do, Vera tore herself away and joined Tatyana. That did not help. The ensign sat on and waited.

'Well, and when is he going? One can die of boredom with him,' moaned Vera.

With her strong arms akimbo, Tatyana tried to quiet the young lady. 'Don't worry, let him sit awhile.'

Having waited alone in the drawing-room for an hour, Yankovsky at last prepared to go away, rattling his sabre and shifting chairs about.

On the following Sunday, he again came to tea. There was no getting rid of him. Three times he made a formal proposal to Vera and three times he was refused. With soft determination he continued to make his calls, ask his usual questions, sigh, and glitter with his gold-rimmed glasses. In the end, we got used to him as we might to a piece of furniture, and we paid as little attention to him as to one of the chairs. He even turned out to be an 'essential object' at tea-time on Sundays and, if he happened to absent himself by chance, everyone asked:

'Why hasn't Yankovsky come?'

'I hope Yankovsky isn't ill?'

His regimental comrades tended to avoid him. 'He's a bore. There's no life in him,' the young people said. The higher authorities kept him for years on the lower rungs of the service ladder. He suffered it all and preserved a stolid silence. Father alone found themes for conversation with him and talked to him for hours, evidently sensing the loneliness and flatness of the young man's soul.

When after many years of stagnation as an ensign, he was at last promoted as an officer to one of the emaciated provincial regiments, he appeared in all the glory of his new rank and proposed for the fourth time. On being refused again, he disappeared altogether and for ever from our horizon.

Vera also had another admirer—'Stepanich'. He always paid his visits in the company of other officers, engaged in gay conversation with Father, joking with Nicholas. In his company time passed quickly and interestingly. His comrades liked Stepanich for his culture and erudition, while Nicholas respected him for his superlative decency. Father sensed in him the longing for a better life for all people.

In the kitchen he was discussed, too, by Tatyana.

'He's a good *barin*, and so kind. He's clever, too, very clever. And he's got a soul like a heavenly angel,' Tatyana would muse aloud.

'He drinks a lot! And he's not at all handsome!'

'What if he does drink? He may be drinking for grief. You're very particular, young lady, and not very attentive towards him into the bargain! Yes! A pernickety bride will stay an age-long maid. You say he's not handsome. Well, what of it? We don't drink water off people's faces. But as for love, he will know how to love all right. "Grandfathers, grandmothers!" Remember my word, I know.'

Vera would let her head fall and ruminate silently and long. She kept silence also because the time had not yet come to reveal even to Tatyana that vast new thing which was inevitably invading her and binding her with incomprehensible force. She knew that when the young lieutenant Zhdan Pushkin, handsome, strong, and jolly, visited us, she saw a dancing rainbow before her eyes; the room and the furniture seemed to swim away somewhere while in her youthful breast her heart beat in alarm.

In the innocence of her white room, Vera would sit for a long time undoing her hair and trying to reason out the, to her, unknown and incomprehensible magic. 'Stepanich, I know, is a man of good heart, I feel as if he were a brother, and everything is clear and in its place. But I only have to hear Zhdan Pushkin's voice as he enters, and my face flushes, my hands tremble, and I feel at the same time like running away and staying with him. But he does not pay any attention to me—he has his own friends, his own conquests. And everybody likes him.'

In her long nightdress, with her waving hair undone, and as tiny as a little girl, Vera prayed for a long time, kneeling on the floor before the ikon. From the kitchen came the sound of Tatyana's heavy steps as she washed up the dishes.

XXVII

VICTOR set up as a local doctor in a small provincial town, some forty kilometres from Moscow.

The town was a drowsy one, surrounded on all sides by mills and factories; it had no distinct character of its own and depended mainly on its proximity to the capital and on the local weaving industry.

The inhabitants preferred to go to Moscow for their purchases rather than pay three times more on the spot. And besides, the goods there were stale and often long outmoded. The choice was not very great either. So trade there had stagnated, and nothing was now left in the town except grocery stores and meat and fish shops.

But by contrast the factories were flourishing. The weavers, those of them that had sense enough, were putting money by. They opened up on their own; their business developed, they grew prosperous and finally they had huge blocks of weaving and spinning mills put up. Thus, little by little, the suburban factory region had grown up and had closely surrounded the little town.

The inhabitants of the factory region, because of their importance, ended by dominating the town; and it simply lived a sort of vegetable life, not daring to raise its head.

The mill-owners, in spite of the proximity of Moscow, held to their old customs here, and led a patriarchal life as of old, the sort of life that had long ceased to be lived in the bigger centres. Here there were no secrets. Each knew the other as he might the fingers of his hand. Here one's Moscow habits had to be concealed and one had to live like everybody else—the 'good life'. Here you did as everyone else did, and you had to be careful not to do otherwise!

Often several families would be found living under the same roof. The head of the family, formerly an ordinary cloth-weaver and now a leading manufacturer, a respected citizen and a 'cavalier', did not part with his sons, but held them all together in his fist, with their wives and children, all in the same house. These bearded merchant sons walked about on tiptoe on the parquet floors of the splendid paternal marble halls.

Papasha, or, as he was called behind his back, 'Himself', or 'the Patriarch', lived in luxurious chambers, while the sons would find refuge somewhere in the *entresol* or on the ground floor in dark neglected rooms, sleeping like pigs among filth, and feeding the bugs.

Their wives were jealous of each other, quarrelled and often hated each other. When the old man died, the family would usually fall apart. They would divide up the inheritance and go their own way: shares would be bought out, and gradually the business would be concentrated in single ownership, that of the most capable and strongest inheritor. And, as he consolidated himself and expanded, and finally grew old, the history of the 'Patriarch' would be repeated.

The marriages were almost exclusively of a local character. The Prohorovs would be matched with the Glukhovs. The Nechayevs would take their husbands from the Korzinkins. All these people 'belonged'—they were of the factory circle, of immemorial faith, tempered in the old ways. The importance of the bridegroom's or bride's 'firm' came first. And so, little by little, as the years passed, five or six families would assert themselves, and their opinion would have weight with the whole of the factory region, the town administration, and the ordinary inhabitants.

If the Korzinkins took a liking to the newly appointed chairman of the town council, his career would then be made. But if the Prohorovs took a dislike to the town doctor, then he might as well gather up his belongings and go to the four corners of the world.

Victor rented for himself a small detached house in a remote part of the factory region, had his things transported there, and then set up his own practice.

The one-storied wooden house, with its three windows, stood peacefully in the depths of a yard that was overgrown with thistles. At the back of it two or three rowan-berry trees swayed to and fro. Three steps led up to the tiny hall, from which there was a magnificent view of the doctor's study. There one saw glass jars with medicaments, labelled boxes with powders, surgical instruments behind the glass of pinewood cupboards; anatomical diagrams and phrenological maps on the walls; notices 'Please do not smoke' and 'Please do not spit on the floor'; and finally, the surprising cleanness of the room and the formality of the furniture arrangement, introduced one to the chilly atmosphere of a doctor's reception room.

Only when it grew dark and there was a cracking in the stove, and the vibrant reflections of the fire danced on the polished floors, only when the jars and the labels and the instruments were engulfed in the darkness, did it grow warm and cosy in the small reception room of the wooden house.

In the morning, Victor cycled to the county hospital. The low spread-out wings of the hospital stood on the edge of the factory region, close by the wooden bridge of the river Yauza. Energetic work went on here the whole day. The reception of out-patients came first; then there was the round of the wards; and sometimes an inspection of the isolation wards. The doctors, the assistants, and the nurses, in their white overalls, joked gaily and smiled, while on the beds patients groaned, paralytics moaned like beasts, and cholera cases twisted in convulsions.

It was all very interesting! There was more than enough work—one could not do everything. In the evening, from eight to nine, there was the reception of patients at home. Sometimes in the evenings, at irregular times, he might be called to the hospital to deal with an emergency case. On such occasions Victor would light his bicycle lamp and cycle back to the hospital—carefully so as not to make the horses shy.

From the bridge, the hospital with its lighted windows looked vast. Sitting in their doorways, the factory people would refer to him jokingly:

'There he goes again, the new doctor, to have his house-warming with the nurses.'

Sometimes, Father went to stay with him—for 'a week's airing', but he usually returned in a couple of days. There were never any disputes at Victor's, but the whole tenor of his life was alien to Father.

'You might think he was a sort of Chichikov,' Father would say on his return. 'Everywhere numbers and labels—and no spitting if you please!

'You can't sneeze or breathe even—exactly as in the offices of the Town Governor. It's some sort of mechanism, but not life. You can't do this, don't touch that—You'd think we weren't living people—You could die of boredom!'

A regulated life was alien and incomprehensible to Father. His soul was opposed to mechanical things; he could not bear pedants, and made fun of them. 'Why be over-clever? It's a simple matter—But they insist on being clever while "there's nothing wonderful in it". Life knows what it's about—and ours is a simple business: "each cricket, his own hearth".'

But the cricket—Victor—obstinately refused to sit in his own hearth. Whenever he visited Moscow for a few days, there was a hurricane blowing about the house. Everyone got it 'hot'. There was Father: he was throwing money about, drinking too much, smoking, ruining his health. And Nadya too: she was at the watering-places, revelling, engaging Tartar guides—all that loose rich living would bring her to catastrophe. And even Vera was dreaming of officers! Volodya was a loafer, with his nose in French novels instead of working on his 'maths'. And as direct proof of this, Victor would angrily point to a ragged book which had just been confiscated from the younger brother.

There was much truth in Victor's reproaches; but it was somehow a formal truth of facts, picked up separately and not related to reality, with no wish to understand, to clarify or even to forgive when necessary. Like a mace, the iron logic smashed down right and left, knocking down the innocent and the guilty, and allowing no one to get up again.

All Father's principles, his whole approach to life, as Victor was convinced, were leading to inevitable bankruptcy, catastrophe, and a terrible end.

'Wait, you will see,' he prophesied obstinately, looking at the future with the eyes of a fanatic.

' "If the thunder peals not, the peasant will not cross himself." And that's what you all are.'

Passions flared up. Father sat with his bottle of beer, silent at first, and then he would try to turn the conversation on lighter topics. But jokes did not help. On such occasions, jokes only wound Victor up; he would lose control of himself; with his eyes glinting angrily, he would forget where he was or to whom he was talking.

'There you are, joking all the time. But I am speaking the honest truth—For don't I know everything—'

And then Father would begin to be irritated. He would empty his glass, nervously fix his spectacles, and start off with a hardly perceptible sarcasm in his voice:

'Well, here's a son a-visiting, it's a long time since we've seen each other—'

'The Devil take him,' he would unexpectedly conclude, rising from his chair.

But Victor was not to be repressed, and he continued to stigmatize Father even more pitilessly. From his accusations it would now appear that there were no mistakes, sins, or crimes which Father had not committed. Everything, even Father's admittedly good acts, were now interpreted by Victor as inadmissible licence, the violation of social order, unforgivable folly.

It might seem that it was not a kind and peaceful man sitting in front of Victor, but some fiend or contemporary Jack-the-Ripper. In the end Father was beside himself. He got up from his chair and looked angrily at his son with his fine eyes.

'Why are you lecturing me?'

'I have already forgotten more than you ever knew.'

'My God, my God, what a child I've nurtured! Nursed and fed him—and he's grown up a hyena! Look at him! He's been educated at a University, the monster!'

Nicholas would then hurriedly lead Victor away into his room, where they talked long and excitedly, after making sure that the door was firmly shut.

Meantime Father paced the room with large strides. There was a weight on his soul; and an ache in his heart. He had a sense of gnawing injury.

'Why all this? What for? Who will feel the better for it?' he asked himself. 'Well, he came and did his bit of shouting. He thinks he's achieved something. He's only stirred up anger and roused my bile.'

But it was painful, he thought, to hear such cruel accusations from the mouth of his own son. Yes, it was true, business was going badly, falling out of his hands; it could hardly be worse. Perhaps it would not be long—and suddenly the terrifying picture of ruin rose up before his eyes. Bankruptcy, his possessions auctioned, the children weeping. His knees shook, a grey mirage flashed before him. He leaned against the door-post and hung his head.

From Nicholas' room came the muffled sound of voices; in the kitchen Tatyana was rattling the pans about. Then Vera entered the dining-room and her luminous eyes fixed on Father with unbelievable sadness. Their eyes met. They both understood how dear and close they were to each other.

When Vera had gone, Father sat down in his accustomed place, put on his spectacles, and involuntarily returned to his thoughts. Now he no longer felt so hopeless—his daughter's compassionate eyes had warmed his soul. But what was he to do about his business?

Competition was little by little, and step by step, seizing the best business out of his hands. Something was still left, there were some affairs on hand, but all that was held together by old sympathies, friendship, and habit. It all might go to pieces any day. And what would there be then?

Victor says: stop drinking and smoking, be economical, keep a sharper eye on the clerks. But how would that help? If I drink or I don't, the orders will not increase and the competition will not be eliminated. The firm soil was again slipping from under his feet.

Evidently it was fated from birth. He sighed. There was nothing to be done about it. Fate, fate. And an acute, inexplicable anguish gripped his soul. What was he to do? Where was he to turn? To whom could he unburden his sorrow?

It was growing dark. The lilac glints of the snow were fading on the roof and the bell-tower. The glimmer of a dying stove flickered feebly on the parquet. There were no sounds. It seemed as if the thread of life were broken.

But suddenly the velvety peal of a church bell sounded triumphantly through the courtyard and, creeping on, resounded through the room and reverberated in the window-panes. Father started at the unexpectedness of it, sighed heavily and, fixing his spectacles, made his way on tiptoe to the hall. It is better to turn one's back on evil, he decided, putting on his galoshes.

When, later in the evening Victor was departing before his normal time in a state of agitation, we stood with a chill in our souls and listlessly followed him with our eyes. Below, by the front stairs, it could be seen how he finally broke down. He gripped the door-post of the open door and, his body shaking all over, sobbed like a guilty schoolboy.

'Go on crying! We also had to cry, thanks to you,' thought Volodya resentfully. Vera swallowed a tear and involuntarily clasped Tatyana. Nicholas was descending the stairs to quiet Victor.

Once in the cab, Victor stared indifferently at the lighted shop windows and the soft flakes of falling snow, thinking the while about Father or, to be more exact, about himself. Why was it that, with all the best intentions towards everybody and Father in particular, he was yet unable really to help people? Did he not speak the truth? But people were only offended. If he were not to speak the truth, but paint everything in rosy tints and flatter, then they would all love him. What, then, was the truth? It was the same with Father. It is true, he admitted, he had been heated. He had said a lot of unnecessary things to Father. He had failed to control himself. And thinking of the past he remembered how Father—. But he felt ashamed and covered his face with his gloves. He should not have remembered that. Ah! 'Our tongue, our enemy', he automatically repeated Father's proverb. But then: 'The word is like a sparrow, You won't catch it once it's flown—'.

And all the way a gloom settled upon him, like a vicious circle of futility and bitterness sweeping him round with the flakes of falling snow.

In the meantime, Father was sitting in the brightly lit Tartar Restaurant under a colossal organ-like music-box and was enjoying the thunder of Turkish drums, the clarion voices of the trumpets, and the whole lively animation of the festive crowd.

Tartar waiters ran about with silver plates and hot dishes; champagne corks popped, and women in fashionable evening dresses flashed their eyes. Here, in the midst of strangers, he forgave his own folk. He forgave Victor, and forgot all the offences and unpleasantness. It was Nirvana! 'You're running away from truth. You'd like Nirvana to be served up to you,' he remembered his son saying. Well, what of it. Let's live in Nirvana. For man must live! Without that, one might as well put one's head in a noose. Each man has his own Nirvana. One saves money, another keeps a ballerina, while others strive to

become professors. And as for me, I drop in here and order myself some red wine. I sit here quietly, interfere with no one, get
on nobody's nerves. However much one may fret and worry
here, it won't help matters.

'Waiter! Bring me another half-bottle!'

'Yes, *barin*.'

The music-box started playing a crackling Persian march.
Father watched the machine through the glass case with great
curiosity. Like an unshaven landowner sprawling on a couch,
the bristly cylinder slowly turned on its axle; the hammers beat
a tattoo, bells tinkled, trumpets blared, the kettle-drums
shivered. Half-a-dozen big drums beat out in savage rhythm.

'A corpse would not stand it without coming to life, it's such
a symphony.' Father smiled to himself as he asked the waiter for
his favourite piece, a 'Pot-Pourri of Russian Songs'.

He felt drawn to the Volga. When summer comes, I shall roll
up the Mother Volga. It's fine on the steamer. One sits on deck
there, with boiled sturgeon and Kahetian wine served up, and
the views! Sheer beauty. God's own land!

The music-box was gaily pounding out the 'Hunting Song'.
And Father imagined himself wading in high boots through the
marshes, a gun in hand, in search of wild ducks. An English
setter ran in front of him. There they go—Bang! Whang! And
afterwards a rest—a cold luncheon, anecdotes, big 'salted'
hunters' tales. Or he might be sitting on the edge of a drowsy
pond and pulling out meaty carp. Oh, for one now!

The music-box fell silent. It was late already. Getting on to
midnight. Nirvana was over. Well, what of it? 'It's not all
pancakes for the cat, there's lenten fare, too.'

At home, there was a light still in Tatyana's kitchen. Father
rang timidly so as not to wake everybody. Watchful Tatyana
jumped out of bed and ran into the hall in her bare feet.

'Are they asleep?'

'Yes, *barin*, they're sleeping.'

'Please wake me tomorrow at eight. I've got business.'

'Very well, *barin*.'

Father undressed by candle-light in his spacious bedroom and looked at the empty double bed.

'Ah, Olya, Olya! Much-suffering Olya!' he whispered bowing his head.

And in the morning it was the same story.

'Papochka! Three roubles, please! It's absolutely essential!'

'Why do you want it?'

'For provisions and expenses.'

'But I gave you some money yesterday! Absolutely necessary —don't try and fool me.'

'But it is essential!'

'Absolutely! Absolutely!' Father teased, irritably pushing aside his cup of tea. 'Do you think I have a press to print notes for you?'

In Vera's eyes tears began to show. Father adjusted his spectacles and pulled out two roubles.

'Here, take them and leave me in peace, for God's sake!'

'Papochka, one more rouble. I must have three, it's essential!'

'Ah well, here you are, drat you! Take all I've got!' And with a sorrowful gesture he threw his purse on the table.

Vera's bright eyes had already filled with tears, while Father, angrily wrapping himself in his dressing-gown, disappeared into the bedroom.

The rent for the apartment was due very soon, the warehouse rent and the wages of the staff had to be paid. A whole half-year's schooling had to be paid for the youngest son: a hundred and seventy-five roubles, that was no joke! And where was he to get them? 'Where am I to get them?' he asked himself, as he knotted a brightly-coloured tie in front of a mirror. 'How shall I collect it? Everyone has to look after himself. Everyone has his own worries.'

Outside it was thawing. The roofs were dripping. The snow had turned black, the sledge-runners creaked and scraped against the cobbles. For the sake of economy, Father first decided to take the horse-tram.

'No! It will be better to walk.' But then he changed his mind and took a cab. 'After walking two or three streets you get tired. Time is money!'.

There was no one yet in the warehouse except Boris, who was sitting at the counter and reading the *Police News*.

Catching sight of Father, he hid away the paper, got up and handed him the letters, the papers, and the bills of lading. Father then went into his office and settled down in a deep grandfather armchair and became plunged in thought.

Fragments of the 'Persian March' sounded in his ears; his daughter's bright eyes looked reproachfully at him. Here, in the chilly atmosphere of a dark, dank day, fear for the future crept into his consciousness. Some uncontrollable force was pulling him down. Father shut his eyes, and it seemed to him that he was rolling down from some giddy height somewhere lower and lower—into an abyss.

'I shouldn't have ordered that second bottle yesterday,' he thought, as he settled down to the correspondence.

Among the usual business letters with orders and bills there was a 'private' one from Kiev.

Puzzled, Father fingered the untidy yellow envelope: who was it from? He did not know anyone in Kiev.

'Good Heavens! Alive! Ivan Aksentiev!' and he greedily devoured the letter.

'Having climbed the last rungs of life, I fall at your feet. . . I am at my last gasp. My only hope is in your mercy. . . Look down on me from your peak . . . . ' Father smiled sorrowfully. 'In my degradation I shall pray eternally for your children!' Father stopped. The terror of life, a hopeless gloom gripped his soul.

His friend, the gay guitarist, his boon companion, had now suddenly found himself in this situation—providing food for bugs in a doss-house. At once all of Father's worries, fears, failures, fell into the background. Only one thing mattered now—to rescue, to save from want, his old friend Aksentiev.

They had not seen each other for thirty-five years. For thirty-five years there had been no word from Aksentiev. Like a stone he had been swallowed up in the waters. And now suddenly this cry for help from one lost in the desert. 'I am perishing in a doss-house!' O Lord! What a life this was! Agitated and, as it were, newly awakened by an invisible shock, Father sensed all the greatness and significance of human existence.

'Boris!' he called to the clerk in a voice of renewed strength. 'Has Filipov's payment come in?'

'It has, sir.'

'How much?'

'Thirty-seven roubles, the usual weekly amount.'

'Put down twenty-five of that to my personal account and the remainder for the warehouse.'

'All right, sir.'

Having counted out the money, Boris put it down on Father's desk.

Without giving himself a moment to reflect, Father inserted the notes into a large envelope with the firm's address, wrote on top 'Money Order for Twenty-Five Roubles', and, having spread out a blank sheet of paper, quickly wrote: 'I am sending you, my old friend, what I can. Take up thy bed and walk. Have a bath, shave, dress up and make for Moscow by rail. Come straight to my house—then we shall see! Don't despair, friend! We are all human beings!'

Already Father was more cheerful and smiling as he recalled past memories. As boys together, Aksentiev and he had gone pigeon stalking. The pigeons had settled in the arch-priest's garden. The Antonov apples had just ripened and the garden was very strictly guarded. In a flash Aksentiev had conceived a plan: Yasha was to approach the keepers and tell them he had come for the pigeons while he, Aksentiev, biding the moment when the keepers were giving chase after the pigeons, would climb over the hedge and get under the apple-trees. He had time to throw some three dozen apples over the fence, and these they later picked up. And how he used to play on the guitar. What was he like now? After all, more than thirty years had elapsed. How time had flown! It seemed as if all that had happened but yesterday. Not for a second did the slightest doubt suggest itself that, in the course of thirty years, life might have transformed Aksentiev. He had no suspicion that the 'real guitarist' had turned into a 'real swindler'. He was merely aware that an old friend had touched rock-bottom, that he needed help—immediately, without delay, that he must be fed and afterwards fixed up with a job.

Father made certain arrangements in the warehouse and went on a round of his merchant acquaintances in order to place his new protégé. He was received indifferently: some listened to him and made promises; others, made wise by experience, coldly refused.

'Yakov Akimovich, why do you always bother about other people?' Soon Belikov was to complain: 'Your protégé has played us such a trick, we don't know how to straighten things out. You started the stew, but we have got to finish it! You're too kind-hearted, you believe every passer-by.'

Father heard them patiently, adjusted his glasses and, despite the protests, persisted: 'I'd stake my head for Aksentiev. He is a childhood friend!' And with his fine blue eyes he would look closely at his severe adversary. But the hard-headed business man would not give in.

In business, in pursuit of profit, the human soul grows hardened, but Father's unselfish intercession for 'the orphaned and the poor', his childish trust in Goodness, would in the end soften the hardened soul. His merchant friend would stop protesting, would become thoughtful, and finally yield.

'Ah, what a generous soul you have, Yakov Akimovich! A pity there aren't more people like you—life would be easier! Well, let your friend be, no doubt we can put up with him.'

On the wings of hope, Father would rush home, imagining that he would find Aksentiev happy, cheerful and fully satisfied, with a swarm of welcoming children gathered round a festive

Father in 1894.

Father with grandchildren.

table. At home, Aksentiev's coming had been triumphantly announced as a great event of unexpected 'joy'. 'We'll manage to find room for him somehow! We shall set up a screen in the corridor—he doesn't need much! He's a simple man, he will understand! He's a great-hearted man! And how he plays on the guitar!' And with childish joy Father would look at us all, expecting enthusiastic replies. But we were all silent. We had no strength to destroy the joy of his illusions by asking sceptical questions, even though we knew by experience all those 'childhood friends', 'outstanding artists', and so on. When, after several days, a bell rang timidly and a man with a worn face, wearing a light coat despite the frost, carrying a lean suitcase and a guitar under his arm, entered uncertainly into the hall, we all stopped talking, so unexpected was the transition from the expected image of 'the great-hearted man' to the wretched figure of the confirmed alcoholic.

'Aksentiev!'

'Yasha!'

The old friends rushed to embrace each other.

The suitcase dropped, the guitar in its worn case gave forth a mournful note. Spontaneous, joyful tears flowed down Father's cheeks.

'Well, go and take your things off! Come and sit by the fire, old friend! You've still kept your guitar, I see. Good for you, Aksentiev!' And not knowing where to find a seat for his old friend, Father fussed about the room like a nervous schoolboy.

The 'great-hearted' man took off his things, his 'fish-fur' coat, brushed off a piece of fluff from his worn black jacket and timidly, as though not believing himself, came into the sitting-room.

His small tearful eyes ran round the room, his restless hands kept touching his neck, his cheeks, his bald patch, and then fell back again. He moved mechanically, started at every sound, as though he expected someone suddenly to shout: 'Where have you come from! Get out!' And like a stray dog which was accustomed to be kicked by passing boys, he was searching for a way of escape, some hole he could creep into, in order to escape the blow he was expecting.

The table was already laid. The 'dear guest' had been awaited since morning. Now the 'dear guest', the 'great-hearted man', sat on the edge of a chair, like a frightened hare, next to Father. He declined everything and was obviously in a state of confusion, but gradually matters improved. One glass of vodka after another, one meat-pie after another—soon he was emptying his glass like an expert and eating with the appetite of a hungry shark.

His sixth glass of vodka he drank only because the salted mushrooms were 'incomparable'. His second plateful of cabbage soup and meat he finished off only out of respect for the cabbage. 'Such cabbage has not been heard of in Kiev,' he explained. Father treated him, offering him helpings with evident pleasure and begging him to eat, like a mother feeding her child. Towards the end of the dinner, the mistrust and the awkwardness of the 'prodigal son' gave place to a verbal playfulness. For each thing he used a diminutive expression, an endearment: 'Those dear little mushrooms', a 'teeny-weeny glass of *pertzovka*'. Vera he addressed in no other way than as 'My little lady, my darling soul' or 'My priceless treasure'. It was a regular flood of mellifluous streams, milky rivers, and syrup, in which one could sense the petty falseness, the artificial tenderness of the flat soul of a lonely, empty man. Father alone accepted everything in good faith. He was astonished at the warmth of soul, the delicacy of manner, of his childhood friend, who had suffered a catastrophe.

By the time they went into the sitting-room and sat down near the well-heated stove, Aksentiev really felt himself at home. Out came the guitar of an old respectable make. The lacquer had rubbed off, the wood on the sides had worn thin, and it looked as shabby as its lonely owner. The strings began to strum. Long-forgotten melodies of polkas, quadrilles, once fashionable romances, the lancers, poured forth in an endless stream—in a word, the hackneyed motifs of an insipid soul, of an insignificantly spent life. But they meant something to Father, reminding him of his youth, of roisterous evenings spent with friends, of the brightly painted church of the Yamskoy Slobody and the chanting voices.

Each motif reminded him of some part of his past life. To that quadrille they had once executed such *entrechats* at a ball at the Nobles' Assembly that even the Master of Ceremonies was nonplussed. Aksentiev and his lady formed the second pair, and he outshone everyone by the studied, unexpected movements of his knees. To that mazurka, Vanya Puzanov, having slipped on the polished parquet floor, knocked down six dancing couples. How he had skidded across the floor to the scandalized amazement of the throng—even the Governor could not help laughing! And then there was Masha, the gipsy, a real beauty! And how she sang 'A Beautiful Maiden Beyond the River'! One was ready to give up everything for her! There was no singing like that today—that 'quality' had gone. Listening to Father, Aksentiev kept on playing the guitar. When he himself spoke, he played more softly, and the barely audible melody was accompanied by his reminiscences.

'Do you remember Noah?'

'Ha, ha, ha!'

'Do you remember how the Protopop threatened us with his stick? "You godless rascals," he called us. "I'll get you even if I have to go before the Holy Synod!"'

'Sing it, then, if you haven't forgotten it!'

Tuning his guitar, Aksentiev played the liturgical tune, and in a thin, feeble tenor voice started off:

> *When Noah came out of the Ark*
> *He saw the Creator, his Lord.*
> *The Lord liked the sacrificial smoke*
> *And was benign in His speech:*
> *And the Creator said to him,*
> *'Ask Me what you will.'*

And humbly Noah replied,
'O Lord, how I loathe the waters.
In them are buried now
The sinner and every sort of beast.
If only you, O Lord of Strength,
Would let me quaff another drink!'

And of a sudden from the breath Divine
Did sprout the glorious vine.
And the Lord spoke: 'Care for it now!'
And all things He now revealed:
How to plant the grape
And how to make the wine.

Having played the ritual piece a second time, Aksentiev began with emotion to sing:

To the glory of the Creator
A bottle more of wine
Did Noah empty now and then
And felt no worse for it.
And as the Bible says,
He lived for three hundred and fifty years.

And then he finished up by singing in a moralizing tone:

And from this we can conclude
That wine will harm us not at all;
But for Christians it is sin
To mix with water wine;
For in this water buried are
All the world's impurities.

For a long time yet the childhood friends went on recalling their past life; the red wine flowed and the guitar played on.

Confidences and laughter alternated with the mazurkas and the quadrilles. Without letting go of his guitar for a minute, Aksentiev confessed his sins and narrated his 'path of torments', explaining how he had sunk to 'such a life'.

He had come to the end of his tether! He had been on the edge of a precipice! At first he had gone the rounds of the gin shops with his guitar in the hope of earning some pennies. Then he had come to the doss-house, but soon he could not afford even that! He had become shaggy and ragged. He looked like a scarecrow. He was afraid to venture out into the streets in daylight: he felt ashamed. He hid himself for days on end in an empty house in the suburbs; at night he used to steal potatoes from a garden!

'Well,' I thought, 'Sinful son, your last days have come. You must try and get out of this mess! You've had your fling, that's enough!' Oh, it was hard, Yasha, so hard—one can't even explain. But one has to eat: and I finally became a latrine cleaner, alas, alas. Ough!—I just could not do it—I felt sick, nausea gripped me. I'd rather put a noose round my neck or throw myself into the Dnieper, "the deep and wide Dnieper" as the song says. And I had no news from any friends, may the devil take them! If only one of them had lifted a finger. So I said to myself: "Let me hold a last inspection of the forces and see what military ranks there are among you humans." I took a risk and spent my last farthing. So I wrote to Perepelkin, a wealthy man, to you and to the Korennaya Monastery. If they don't help, it's the end of me. Left turn, to the devil, march! I had a drink on what remained, crawled into the empty house, and lay down there, waiting for—death. Oh, it was hard, very hard, you wouldn't believe how hard.

'I'd been lying there for three days and had come to my last crust of bread, thinking the end was near. I had grown weak and was beginning to feel indifferent to everything: to live or to die seemed much the same. You know the refrain: "It's all the same, to love or not to love, to suffer or be happy",' he hummed, accompanying himself on the guitar.

'But that evening, I suddenly heard a boy calling me. "Uncle Aksentiev! Uncle Aksentiev! Are you still alive? My dad has sent for you. The postman with the whiskers has been searching all day for you! He says there's a money order arrived for you! He'll be round again tomorrow morning!" I was thunder-struck—"Blessed be, O Lord!" My weakness vanished. But-toning my trousers, I ran to a friend's. There they fed me and gave me a bench to lie down on, but I could not sleep. I kept thinking, "It may be Perepelkin, the rich one, who's sent me a thousand roubles, just for the feel of it! Or maybe," I thought, "a charitable institution has sent me a rouble in response to a request I made long ago. " You can't get far on a rouble! But as for you, my benefactor, you never entered my head. And so I could not sleep all of that night. In the morning the postman with the whiskers did actually turn up. "You," he asks, "are you so and so?" "Yes," I replied, "I am here in person." He looked me over, stared at the ragged clothes, at the "pale colouring of my armour", said not a word, and began to search in his bag. "Are you literate?" he asked. "Will you sign this receipt for twenty-five roubles by postal order from Moscow?' My head went round—bands of red crept over my forehead. My own darlings! Yasha Andrashy! You saved me!' Without stand-ing on ceremony, Aksentiev poured himself out a glass of vodka and drank it at a gulp, and then continued in a quieter tone:

'What a story! I had counted on you least of all. We had not met for thirty years—there had been no sign of you. What was Aksentiev, the scavenger, to you? But the test proved that Andrashy was one of the family, he had been and remained Andrashy! I remember when I got that twenty-five roubles—I first of all bought a ticket for Moscow; then I took my guitar out of pawn—for years I hadn't had it in my hands!' Tears appeared in Aksentiev's eyes. 'Yes, I went to the baths and gave myself a good wash, had my jacket mended in the old clothes market, got myself a shirt-front and starched cuffs. But there is *nothing* underneath!' And unbuttoning his shirt-front, Aksentiev bared his hairy chest by way of a demonstration. 'But that's just to illustrate the situation,' he added. 'Yes! So I got into the railway-carriage, sprawled on the seat like any land-owner, but I was frightened. Until the train moved I was afraid I might be dreaming. What if suddenly the Day of Judgement came and the trumpet sounded: "Your turn next, you're for it, please!" Ah Yasha, Yasha, you have saved me from death, you have taken me into your family, you have made it possible for me to behold an angel in the flesh!' And genuine tears flowed plentifully from those drunken, watery eyes.

It was already late. In a neighbouring garden cocks were crowing for a second time. The early morning goods sledges were creaking in the streets. Holding a candle, Father conducted Aksentiev to his bedroom.

'Tonight you will sleep in my son's bedroom—he's away on a mission, but tomorrow we shall fix up a "Palazzo" for you! I hope you won't mind. We haven't got much space,' Father said in some confusion.

Aksentiev was left alone. Groups of soldiers in narrow frames, strategic maps with red flag pins looked down on him from the walls. A writing desk with neatly spread papers stood by the window. In a corner was a small iron bedstead with snow-white sheets. Stopping uncertainly on the mat, Aksentiev meditated awhile, and then, having resolved on something, began to undress. First, he took off his jacket, unbuttoned his shirt-front, pulled off his cuffs and trousers, and stood there absolutely naked. Then, wrapping himself, head and all, in a rug, he lay down on the mat, placed his jacket and trousers on top of himself, and instantly fell into a dead sleep. When the maid, after breakfast, came to do the room, she was very astonished to find the bed untouched. 'A strange gentleman!' she thought. 'He was walking about all night and hasn't slept.'

But by that time Aksentiev was lying on the upper benches of the Sandunov Public Baths and ordering the bath attendant to 'steam up!' 'Let the heat get to my bones!' he exclaimed.

At last he was no longer troubled with the lice which he had brought with him all the way from Kiev.

XXVIII

IT was spring. The first double window-pane was being removed. The thaw had gone on the whole week. The snow had turned a dirty grey and was creeping down the slopes. Only in the hollows, where the occasional sun did not penetrate, did it preserve its pristine whiteness and firmness, and with its consolidated layers resembled the sugar cones of grocery shops.

The sky was the grey of soldiers' cloth, and hung low over the roofs like a blanket. It seemed as if one might touch it with outstretched hand. The roadway was bared in places. Wheels were already in use, and their clatter, to which one had become unaccustomed in the winter, burst noisily into rooms. But at times the grey sky would be rent, as it were, and would send its gifts to the earth: damp, shaggy flakes of snow. These hardly reached the ground, melting away in the air. Then unexpectedly a dull March sun might peer out, clouded, impotent, and sad. But that did not last very long. Without time to warm the earth, the shy sunlight hid itself once more as if embarrassed by something behind the impenetrable blanket of sky. Flocks of jackdaws and rooks were perched on spires and telegraph wires, and gazed silently in one direction as if expecting something. In a word, it was that tedious phase of weather when winter had not yet surrendered its rights and delayed its departure while spring was still hiding behind the scenes. The air was damp. Stucco houses wept large tears. Mud and slime were everywhere.

'What foul weather! When will the spring come? April should be here!' So seemed to say the joyless faces of passers-by hurrying on their business. On the corner, near the meat shop, a large crowd of people was gathered.

'What's the matter there?'

'Oh, some sleighs have got stuck! They left the village in deep snow, but in Moscow everything is on wheels already. So there they are, and can move neither backward nor forward.'

'Try as they will, they can't move an inch. Two heavy sleighs with sacks have blocked the roadway.'

The drivers were beating the sloping flanks of the sweating horses savagely. The horses quivered all over their bodies, strained their strong muscles, advanced two or three steps and then stopped again. The drivers started their thrashing again in a business-like fashion.

'I say, Mr. Policeman! This is inhuman! It's simple savagery! I am a member of the Society for Prevention of Cruelty to Animals and I demand that the horses be unharnessed at once!'

Unwillingly the policeman gave the order: the horses were unharnessed. The loaded sleighs remained standing in the street. The crowd scattered in silence, encouraged by the guardian of peace and order.

'Move on! Move on! Gentlemen, why are you standing here? What a novelty! Haven't you ever seen a sleigh!?'

'What weather! The devil take it,' the passers-by said to one another as they scattered.

In the Ohotny Ryad, the Zaryady and Zamoskvorechie, there was no way through either on foot or by carriage. The Moscow river had swollen like a pregnant woman. The river looked black and turgid, and almost reached as high as the middle of the Kameny Bridge. Frightening to cross it: what if it collapsed? One would get a ducking then! It had happened before.

What weather!

Father was not feeling well. He was sitting at home in his dressing-gown, gazing out of the window at the yard below, at the spire and the rooks. The weather had a depressing effect on him. It was quite a time since he had spent his mornings at home, and now everything here seemed strange to him. There was not a soul at home, all was dead silence: everyone had gone about his business. Nicholas was at the barracks; Volodya was at school; and Vera and Tatyana had gone out shopping.

Where the devil were they all?

There would be nobody to open the door if the bell rang. As a result of his ailment and the weather, everything seemed wrong to him. Where had they all gone? And why did they go? In his mind, of course, he knew full well they had all gone out on business, but for some reason his heart ached sadly. The strong tea, with a dash of rum in it to keep off the chill, also did not taste right. The papers were uninteresting; there was no *feuilleton* that day—and one subscribed twelve roubles a year! It was a swindle! He must change his paper; he was tired of the *Russian Word*, always the *Russian Word*. And so he grumbled on like a dissatisfied bureaucrat. Now, take the *Moscow Leaf*, it has a *feuilleton* every day, but Victor calls it a boulevard rag. Ah, if he could but go away somewhere, to a warm clime! Find a corner somewhere amid green grass and flowering fruit trees, where all is peace, repose, and divine grace! No conversations, no alarms. Man does not need much! And here it was all dirt and damp and mud. Each one tries to push the other out of the way, they put a knife to one's throat. But why and what for? There is enough for everybody!

And the wickedness and greed there is on earth. O Lord! What is it all for? They will die all the same: six feet of earth is each man's measured portion! You might as well try and grasp the stars out of the sky: the end is one—death and the weeds that will grow. Ah, ah, ah, Father yawned before falling imperceptibly asleep.

When he awoke, it was dark already. The ikon-lamp was glowing peacefully. Trying not to make a noise, Vera was laying the table for supper.

'Well, and I have slept. I closed my eyes for a minute and here's night-time already. I saw a peculiar dream—as if we were living in hot lands: palm trees and monkeys everywhere; and we walk about dressed as we were born—stark naked!

Only Aksentiev sits alone in a bearskin coat, wrapped up in it strumming on the guitar.

' "What's the meaning of it," I asked him. "Why are you all dressed up?"

'And he took his cap and began to say something—and then I awoke! What nonsense one gets into one's head!'

After his sleep, Father felt much better, his cough did not disturb him, and it was peaceful and quiet in his soul. Somewhere in the hidden depths of the soul joy was beginning to awake.

On the following morning the scene in the street had changed beyond recognition. The sun was broiling, and noisy streams of melted snow were coursing down the roadways. The birds were flying about crazily, calling stridently from roof to roof; and the dogs vied with each other in friskiness. There was clarity and joy: the end of a long winter had come at last.

Within a week the first shoots of young emerald grass had appeared; the buds were swelling on the trees and the earth had been warmed and dried. In the street passers-by greeted each other, smiling warmly, exclaiming on the same theme:

'What fine weather! Spring has come, by God's grace!'

'It must be marvellous out of town now! What Paradise! It's so lovely and mild!'

Father could not remain cooped up in his warehouse for long; he was drawn to go out of town, as far as possible, somewhere among birch-trees under blue skies, surrounded by renascent nature. He stopped an *izvoshchik* and had himself driven to Zamoskvorechie.

On the canal near Bolotny Square, where he had once stayed with friends as a boy and where many years ago Emelyan Pugachev had laid down his rebellious head, a plump floating quay was moored. Swift steamers were speeding to and fro, to the Sparrow Hills and back. Father made for the quay. A shrill steam whistle suddenly pierced the air, the engines started, and the little steamer quivered and cut slowly and smoothly through the still waters of the now abundant and brimming river. From his comfortable place on the prow, Father could see everything as on the palm of his hand. They steamed past the granaries and the shops of the Zamoskvorechie where there was a hum of activity, the sound of voices, and a variety of riverside smells. Then the squat houses of the merchants could be seen, as well as the vacant detached houses, white-columned, of the nobility.

Then came the factories, the monasteries ringed by fortress walls like medieval castles, and the near-town estates of more important nobles, now for the most part transformed into hospitals and charitable institutions. Sloping down to the river, the spacious park of the Neskuchny Palace was already showing its green tree-tops.

The palace of the 'Eagles of Catherine' was astonishing for its size, luxury, and taste. Here once upon a time the famous horn orchestra could be heard. Pairs in powdered wigs might have been seen moving rhythmically to the tune of a minuet. Here leading notables lost thousands of roubles at cards in the summer-houses. In the park there were century-old oak trees, alleys of lime trees, little bridges, arbours, pavilions—witnesses of love, drama, jealousy, and intrigues. Later, along these alleys, Orlov's orphaned daughter might have been seen walking pensively in nunlike isolation and weeping the fate of her sinful statesman father. 'Where has all that gone?' thought Father to himself.

Only the stately Orlov race-horses and the Neskuchny Palace remained as sad witnesses of the past. People had lived, made efforts, climbed higher and higher, and now nothing was left of them. Perhaps they had only lived for their own pleasure? But who knows? There was the millionaire Pospolitáki, as one's father used to relate: he used to extinguish the candles and sit in darkness; 'We know each other,' he would say, 'We can talk like this, for a candle costs money.' He had lived and died a prize swine! Men like these had lived their life for nothing, not even a trace of them had remained. No, money and luxury do not bring happiness—that much was clear. There was one good thing in life, and that he knew for certain, and that was to sit quietly and observe how life went on around one.

Life would be seething around, a bird would sing on high, a fish would splash in the water, a crab would crawl up a river bank. Ah! It was marvellous then! One felt as if one were living.

When the steamer had passed by the monasteries on the outskirts, the river turned sharply to the right and became wider still and more flooded. In the distance woods could be seen advancing up the hills towards the very summits. Moscow had already been left behind: its spires, towers, and houses were now bunched together as if forming a solid wall. The sun was playing on the church cupolas, glittering on the church crosses, and infusing the moist atmosphere with its rays. Two or three boats with people rowing passed the steamer. The company in them was gay and their laughter could be heard as the boats fell behind, rocking in the steamer's slight wake.

A lonely fisherman, an unsuccessful one evidently, was nodding in a tiny boat. Along the banks peasant horses were trudging with harrows. A herd of motley cows with dully fixed eyes gazed in amazement at the puffing steamer, which, groaning and vibrating, went on its unhurrying, diligent way.

Ahead was a small floating quay on which could already be distinguished the multi-coloured dresses of waiting peasant women. The steamer's whistle blew and the tops of trees gave back a pitiful echoing moan; the steamer quivered for all it was worth, and then reversed like a crab and softly struck against the sides of the tiny quayside.

'We've arrived, please!'

For the town-dweller this had been a tour of the world. Who knew what accidents might not happen. 'During the spring floods, you need a sharp look-out or the steamer might get stuck in the shallows. And it would have to sit there. And if you keep to the deep channel, the current is mighty strong. It might sweep you away for twenty miles or so, the devil knows where,' the captain, a huge man with a ginger beard and bottle-shaped boots, was saying tutorially.

The passengers follow each other down the slimy quivering

gangways; they all have one goal—the Sparrow Hills. The narrow path winds higher and higher up the hill, loses itself in a wood and, breaking out once more, winds serpent-like to the very summit. At first everyone walks quickly and cheerfully, but little by little the path becomes steeper and steeper. The passengers fall into groups: the children run on in front while the merchants' wives and the young ladies come last, moving with difficulty. When the company reaches the wood, it grows darker there and cooler, and the sound of voices is muffled.

'Ah, ye holy fathers, let me get my breath back. It's mighty steep, I'm quite winded,' says a stout matron stopping. The company pauses to look with displeasure at this plump Zamoskvorechie dame.

'What is she doing here? Why doesn't she stay at home and sip tea? Fancy coming to the Sparrow Hills with such a corporation!'

In another group, a tall man with city manners is saying something severely to a lady in ostrich feathers, who is strutting along with small steps.

'To think what a road we are treading! It makes one fearful to remember. Napoleon himself, the "enemy of the peoples", the exhalation of Hell, one might say, set his feet here, in lacquered boots, along this path. Yes! It's God's truth! "Give me," he says, "the keys of the capital, of the First-Throned One." See what he was after? But our *bátiushka*, Alexander the Blessed, may he reign in Heaven, took him by the scruff of his neck and gave him what for. "What," he said, "You son of a bitch, where do you think you're going?" '

'But listen,' says a schoolboy, 'Do you think Czars behave like that? And besides, there was nothing for Napoleon to do on this path. And it isn't known if it existed at all at that time. He marched above there from Mojaisk towards the Dorogomilov barrier and waited on Poklonnoy Hill for the arrival of a deputation.' The boy was reading out a regular lecture. 'And you say, "took him by the scruff of his neck". It's quite improbable.'

A middle-aged gentleman in a bowler hat, carrying a cane, was walking beside Father. He was twirling a pair of gold-rimmed glasses in his hand and was saying with assurance:

'In the first place, you order a borsch—for satiety.' The gentleman turned down the index finger of his left hand. 'A boiled sterlet with olive sauce.' He turned down the next finger. 'Boeuf Stroganov, with onion, mustard, and pepper, first class: there will be no need to die. That's three,' he turned down the third finger, '*Guriev kasha*, but the real sort, no imitation. That's four,' and he turned down the little finger. 'Roquefort! A symphony of tastes. That's five,' and the thumb was turned down. 'Coffee with cognac. Fine champagne! Three stars. That's six,' and the little finger was pressed down to the palm of his hand.

It was not certain how many more fingers he would have required for the fulfilment of his gastronomic programme, but at that juncture a party of sightseers descending the hill separated them for a while, and when the path was clear again, the gentleman in the bowler turned out to be in the tail of the procession.

The wood came to an end and they emerged into a meadow. It was not far from here to the top, or, to be more exact, to the spacious restaurant built on the historic spot where, according to tradition, Napoleon had stood gazing at Moscow. On a wide terrace dotted with tables many people were already seated. It was as noisy and animated as in a Moscow beer-hall.

And there below unrolled the long-familiar spacious view so dear to the heart of any Russian—the panorama of the capital, Moscow.

> *Ah, Moscow, Moscow, Moscow,*
> *Golden-headed town,*
> *Ah, Moscow, Moscow, Moscow,*
> *White-stone town. . . .*

Below was an expanse of green forests; and the river stretched in a steel ribbon over the meadows. The steamer was already far away from the quay and was puffing out smoke unhurriedly as it made toward the city, while in the distance one could see a countless number of churches, monasteries, fortress walls, and the towers of the white-stone Kremlin.

What space. What quiet. One might sit here eternally and gaze into the boundless horizon. It was quiet and peaceful and so satisfying. Enchanted by the evening that was drawing on, Father plunged into that state of quietude when the whole world harmoniously integrated, when all the manifestations of life, grief and joys and all the misfortunes, seemed to be part and parcel of the Cosmos. In these rare minutes, the soul became reconciled with misfortune. With His healing hand the Invisible Almighty God touched the bared wounds of simple mortals. The pain was stilled and simple ingenuous life appeared endless, bright, and joyous.

It was growing noticeably darker. A spring breeze sprang up. Great droves of birds circled over the tree-tops. The red-hot sun was sinking slowly on the horizon—until finally it was hidden. Thousands of windows in far Moscow blazed up in a dazzling fire. It seemed as if the town were in flames once more, as it had been at the time of Napoleon, when it was set on fire by 'the avenging hand of an elusive giant'. The sun was bidding its last farewell to the stilled town. The red eyes of the windows shimmered in all the colours of the rainbow. Gradually they were dimmed and at last were imperceptibly extinguished. The sky was a-glow with a red fire, the city was sunk in shadow and, dissolving, vanished from the horizon as if it had never existed. The immensity of the dark abyss below and the final glow in the sky as by magic transported the imagination into an unknown fairyland.

Shaded candles had long been lighted on the restaurant tables, and moths were fluttering round the candle-flame and were falling scorched upon the tablecloth. The terrace had emptied. Here and there in the shadows the voices of belated tourists could be heard; it was already late and time to go home. Father looked at his watch: three quarters of an hour to go before the departure of the steamer.

Nadya with son.

Vera with children and Tatyana the cook.

On the way back the landscape had changed so much it was unrecognizable: Moscow was beginning to glimmer with nocturnal lights. Myriads of little lights, no greater than pin-heads, ringed the bluish vastness of the city in all directions like a fantastically luminous and decorative necklace. And once more the vanished city uprose from the void, illuminated by a million lanterns.

> *Lanterns, little sirs,*
> *Burn and shine and glow.*
> *What they've heard or seen*
> *Of that they do not speak.*

Father recalled to mind this ancient verse as he was carefully descending the steep path. Out of the darkness below, two eyes, green and red, were advancing slowly in his direction: the last return steamer was coming up like a terrifying dragon from a legendary land. The path now twisted toward the wood, and it grew so dark that the existence of the path could only be guessed by the light of the kindling stars.

'I started too late, I might come to grief here,' thought Father as he felt his way carefully along the path. As if to confirm his premonition, he slipped. Something struck his leg painfully and he lost his balance and rolled down the slope.

He was brought home at night by strangers; his leg was broken and he had lost his spectacles and hat.

For many weeks Father lay in his bedroom, his leg in splints, asking himself whether it would mend. Victor would arrive and examine the leg with a professional eye and find it all in order. But on departing he could not resist a dig at Father in spite of the circumstances.

'Why are you always so restless? Isn't it time to stop playing at Rocambole? It's just as well it did not end worse. You might have fallen on your head, and you would have been in the Vagankov cemetery by now. Well, there is nothing for it, but lie there and rest. I shall come again in a week's time and have another look. It will mend all right!'

In a fortnight the bandages and splints were taken off: the leg could not have set better. To begin with, Father hobbled about on crutches and, like a child, learned to walk anew.

'It's a wonderful business,' he said to a visiting friend, 'Look what they can do now. The bone was broken clean in half but it has set again. It's like a new leg,' moving his leg and rejoicing like a child. 'A great thing, science!' he concluded with conviction.

XXIX

ON the hilly side of the Volga, some three miles from
Yaroslavl, a camp of grenadiers—a whole city of tents
—had been set up. They were ranged in straight rows
a mile long, like soldiers on parade, wearing white tunics.
Company field colours fluttered in the breeze like birds and,
indeed, the whole camp reminded one of a giant bird ready
to take flight.

In the centre of each regiment, in the front line of tents,
stands the duty tent. In front of it are the money-boxes of the
regiment, on wheels, and with huge locks, and the regimental
colours on an oil-cloth, set on a trestle. Two sentries guard
them. The soldier on duty, in a white tunic and with a bayonet
at his side, calls out the officer on duty. Entry into the camp is
forbidden except by special pass. The officer on duty in full
uniform, with a sword on one side and a revolver holster on the
other, looks as if he had not slept all night and hands out the
pass without a word.

The duty-soldiers are posted on the boundaries of each
company and they call out the pass.

'Send the duty-soldiers to the centre of the regiment,' comes
a cry from somewhere near, uttered in a full deep voice, and a
high tenor an octave higher takes it up: 'Send the duty-soldiers
to the centre of the regiment!' And so this verbal post travels
further, sounding muffled in the distance and filling the air
with varied sounds. Similar calls can be heard making their
rounds of neighbouring regiments.

In the tents there is a subdued hum of conversation, the sound
of the accordion, and the bluish curling smoke of *mahorka*.
Grown men in white tunics can be seen sitting or lying down

and enjoying their Sunday rest. Twenty thousand young men are assembled in tents here, all grenadiers, in white tunics, black breeches, strong boots. Five men in each tent!

It is light and pleasant to sleep under canvas, covered in a soldier's greatcoat, but when it rains the water soaks through the canvas as through a fine sieve, and the tent is full of steamy dampness. The young men take it all as a matter of course, without grumbling.

> *That's the sort of life we lead,*
> *Under canvas and the open sky we feed.*

Now it was all right. The sun shone out and warmed. Under a steep bank, the Volga curved in a broad blue ribbon. Barges with unfurled sails were floating along in the wind; and on the green flat plain of the bank opposite, villages could be seen and the lonely bell of the Tolzhsky monastery could be heard tolling.

It took Father a long time to traverse the endless streets and passages of the canvas city. There seemed no end to it, and he might have got lost there, as in a forest. Now he had reached a row of more spacious tents: he had evidently come to the central section of the city. The tents here were roomier and festooned with red edges; there were also stockades, flower beds, and wooden porches in front of these tents. Each of them had its own individual features, and was set up apart, according to personal taste and inclination. Here geometry was superseded by the reign of fantasy. The orderlies, a dandified and spoiled lot, were fussing about near the tents. The domestic surroundings relaxed the discipline somewhat, and the orderlies resembled private citizens more than soldiers. At the entrance to Nicholas's tent, his orderly Sadykov, a Tartar, was squatting down and fanning with his boot the charcoal of the nickel samovar Father knew so well. Sadykov came from Kazan; he was a taciturn and hardworking dark man who yearned for home, mare's milk, and his droves of horses.

'He's gone to Assembly. Return immediately,' he said in his funny dialect, smiling good-naturedly with his kindly Asiatic eyes.

'All right. I'll wait,' Father said.

In Nicholas's tent Father saw a camp bed, a ticking watch suspended on a nail, two or three books on a small wooden table, and three chairs. The tiny wooden house with floor, nailed over with canvas outside, was the usual type of officer's tent. In the autumn the canvas is taken off, and these card-houses are left to spend a solitary winter until the advent of summer, when they revive again.

Sitting down on the bed and gazing round this monk's cell, Father thought of Nicholas. 'He leads a real monk's life. He doesn't allow himself any liberties. Not at all an officer's life. It's a miracle. One says to him, "Why do you live like a cloistered maiden? Why don't you go on the spree and enjoy yourself? But you're always poring over fortifications and all kinds of chores, and in the meanwhile time is running away." '

Father listened. In the next-door tent a gay company had gathered and was evidently settling down to a game of cards. Abrupt exclamations could be heard. 'Pass . . . . No trumps . . . . I say, what was your lead?' The scratching of chalk on the green cloth and the tinkle of silver coins could be heard. There was a sound of carefree laughter and of youthful voices.

'Our "top bunk" got tight last night, so tight it pricked one's conscience to look at him. We began as usual with *zubrovka*, all above board. Then the Fanagoryitz dropped in, all cock-a-feathers. And "top bunk" plunged in. Starting arguing. They made a bet to down ten glasses of vodka at a gulp. To see who can drink it all down in one breath without any *zakuski*. A Fanagoryitz got there first. "Top bunk" got stuck on the seventh—"I'm out of training," he says, "Had no practice lately. We must repeat it." So they began again. And then they rolled into the town, beat up some civilians and smashed up the bar at the Big Yaroslavl station. The "top bunk" was brought into the camp at night "all stewed". There was a complaint before the commander this morning; they are threatening him with a court-martial. Quite a scandal! The devil of an affair!'

'And have you heard our Don Quixote, "Vassichka", has distinguished himself?'

'No, what has he done?'

'We learned yesterday that when he was on leave, he suddenly heard cries coming from a hut as he was walking down the village street. A woman's voice bawling and swearing for all the neighbourhood to hear. Well, Vasya's knightly heart could not resist it.

' "What," says he, "A woman being beaten? I won't allow it."

'He burst into the hut, scattered all the people there, knocked over a bench, all in the best style of Prince "Bova". And then he sees a woman lying in bed and groaning like an animal—she was in her last birth-throes, in the act of giving birth, it seemed. Well, when she saw Coeur-de-Lion Richard—Vassichka—she just went up in smoke! Birth went wrong, and there were all sorts of complications. And now there is an unpleasant case coming on in the Courts. No one believes in Vassichka's knight-errantry; a hooligan, that's what they think he is, and a violator of home and happiness. Ha, ha, ha! Vassichka never had any luck with the opposite sex.'

At that moment Nicholas entered the tent. He was in a white tunic, and he had official papers under his arm; he looked sunburnt and younger from being out in the fresh Volga air.

'Well, how are you, Nicholas? You're looking fit.'

'Why didn't you warn me you were coming, Papa? I'd have met you at the station. Well, let us have a glass of tea. Sadykov,' he shouted to the orderly, 'Is the samovar ready? Bring it along, chump, quickly! And there I was straightening out these orders —they'd got everything in a tangle in the office.'

Sadykov brought in a tray with glasses, set down the steaming samovar, and spread a clean napkin on the table in place of a tablecloth. Father did not like drinking tea in the middle of the day, but it gave him much pleasure to watch Nicholas's domestic efforts. The 'Cachalot' dropped in, in a soldier's tunic with an engineering badge on his chest, and with a black beard that crackled with health. He seemed a giant in the tent.

'Look out and don't break a chair again, you lump,' said Nicholas. 'You'd better sit on the bed. See what a mountain he's grown. God knows where you'll end!'

Cachalot bared his teeth cheerfully and the whites of his black eyes flashed with pleasure as he sat down to tea with lemon.

'I'm always being told off here,' he complained to Father. 'They won't even let me sleep in peace—always projects and projects. You're an engineer, they say, so you must construct the camp. And see to the sanitation. They want me to do it, *me*, an engineer mechanic of the first class—latrines and all that! An order is issued and I read in it: "Volunteer Puzanov is appointed in charge of the sanitary section of the last row." Me in the last row! What else?' And Cachalot guffaws with laughter. 'They don't give me any peace.

' "Why," they ask me, "is your project of the rears not ready these five weeks?" I answer, this and that, and that the consulting engineer has not yet arrived from divisional head-quarters. And without a consultant one might easily go wrong. Ha, ha, ha!'

'Loafer, that's what you are, a loafer. And you'll remain one,' says Nicholas good-naturedly. 'They didn't thrash you enough in the Technical Institute. It wouldn't take a couple of days to get the project going.'

'Ah, but one must think it over, brother.'

Nicholas knew well Cachalot's character. Everything with him moved tightly and ponderously, he had to 'think every-thing over', discuss it and examine it from different points of view. The business moved on as slowly as a crab, and, to tell the truth, there was no reason to hurry.

'If I'm a loafer, then that's what I am. It's not exceptional,' Cachalot defended himself. 'If the w.c.s are ready or not, does it matter very much?'

'That's why everything fails with us Russians,' concluded Nicholas seriously.

Other officers known to Father called in at the tent. Here in camp everything somehow seemed simpler and freer: the tunics were unbuttoned and people's souls were open.

They supped on the open terrace of the officers' mess. The waiters, soldiers in tunics and white knitted gloves, wended their way deftly amid the narrow passages between the tables and served the dishes smartly. They filled up the wine-glasses without spilling a drop, and managed to preserve a respectful air. There were some three dozen officers at supper at the long narrow tables. The dishes were served according to rank. Each drank his favourite drink. The conversation was general from table to table, and it was not always clear who was speaking. When they laughed, they laughed all in unison; the servants did not join in the merriment. Only when they reached the kitchen after clearing the plates did they venture to relax into laughter.

'That was a good crack of the lieutenant's! Straight on the ribs! Don't stand about here idle, you green devils! Take the cutlets round before they freeze!' yelled the moustachioed chef, deftly sorting out the cutlets on to the plates.

The waiters once more assumed serious expressions, and went on to the terrace with steaming plates. The animation increased on the terrace. A grey-haired captain with pale fishy eyes was relating how they had been quartered in Poland and had amused themselves beating up the locals, courting Polish girls, fighting duels out of boredom, and taking estate farms by storm.

'Yes, we had the time of our lives! Now, one can't live like that,' the bald-headed captain was saying sadly. 'Now there are rules and regulations about everything. Can't do this, can't do that. One has to be careful not to get court-martialled. The honour of the uniform, that's a new idea they've invented. But did we not uphold the honour of an officer's calling? Ah, gentlemen, we wore our uniform with no less honour than you do. What if we did beat up a fellow—one would give him a slight beating, not too serious, and the next day a three-rouble note. And what of it? He was pleased, and we had some quiet amusement.

'As to the young ladies, that was a young man's distraction. Many of them married the officers and got their percentages. There were some tragedies, of course! I remember one case: a young hussar officer, I don't remember his name, perhaps it was Yanov—something like that. Well, he eloped with a fine young girl, the wife, I now recall, of the land-owner Popyalovsky. But she had forgotten her Polish husband. They settled down together and were living like a couple of doves, not bothering about anything. Well, we thought, this has the makings of a tragedy. Popyalovsky will ask for satisfaction. But it didn't turn out quite that way. He shut himself up on his estate and would not let anybody near him. But three months later we found our hussar with a bullet in his head; he was lying on the carpet with a letter gripped in his left hand. Well, they finally got to the bottom of the affair. There was no duel; they merely cast lots as to who should live with the lady and who should visit the next world. The hussar was unlucky that time. There was no needless chitter-chatter. Pop, and that was that. The proud Pole apparently did not recognize duels, and the luck was on his side. The poor hussar died in the flower of his youth: he upheld the honour of his uniform.'

The conversation now turned on duels. Opinion was divided: some thought the duel a false survival of barbarism; others justified it as the only solution of tangled situations, as a noble school and as a traditional institution of military courage.

'But listen,' said a tall lieutenant with pointed moustaches in the style of Wilhelm II, 'Courage and nobility, that's all right. But if somebody treads on your foot, are you to send him to join his forefathers the next day? A corn and human life! What terrible incongruity!'

'But it wasn't only on Pushkin's corns that they stepped, it was a more serious matter,' protested little Vassichka, the unsuccessful champion of pregnant women.

'And why did Lermontov perish?' the tall lieutenant went on unheeding. 'It wasn't for a pinch of tobacco—but for such a great poet to die at the age of twenty-nine—bang and that's all! A great poet died, and muted his lyre! Of what verse of genius was the world bereft!'

'Nonsense! It wasn't bereaved at all! An end is fated to each man! It's all written down and predetermined. It was fated in the Book of Life for Lieutenant Lermontov to write a certain number of verses, so many pages of prose, and that's all!'

'If he had lived another hundred years, he would not have written another line of sense,' a younger Colonel added. 'Take Griboyedov, for example. He wrote *The Mischief of Being Clever* and then no more. All the rest was just "water".'

'No, gentlemen, each man lives his full cycle. It would be comic to think that if Napoleon had not been suffering from spleen at Waterloo, he would have won in the end. All that was predetermined by fate. Everything is already noted down in life's account book. You've rung your peal and so get off the bell-tower,' he finished with conviction.

The talk now turned on war. They made fun of the band-leader, a stout, soft and pink-faced German, Hektor Arnold-ovich, and told how he went into an attack with a Turkish drum.

'But you'll desert to your folk, Arnoldovich, when we fight the Germans, won't you? I'm sure you'll desert? Well, tell us, Hektor Arnoldovich, tell us the truth,' the young officers pestered him.

The German puffed heavily, waved his hands and muttered, 'What you think of me?' It was clear to everyone that Hektor Arnoldovich would go over to the Germans, but in the mean-time he was a fine fellow and no fool at drinking—a companion-able fellow, in fact.

The coffee and the liqueurs were brought in. There was red apricot brandy, curaçao, and fragrant benedictine. Over coffee they passed on to anecdotes. Talk of women was the theme that engrossed everyone. Now all attention was concentrated on

Staff-Captain Pchelko, a real poet where scabrous anecdotes were concerned. He knew hundreds of them and, like a butterfly, he flew from flower to flower, and one anecdote succeeded another. 'Ha, ha, ha!' roared out the youthful voices in the captain's vicinity:

'What a cynic you are, Pchelko. How does the earth suffer you?'

'Eh, brothers, who's with us? Let's go to "Nastya," an elderly captain said, calling for recruits. 'The devil take Pchelko, he's a pimp. The Scriptures say, "Thou shalt not tempt my soul".'

Three or four officers, who were well in their cups, took the inflammable captain under the arms, and they vanished together from the terrace. The staid officers scattered to their quarters, while the remainder of the youngsters prepared to go on a boating expedition.

'Let's have a picnic, in the moonlight with nice girls. Weather couldn't be better, and it's warm. *Ai da*. Left turn, wheel, march—No, wait. Wait till the moon rises, then we'll go!'

The orderlies were preparing baskets with *zakuski*, wine, and plates. Some of the officers went off to find the girls. About ten o'clock they were filing down the steep river bank towards the Volga, where the boats were awaiting them.

'Careful, careful, gentlemen, don't fall in,' Nicholas warned them, vigilant as ever over matters of general security.

It was already quite dark. The Volga appeared forbidding, mysterious, and bottomless. The moon would rise any minute now and throw a silver shimmer over the boundless waters of the mighty river.

Belated birds flashed mysteriously and silently in the high heavens. The silence was such that is seemed one might hear one's own heart beating. Then it grew lighter on the horizon, and it was as if a solitary lantern had been lighted.

A huge red moon slowly appeared behind the opposite bank, and it rose vertically like a giant balloon. Phosphorescent glimmers ran about the water; the river came to life and unrolled its wide highway, lit up with blinding light from one bank to the other. One had the illusion that one could walk upon that compact roadway as upon a pavement; and the mysterious deeps of the river were no longer terrifying.

The boats floated after one another smoothly down the lighted highway, and whenever the current deflected them into the dead shadows, oars would come into play and bring the boats back to the main road.

'Gentlemen, keep in the light, otherwise a steamer may run into you,' Nicholas shouted.

A voice suddenly burst into song. It was Zhdan Pushkin, with Stepanich and their young ladies, singing a melodious Volga song in the second boat. 'Down the Volga river, from the lower town, the boat is coming, like an arrow coming—'

In the silence of the warm night these youthful voices were wafted somewhere into the distance in the wake of the ripples of the great river. Father was sitting at the helm, his favourite place, and he was breathing in with pleasure the warm exhalation from the river. Lulled by the even rhythm of the oars and by the youthful voices of the singers, he thought of the past and of his experiences with a refreshed feeling of tranquillity.

'Well, what if I am almost fifty,' he thought. 'Life is still as fine as it was in my young days. I am not as I was, but the young people are growing up. And what a fine generation they are! They take life somehow more broadly and freely. They haven't got the same fears and depressions that we used to have. They're bolder, and "who has courage, he's worth two". And so it should be!'

'Pull in this way, otherwise you'll run into a steamer,' Nicholas shouted. The boats went faster, and the laughing oarsmen began to race one another, the muscular Cachalot performing miracles. A terrifying monster, glowing with phosphorescent light and with green and red eyes, was bearing down upon the merry company, puffing and groaning.

The distance diminished. Now the silhouettes of passengers could be distinguished on the lighted deck. The sounds of a waltz, 'The Blue Danube', evidently played in some cabin, drifted ever more loudly towards them. The unexpected intrusion of progress and civilization into the quiet and peaceful stretch of the Volga seemed somehow strange and surprising. In a minute there was only a remembrance left of the steamer. and all was quiet again, and in the soul there was profound joy.

Now the moon stood high. The golden shades had vanished and only the silver melted and shimmered on the ripples. A strong tenor in the front boat poured itself out upon the silver, soared to the sky, and was repeated as an echo on the hilly bank.

> *To love or not is all the same,*
> *To suffer or be happy;*
> *So let the world forget me!*
> *It's all the same, it's all the same. . . .*

The chorus caught up the last line in unison: 'It's all the same, it's all the same. . . . '

Somewhere the river birds were startled and, with beating wings, they rose and found a safer retreat. The song evoked great love and happiness in spite of the hopeless refrain, 'It's all the same'. It was clear that nothing else in life mattered: only love was important and all-embracing happiness.

Each thought to himself of his love. Only the singers, like birds of heaven, created their prayers without a thought, unconsciously.

The song stopped. Eternal silence opened wide its giant wings.

XXX

VERA and Father were now quite alone, unless one counted little Volodya, 'our last-born', as Mother, now spending her third year in hospital, used to call him.

Nadya was disporting herself at some spa or other. Nicholas was with his regiment. And Victor, who had more or less severed himself from the family, was engaged on his Council work, fighting for justice and progress and quarrelling with everyone.

On his rare visits home he would arrive full of the best intentions and leave with tears of rage, insisting that Father's happy-go-lucky ways were heading him for inevitable ruin. After his departure Father would sit sorrowfully by himself until late at night, drinking glass after glass of tea with cognac, and staring fixedly at the ceiling.

'Teaching his grandmother to suck eggs! And his mother's milk not dry on his lips! Lecturing me!'

And yet, more than anyone else, he knew that all Victor said was true. But what use could the truth do? The problem was how to improve a business which for ten years past had only been held together by his customers' goodwill towards himself.

'It is only because of their feelings towards me that they do not take their custom elsewhere. Our stock is rubbish. There is no other word for it! Many a time, just to save our faces, we have had to buy goods elsewhere, stick our labels on them, and dispatch them to disgruntled clients. But it makes no difference to that pot-bellied German partner who imagines that because he was able to fatten himself for thirty years when there was no competition, he can go on blissfully raking in his dividends by selling trash.

'I have told the fat devil, but his only concern is that his dividends shall be guaranteed. Dividends! How the deuce does he expect dividends when all our customers are sending back his wares, refusing to have them even as a gift!

'And on top of all this the "Professor" turns up and gives me the benefit of his lectures.'

'You are wasting too much money, Father. You'll end up without a seat to your trousers.'

'I knew you before you wore trousers, but whether you see me without them is another question. Business is no concern of yours, and I'd ask you not to speak to your father as you do!'

'Father or no father, the truth remains.'

'I was familiar with truth when you were a brat.'

'You were one yourself once.'

'And when I was, I never spoke to my father, your grandfather, as you speak to me. I respected him.'

'I only respect a man who earns my respect.'

'You swine! I've fed you, clothed you, sent you to a university—and you as good as tell me that I have not earned your respect. Go to the devil before I throw this glass at you!'

'If you're reduced to cursing, I'd better go.'

'Go, and good riddance! You're unwelcome here at any rate.'

Poor little Vera was all this time running around like a squirrel on a wheel. Her sympathies were all with Father, and she did her utmost to persuade Victor to make peace.

'Words won't help! Do leave off quarrelling. It is wicked to disregard God,' and, as she prayed for reconciliation, big scalding tears welled down her cheeks.

But it was no use. They were both ablaze with passion— Father unable to forgive his son's cruelty, and the son unable to conceal his complete lack of respect.

'There,' Father complained, 'is the result of all my anxieties, sleeplessness, and sacrifice. That is the gratitude I get.'

He was so utterly downcast that his sorrow was like a physical pain, catching him beneath the heart. His hands trembled, his eyes grew dull. He longed to give up, to go away to the ends of the earth, and wandering through the fields and meadows, a pack on his shoulders, to meditate on God, death, his own sins, and the weakness of humanity. Perhaps God would comfort him and take from his soul its stifling load.

Yet where could he go? And how leave home and children? However bad he might be, things were worse without him. Besides, he had his habits to consider: life had spoiled him. He would not get far with his pack before he started wanting caviare. There was no getting away from that.

The more he tried to clarify the position which now existed, the more did its hopelessness grip and strangle him like a noose round his neck. Was there really no way out? There must be, for there was 'no situation from which there is no escape'.

Again a vague hope kindled in his heart. His brain cleared. But it did not take long for the hopeless mood to return again and benumb his soul with pain. No, he could not go on like this. Something must be done. He would lose his reason if he sat still and watched ruin overtake him.

'I am a man, not a weak-willed child! I have surmounted difficulties and extricated myself from dangers before now. I have thought, "This is the last straw. I'm done!" and then some unexpected trifle of good luck has come my way, I have seized it, and all has ended well. It has been funny to look back on.'

But this was no longer a laughing matter. There could no longer be any doubt that each succeeding day was leading him to bankruptcy, ruin, and death.

Yet, when the soul is weary, death is not so terrible.

It was the trifling worries of everyday life that were terrible —the grey days, the family separations. 'They were all so innocent, why should Fate bludgeon them?'

However well one argued one must come to the conclusion that the greatest blessing in life was children—healthy, active, self-reliant children. 'And I went and lost my temper with Victor, an honest, solid fellow, unafraid to speak the truth, and intolerant of insult.'

Nicholas, Colonel of Grenadiers.

Victor, the doctor, in old age.

Father had had nine children. Five were very much alive. Three had died in babyhood, but poor Peria had been a sturdy little boy when his life had been crushed out of him. Like some terrible, forgotten nightmare there arose before his mind's eye the vision of the bleeding body of his son and the sudden illness which had then descended upon his wife. His wretchedness increased.

Where could he find escape from these memories?

'It must be that my end is coming. Life has dried up in me. I have nothing to live for.'

Early next morning he packed and strapped up his trunks and gave his parting instructions. A sleepless night had left him with a pale face, trembling hands, and twitching eyes. It was painful to see how bent he had become, how deeply cut the furrows on his brow, how in one night his hair seemed to have become greyer.

No one dared ask him where he was going, and it was only after the cab had been ordered that we knew he was going to his native town.

Sitting in the uncomfortable cab, he clung obstinately to one thought. His position must be cleared up now. He could not put things off any longer. Cost what it might, he must knock some sense into that fat German, his partner Petchke. He must convince him that his policy of slackness and stagnation had outlived its day. He must finally drive home to him that only by the most energetic measures and hard work could the business be saved.

Yet deep in his heart he knew that it was impossible. But as a drowning man clutches a straw, so did he decide to put his luck to the test for the last time. Win all, or lose all!

The bustle at the station, the first-class refreshment room with its pyramid of bottles and platters of *zakuski*, the variegated crowd of porters, passengers, and leave-takers—all alike failed any longer to interest him. Like a wounded beast crawling into its lair to lick its wounds, so he ensconced himself as soon as possible in a corner seat on his train, unfolded his newspaper, and made a firm resolve not to enter into conversation with his fellow travellers, however friendly they might be.

With all his soul he was yearning for his birth-place, where he thought that even now the kindly shades of the past would linger. There his old mother had caressed little Yasha, and now the thought that he was getting nearer home was enough to wake some sort of hope. Of what avail were grief, disappointment, and anxiety, when the world was so good a place?

He looked out of the window. The train was racing past green fields and lowering forests. Little wayside stations flashed past. Tra-ra-ra, tra-la-la, thumped the wheels. All was as in times gone by. Life went on without pause from one tenderness to another, from one sorrow to another. People lived and had their being and suffered and struggled. What remained of this ocean of endurance?

'Thus it was and thus will be.' What was the meaning of it all? However diligently a man might seek, he would find but little joy in life, and what he found would be solitary islands washed on all sides by a sea of misfortune and suffering. Who was to blame—people or life itself?

Some held that the system was at fault and that life itself was not concerned. 'You have,' they said, 'only to change the system; to share and share alike, and all will be well.' And so they experimented and laboured and set up new constitutions— and there was no less suffering than before. Stop up one leak and another appears.

> *He pulled out his beak and his tail got stuck,*
> *So he pulled out his tail and his beak got stuck.*

Some, with Count Tolstoy at their head, preached a different doctrine, namely that systems did not matter and that the responsibility rested with the individual. 'Let each individual be agreed in his desire to be better and all would be well.' They practised these precepts, sacrificing their possessions to found colonies and communities. At first things improved, but gradually the colonies dispersed and enthusiasm died.

Men had been weak and sinful before Christ, and weak and sinful they remained to this day. Thus it was and thus will be!

'Look at me! God gave me life, saying, "Go, live." And what have I done with life? I have simply made a mess of it.'

As he dozed and dreamed, memories of long-forgotten transgressions crowded upon his mind. They seemed overwhelming in their very enormity. There could be no hope of forgiveness for them. Oh, to turn back time and redeem his sins, right his conscious and unconscious mistakes, forget affronts, and forgive the sins of others while craving forgiveness for himself. He was standing in the market-place crying 'Good people! Forgive me the wrongs I did you!' The heavens grew dark, and saints and devils seemed to be warring with one another for possession of Paradise above, while sinners below were shouting aloud

'Tickets please! Tickets, gentlemen, please!'

The guard was giving Father a shake and the train was running into the station. It was a gloriously fine morning. Father was still under the influence of his dream.

But to be back in the town of his birth seemed more dreamlike than any dream.

XXXI

THE station and its approaches were thronged with people. The *izvoshchiks* threw themselves upon arriving passengers as a pack of hungry wolves might attack a flock of sheep. They almost knocked you off your feet. They demanded exorbitant prices, thrusting their numbers annoyingly into your hands, and then once again like a flight of ravens they swooped upon other victims. Policemen would chase them back to their cabs, not very seriously, but more for the sake of appearance, knowing by experience how difficult it was to control the 'infuriated beasts'.

How attractive was that poor provincial life! Once upon a time, before the railway was built, here stretched endless fields, pastures, ravines, thickets. In their childhood they had made so many happy raids in these places; many adventures, heroic exploits, legendary campaigns had come to pass here. In those days a band of children under the leadership of the fearless Vanya Puzanov played at robbers among the hillocks, pursued jackdaws, destroyed birds' nests, or pitted their strength against an undergrowth of nettles.

There was freedom here and quiet: not a soul around, you could do what you wanted, there was nobody to stop you. Here time rushed on without a pause and the twilight came on suddenly. Here in the glades, men had appeared and had begun to construct the first railway in this district.

To begin with, surveyors arrived: they looked through strange telescopes on tripods, measured out the land, ran hither and thither with striped poles, put up numbered stakes, and did other incomprehensible things. Then they set up tents, built barracks; peasant workers appeared with barrows, spades, and mattocks. Hillocks were levelled to the ground together with the young trees; embankments were built up and drains were dug.

Within a month the locality was unrecognizable: the place was littered with iron waste, with all that was left over from the construction, and the rubbish lay about in mounds. The quiet was gone: the kingdom of birds was no more. But it was interesting to watch how this iron construction work bore on, pressing with its breast against the 'Blessed City'.

And now there was a whole town here, a noisy, hastily built-up town, with many-storeyed houses, wine shops, hotels and tea shops. From the railway station a shining line branched off, turning abruptly towards the town itself.

This branch did not enjoy much success: it was quicker to reach the city in a horse-drawn conveyance. Luckily, the main road, well trodden by frequent use, ran in a straight line to the centre and tempted the traveller by its innocent whiteness. After a long spell of railway travelling, it was pleasant to drive along a smooth road. The horses raced along swiftly, the *drozhky* bumping on its springs; in the provinces it was still the thing, as of old, to drive for the glory of it.

When the road came to an end, merging into the cobble-stones of the suburbs, the pace had to be reduced. Now came the small houses, the old mansions, the wooden fences with the orchards behind them. There was not a soul in the streets; the hens had the run of the roadway, on which the young grass was growing amid the cobbles; the ancient, drowsy 'Blessed City' was baring its breast.

In the centre of the town there was a certain amount of animation: one saw gymnasium pupils with calf-skin satchels on their backs, *chinovniks* with briefcases under their arms, and citizens.

As before, the trading booths were clustered absurdly close to one another in the vast square. The traders sat in the same poses in their shops, as if in the past thirty years life had not changed a jot. The Cathedral was all in scaffolding; repairs were going on, painting and adjustments. The Nobles' Assembly Hall had apparently just been renovated: freshly painted, it towered with its bulk and, like a huge white sail, showed white over the town.

'Heavens! Heavens!' Father sighed, thinking of the years that had passed. It seemed as if each turning of the street, each little house, was saying, 'Do you remember?' Yes. Do you remember how here along Moscow Street you were walking at dawn, feeling drowsy, past the fish stalls on the firm snow? You wished you were at home in your warm bed, but you had to go on to the unheated shop, and sit there behind the counter till the lights came on, nodding your head.

Do you remember how the wounded from Sevastopol were driven along the Eletskaya? And he relived Okorokov and his noisy band.

Those pitched battles of another kind were glorious events of youth and vitality, and the memory of them ran through his mind. How those reserves came up—like the reserves at Sevastopol itself! Slowly Father was ascending the slope. And from the hill-top, as in the early days of youth, the brightly painted church drew one to it. Grandfather's house, all peeling and long neglected, looking on pitifully with its windows appearing uninhabited.

Hail to thee, native corner! Here I am come, sick and weary, comfort me and warm me. I have not the strength any more to struggle with life. Mother, take back your prodigal son!

The old house is silent. Will no dear wrinkled face appear? Will no one hold out their arms: 'Yasha, first-born, dear one . . . . how you have grown!'

No, the old woman is not there any longer: she, eternal toiler, is sleeping in a neighbouring cemetery, side by side with her husband.

At his old home no one knew of Father's arrival. In brother Pasha's quarters, where once Grandmother had peacefully ended her days, there reigned a bachelor disorder: the remains of yesterday's supper not removed, and unfinished bottles.

Pasha worked in the fish market; he had the same job in the shop and the same wages as he had thirty years ago.

'How is it, Pasha, you could not manage to make a better living for yourself?' Father used to upbraid him. 'You should have insisted—it's no joke standing behind a counter for thirty years.' But Pasha would keep putting off his conversation with his employer from day to day; and now, he would say, it was too late—he was lucky to be where he was.

'Ah, brother, brother,' thought Father, pacing up and down the small rooms, 'You are a simpleton, you have got the brains of a hen. You have the soul of a chicken!'

It was quiet in the rooms: it seemed as if his mother's spirit lived and hovered somewhere above, under the ceiling. There were her spectacles, her Bible in its leather binding, and the daguerreotype showing Grandfather and Yasha himself in white trousers and with his hair well combed and parted in the middle.

It was pleasant to sit here alone and to think of the days gone by, of the dear and remote but still familiar past. The grandfather clock with its weights and chains struck midday. Father shook himself out of the trance and went back to the town.

There was noticeable animation at the haberdasher's, at Vanya Puzanov's. The shop assistants were bringing out rolls of cloth, deftly unfolding them, measuring out the yards and cutting off lengths with their large shining scissors, sharp as a razor. The recently opened jewellery and watch department glittered with novelties: watches of different sorts and sizes ticked their different tunes. Precious stones in glass cases shone austerely from their sharp facets.

In his office, hung from ceiling to floor with photographs of theatrical celebrities, Vanya was majestically ensconced at a writing desk, reading press critiques. And even here, in this commercial atmosphere, he reminded one rather of the 'Duke of Alba' than of a merchant son of a remote provincial town.

'Well, well, well!'

'Yasha! Andrashy! What brings you here? How many years is it?' Thus he greeted Father, embracing him thrice and kissing him on the cheeks.

'Are you here for long? On business? Sit down, sit down. You shall be my guest! I shan't let you go now—come and dine with me. You must have a lot to tell me. My wife is not here, she's in the country, and so we're at liberty, we can talk.' And he burst out laughing gaily and infectiously.

Father always submitted to the active, overflowing nature of Vanya Puzanov. Vanya was energetic even in sorrow: he never drooped, but marched straight into danger, like an obstinate bear on to a spear. He had one weakness—he showed complete lack of will-power where his wife was concerned. And Barbara made full use of that weakness, surrounded herself with admirers, local officers, young *chinovniks*, and burned the candle at both ends. That was Vanya's chronic sorrow, and it often drove him to drink.

On these occasions he tore himself away like a wounded tiger and went off to Moscow to Father's; he would sit for a week or two, isolated in a room, drinking down bottle after bottle of red wine. At such times he was terrible to look at, with rumpled hair, unwashed, uncombed and with wild swollen eyes. He would not allow anyone near him except Father, and he stalked about his room like a caged beast far into the night; or he would sob, with his leonine head buried in a cushion of the divan.

It was impossible to help him in any way. One had to listen patiently to all the laments, all of Barbara's cunning treacheries, all the deceits of her suitors, until the period of sufferings came to a natural end. Such travail would usually last for a couple of weeks.

When the fit had passed, Vanya stopped drinking and was transformed again into a handsome and elegant man. Then he would appear in society, visiting his actor friends and the theatres, and thus pacified, he would drive to the station, homeward-bound but always accompanied by Father.

Father loved and understood Vanya Puzanov, sympathized with his sorrows and did all he could to lighten his sufferings during the periods of 'weakness'. In return for this sensitive understanding Vanya valued the modest Yasha more than all his friends, 'the great luminaries of the stage'.

'When affairs get to that state, who is there to turn to? To Yasha, of course. The stage folk have no time for that sort of thing: they are easily diverted and think only of their own successes.'

But Father never mentioned to Vanya his own sorrow and tangled affairs; he understood very well that this would not lead to anything, that it would only be a waste of time.

Soon they were already in Vanya's house. The comrades were now relaxing in the master's study. Stage personalities looked down upon them from the walls: there were many enlarged photographs signed with flourishes, in narrow frames; there were snapshots of Vanya in different roles, and portraits of Yasha at various stages of his life.

Vanya was recounting how he had visited Carlsbad to get rid of surplus fat. 'I'd put on fat; I'd come on the stage, in the role of the Duke of Alba, in tights, and I'd feel awkward with thighs like a draught-horse. So I went to Carlsbad and dropped about thirty pounds, what with the waters, the baths and—not a drop of drink! A diet and all that. And the people I saw there. O Lord! the scroungers there were, most of them Russian. You'd never imagine such scum—the gigolos, the swindlers, Poles and Polish ladies—in fact, cheats all of them, but to all appearance elegant folk, the cream of aristocracy.'

'Well, and how is Barbara?' Father enquired carefully. Vanya dropped his eyes and let his head fall.

'Barbara?' He raised his eyes. 'Barbara is much the same. Officers, always officers.'

'Why don't you take the broom to them, to the whole lot of them?'

'Ah, brother, "I'd love to be in Paradise but my sins will not allow." She sways me overmuch. Believe it or not, I cannot raise a hand against her.' And his leonine head drooped still lower.

'There's life for you,' thought Father. 'A quiet modest girl from a good family has turned into a lioness, and Vanya, the born lion, is lamb before her!'

While he could bear it, Vanya avoided dwelling on his old wounds, even with Father. He tried to forget himself in business, showed amazing energy in his shop, opened new departments and introduced the fashions of the capital. If that did not help, he would plunge with his whole soul into the affairs of the theatre; and although by this participation in play-acting he lost face to some degree among the residents of the 'Blessed City', and also wasted much time, nevertheless this was for him a necessary and extremely important matter. Just now he was in the mood when the theatre, the life of the actors, and his own part in the plays were all-important.

The conversation naturally turned to the theatre. In a few seconds Vanya was unrecognizable. Reminiscences, jokes, and anecdotes all poured out of him. When speaking of actors, he imitated their carriage, voice, and manners so cleverly that it seemed they were all there in person, tossing out their catch-words singly or in chorus. Now it was Gorev parading in Sudermann's *Magda*. What fine acting! 'What nobility—not one false movement,' said Vanya, carried away.

'But the following day, when I called on Gorev at his hotel, I found him sitting on a divan all painted up and powdered, with that impudent actor's air of his, and a monocle stuck in his eye,' and here Vanya stuck a silver rouble in his own eye, 'and there he was spinning tales about himself and his greatness. All other actors were worthless. All actresses without exception were sluts. It was shameful listening to him and disgusting to look at the painted dodderer—but on the stage he was a czar, a colossal talent. So there, and where does it all come from? It's easy, brother, to sum up a man in life, but it's not so easy to judge him on the stage. In life your actors are small folk, far worse than ordinary mortals—but on the stage! They spiral up and whirl among the clouds, it would make your head turn! Take Kissilevsky, for example, how he acts in *Kreschinsky's Wedding!* How well he brings off "It's fallen through" and the breaking of the billiard cue. Once they forgot to saw the billiard cue for him: he pressed on it but it would not break; he had to walk off carrying it—but how he did it! And afterwards, in the wings, he beat up the property man with the cue. "You've murdered me, you villain, I'll kill you," he shouted. And they had to pull him away.

'I remember once two actresses had a fight, a serious one: as they grappled in a deadly hold, the feathers flew, and here were Mary Stuart and Queen Elizabeth settling accounts over a lover. Ha, ha, ha! But about Lensky you cannot say anything bad. He is noble in life as he is on the stage. As King Philip of Spain he is a monster all right, but the noble blood can be felt. His appearance alone sends shivers down one's spine. A wonderful artist, this Lensky, and a worthy man!

'It's like this with an actor: one day it's feasting and the next it's only potatoes. Today he's driving round in a landau, and tomorrow you see him as "Arcady the Unfortunate", counting the telegraph poles. Lying, drunkenness, debauchery, swinishness—the whole caboodle, but in the theatre he's the high priest of great art! "And they awaken the best feelings on their lyre," as Pushkin says.

'But when the time for failures comes or old age catches up with the actor, or when talent dries up—then there is no human image left at all. Then, brother, it's bad. It could not be worse. Such a "type" is to be found sitting in a wine shop from morning till night in a threadbare coat, boasting about his fame to merchants on the spree. His only riches are the posters and press cuttings of his past greatness, worn and faded from their long being carried in his pocket. For a bottle of vodka he will declaim the whole of *Hamlet;* he will weep drunken tears over his perished talent; he will blame everyone and blaspheme before God. The Lord preserve us from seeing anything like it. There's nothing lower or more wretched.'

Vanya pondered for a minute, passed his hand through his tousled hair and then continued more sedately:

'The young ones are better. In the Moscow Arts Theatre it's all one, whether on the stage or in life. They are all people of character, with no actor's caste about it. Whether that is better or worse for the stage, history will show us, but they have something fresh and new there. They impose themselves not by their training or school, but by something else: by their common endeavour—by their work together. Of course, they have their strong and individual points of outstanding quality—young Moskvin alone is worth a lot! There's Kachalov, too, although he was one of the professionals. But he's adapted himself so well to them, that one might think they were birds from the same nest. Well, we shall see!'

The love of the old players of the Malyi Theatre was still so strong, with Vanya, that the attractive innovations of the 'Artists' were still held in some doubt. Father loved and knew how to listen. This rare quality opened souls to him. One felt in him a person who entered with interest into all the details of a story. Two or three questions, Father's replies, and the narrator sensed a sympathetic audience capable of understanding and assessing each detail. And apart from their old friendship, Vanya found himself particularly at ease with Father when discussing doubts or decisions—it was like talking to himself. When the conversation flagged, Father asked two or three more questions, and Vanya's speech again flowed on in a wide flood until the topic was exhausted.

It was already late when Father prepared to leave. About his own problems, he had had no time to mention even a word. And he felt that it would serve no purpose—inescapable fate marched on its own way.

In the deserted streets, lit by dim oil lamps, it was dark and empty. His legs carried him mechanically homewards through the long-forgotten streets. In brother Pasha's room there was a light still: he was evidently up and waiting for him. 'Pasha!' 'Brother!' They embraced.

'Well, how are you? How's the shop? You're serving and serving, but where's the sense of it?'

Pasha's hazel eyes restlessly combed the corners; his short solid figure looked as if it wished to dart somewhere, as if it were hiding something and wished to preserve its secret. He was respectful towards his elder brother, a little afraid of him as he was once afraid of their father and mother and, as he stood now, despite his fifty years, afraid of his employer. He had a fear of everything. 'May God punish me!'—that was his favourite saying.

'Why didn't you warn us by telegram that you were coming, brother? I'd have come to the station to meet you, may God punish me! The master would have let me go.'

'Don't worry,' Father reassured him. 'I came in a hurry, on business, to see my partner, Petchke. I had no time—and then I know the road. Why should I disturb my brother? And how are things? How is everything at home?'

'Everything is all right, thank God! There are repairs to be done—the lodgers upstairs are complaining. But where is one to get the money? We'll chance it as it is.'

'Ah, Pasha, Pasha, you're "living in a forest, praying to the stumps". You're not interested in anything, you go nowhere! Here you are in your old age and nothing to show. You have no ambition, you're always afraid of something, always hiding something. And so you will have lived in vain, without much profit to yourself or to others! And you will not know why you have lived!'

'But I'm all right, brother, thank God! May God punish me!'

'We shall talk it all over tomorrow, it's time for bed now! Vanya and I got talking, and I'm tired from the journey,' Father yawned, getting up from Akim Ivanovich's chair. Lighting the way with a candle, Pasha saw his brother to his bedroom.

Here everything had remained as it was in Grandmother's time: the same furniture, the lace curtains crocheted by her, the same smell of camphor from the chests, the same stillness of a native nest. One of Grandmother's ikons was still in the corner, the lamp lit, and there was a bunch of dried willow branches in front of it—perhaps they had been there since her day. There was the wide bed, the same in which he had been born fifty-five years ago: on which, as a child, he had scrambled up to his mother when he was afraid of being left alone in the nursery.

The memories of dear past things, the pure tears of childhood, the great faith in goodness and happiness, all these bore down upon him joyously in a gigantic wave, drowning all his misfortunes and the agitations of everyday life. How small is man! How insignificant his laments to God! There were such riches in childhood memories alone that no successes in life were comparable with them! Was happiness possible only in childhood?

And he remembered again how as a child he had puzzled over the legend of Kuzmich—Czar Alexander. Having risen to the heights of greatness, he suddenly threw all that aside like an old garment. Yes, it was 'vanity of vanity' that multiplied itself. There was the fate, too, of the 'magnificent Prince of Taurid'— Potemkin, who was raised by Catherine to a dizzy height, but died on the bare earth of the steppe. 'Enough! There is nowhere more to go! Lay me down here!' The cortège stopped in the open fields of the vast country, and he before whom all Russia trembled, lay limp and lifeless on the dusty road. 'And so it is with me,' Father thought, 'I am striving and arranging things, but there is nowhere left I can go. Lay me down here!'

In a few days' time, Father took his leave. His mission was a complete fiasco. After stormy sessions with his partner, the fatal line became more clearly defined. It was decided to wind up the business, give up the store, and close down the Moscow department altogether, after executing the last contracts. In simple language, that was complete ruin. The loss of a means of livelihood! Poverty!

XXXII

IT is hard to face imminent ruin from day to day without
being able to move even a finger to avert the catastrophe.
The mind continues to work ceaselessly, attempting to find
a way out of the predicament. Every minute new combinations
suggest themselves; but fantastic possibilities are a doubtful
solution of the problem. Logic persists in clambering up the
fragile ladder of possibilities. For a moment it seems that it is
about to attain the goal of liberation—one comes to life again
and is glad to be alive. Then suddenly the chain of logic is
broken and everything crashes once again, like a house built
on sand.

And then again, from day to day, there is the repetition of
the same old story. Reason refuses to admit defeat. The exhausting and fruitless work of the mind undermines the organism
hourly, paralyses energy and weakens the sinews of the body.
Existence becomes a burden, an austere fatality, a ruthless
destiny, from which there is no escape. The whole of life
becomes concentrated within one's self, and that inner experience absorbs all vital energy. There are no life forces left
for stimulating external activity. The active external life is at
an end. Time creeps slowly and heavily on from lunch to dinner.
Everything seems unnecessary. Everything that was dear and
precious, everything that made life beautiful, becomes deper-
sonalized, lifeless and incapable of arousing any illusions. Life
is cynically bared and has the odour of death about it. Long-
forgotten mistakes, transgressions, sins, multiply anew before
the astonished gaze of the sinner. Soon they assume such
proportions that it seems they will crush the unfortunate victim

—the unfortunate ego. It is easy to pick out a person who has experienced such trials from among a crowd in the street. His downcast air hits the eye amid the dead silence of the Kremlin Cathedrals, or in the cosy atmosphere of a family tea-party. He is a living corpse, awaiting the trumpet call of the Apocalypse: 'And, behold, a pale horse, and he that sat upon him, his name was Death'. It is terrible to have looked in the eyes of the pale horseman! Many cannot bear that vision and quit this life of their own volition. God will forgive them! Others the 'pale horse' rescues from their lethargy and prepares them for battle —their last encounter.

And so it was with Father. 'If you've lost your head, don't cry about your hair,' he used to say to himself and he applied himself energetically to liquidating his business while being clearly aware that he was at the same time winding up his own life. So let it be! 'You've rung your last peal, so get off the bell-tower.' The vast weight of responsibility for his business, the constant game of wits to make twopence out of three half-pence, was now off his chest. There was no business left now, no stock in trade; there was no need to persuade customers; there was no anxiety left about delivering the goods or the constant appeals to old Petchke to postpone payment. Having had his writing desk and Grandfather's armchair brought from the warehouse, Father sat at home and watched what was happening in the courtyard outside. The square courtyard, the white plastered houses, the steeples of the neighbouring churches with their pigeons, all reminded him of his childhood.

There was little movement in the deserted street. One could hear from afar when a rare *izvoshchik* drove past or the heavy hooves of a cart-horse clattered rhythmically on the cobbles. Every day about eleven old Peter drove by with goods from the railway station. Peter would drive into the courtyard and Father checked his watch—it was exactly eleven; it was all as precise as a chemist. Father then put on his short coat made specially for him from thick cloth, with blue lapels, and went down into the yard.

Father with Volodya while visiting him
at St Petersburg Forest Institute in 1898.

Family group, 1900.
First row: Victor, Father, Mother, Volodya.
Second row: Nicholas, Victor's wife, Stepanich, Vera, Nadya, Cachalot.

'Well, Peter, how goes it?' Thus he greeted the old worker. 'Is everything all right?'

'Everything, glory be to God, master! I sent off five boxes to Nizhny and seven to Lobanov in Yaroslavl. Here are the receipts and invoices, if you please.'

Father would open the cellar. He had made of it his store-house, his receiving and dispatch centre, his office, in fact; it served for all the things that formerly were housed with diffi-culty in larger premises.

Peter kept coughing into his hand (he had chronic consump-tion) as he opened the door of the cellar; he would light a candle-end and descend with Father into the dark depths of the cellar. It was cold and damp there. He helped Father to move heavy boxes, trying to ease for him this unaccustomed physical labour, and thought the while: 'How the master has come down in the world—it's painful to see it. And from such a high position to come down to this and carry boxes himself. Ah, sinful world!' He recalled the times when dozens of carts used to drive up to the store, and when there were men specially there to unload them, so that there should be no hold-up. 'In those days there was a coming and going to and from the stations all day long, and sometimes they could not manage to send everything off on time. Boris was our slave-driver and he could swear: we were always in the wrong; but the master never said a bad word—he was a good master but unlucky. And now what misery!'

When all was finished and the dispatched items had been noted, Father fed Peter's old swollen-bellied mare with sugar and chatted a few minutes with Peter about the news of the town.

'And how are things in town? What is the gossip?'

'Ah, in the town—' Peter waved his hand. 'The Givartovskys are climbing. No one wants to receive our Petchke. Boris has done the dirty on you. I warned you in good time, you should have got rid of him. And now he's sucked up to the Givar-tovskys and is blackening your name round the town.'

The offences of Father's clerk, Boris, still gave Peter no rest. Boris had known how to make money on the side and he had cheated Father throughout his long years of service; and now he appeared as an open competitor for whom all means were fair.

'God will look after him,' Father would reply quietly. 'Every old woman has her past . . . . but how is your old woman?' he said, changing the theme.

After shutting the cellar, Father would stroll about the court-yard, in his short coat with its lapels, like a retired general in his domain; and then he would go upstairs again.

Now he must enter up the bills of lading and the cash book, write two or three letters, and the working day was over. Then he could sit and read the paper, feeling that he had done his duty. Over the absorbing leader of the *Russian Word* the last traces of anxiety disappeared. 'Yes, when you've lost your head, it's no use weeping over the hair.' Reading the paper, he was no longer worried by the money he owed his old partner, by competition or failures. Owing to the impossibility of recovering them, the debts were 'cancelled' and the competition no longer roused his envy. 'Let them profit: we'll manage as best we can. Softly does it.'

Sometimes curious incidents arose: some forgotten debtor would turn up. 'I happened to hear as how you were winding up the business, Yakov Akimovich. So I remembered about my debt. The Lord bear witness to me. Here, take what I've left, and lighten my soul.' And he would empty his pockets of a few credit notes, his gold watch and chain, a pair of ear-rings and suchlike domestic valuables often of doubtful value. One such character brought a fur coat and a Tula samovar with him: 'Take them,' he said, 'I would not part with them to anybody else. Only I was sorry for you and remembered—you're a good fellow, Yakov Akimovich!'

These offerings from forgotten customers touched Father greatly and occasionally roused his emotions. 'Ah, you see, he remembered,' he would say triumphantly, pointing to some article made of Caucasian silver. In these moments he forgot that all these 'voluntary' contributions did not help to pay off a hundredth part of the actual debt, and that they were as good as useless. Thus, one of them insisted on paying off his debt with a worn-out dog-cart, while another dragged along a whole sack of silver coin that unfortunately turned out to be counterfeit!

Father was now completely cut off from town, from the bustle of the trading world, and he spent entire days at home. This pleased Vera better, and she did everything possible to make life more pleasant for him. Expenditure was much reduced now. Victor's visits were no longer as stormy as before— there were insufficient reasons to start a war. It even seemed to Victor that if he were to squeeze himself a little, then Father might yet manage to exist somehow, 'sharing with difficulty'.

Everything now was on a more modest footing. Little by little old companions and friends dropped away; Gushchin, Aksentiev, Bielikov, found little advantage in their old haunt and went in search of more abundant and luscious grazing grounds. Only the band of officers dropped in occasionally, as before, paying little attention to the changes. The fresh caviare, salmon, and cognac had disappeared from the table and given place to tomatoes and onions, sprats and beer. The company of young people seated themselves around Father; they joked and laughed as in the old days. True, it was noticeable now that Father was not the only attraction. Vera's beaming eyes involuntarily compelled some to linger long over their tea. Sympathies and possibilities suggested themselves. From the kitchen, keen-eyed Tatyana noted the rising temperature, and afterwards in the kitchen discussed 'strategy' with Vera. Nicholas played stormy regimental marches or dreamy Ukrainian songs for an improvised choir.

Lieutenant Stepanov, or simply 'Stepanich' as he was called, in particular proved a good companion to Father. He was sensitive of soul and understood Father's sorrow, showed a marked sympathy for him and set high value on his spontaneous nature. It seemed to him that people like Father stood nearer to truth, or as he put it more exactly, nearer to God.

Stepanich had a good understanding of people. Of humble origin, of simple peasant stock, having risen to the higher strata of the intelligentsia, he had learnt to judge people by their worth, throwing aside everything superficial and non-fundamental as so much unnecessary husk. What interested him was the kernel, the human soul in itself; he could dispense with the cultural garment. In this respect, Father seemed to him one of the more interesting men and of close spiritual affinity with him. Stepanich often came alone and had long chats with Father.

What did they talk about? Nothing in particular, but Father's kind soul showed itself in everything. He never condemned anyone, somehow generously forgave all, and always found excuses for others.

'Ah, Stepanich, Stepanich,' he would say softly, touching affectionately the facings of his uniform, 'we are all sinners before God! Each one bears his cross! One must understand, put oneself in another's place, and forgive. For is not God everywhere? He is here in our midst. Here we are sitting and talking, drinking tea and red wine, and He is watching us from on high.' Convinced, Father looked up at the image of the Saviour, hung in the right corner. How could man not sin?

'We are all human. "A horse has four legs but it stumbles too." "Count your chickens in the autumn." Often I thought, "It's the end of me now," but lo and behold: if fortune comes, misfortune helps towards it.'

And Father burst into triumphant childish laughter. These quiet simple talks had a refreshing effect on Stepanich. Father's simple, unsophisticated outlook on life, his unmalicious child-like directness, seemed to him a true approximation to the Christian spirit.

At home life went on quietly and peacefully. In the early morning Nicholas went off to the barracks; returning late, he pored over his military text-books. Vera busied herself with domestic chores, sewed, and did the accounts, trying to reduce the expenditure. The tousle-headed Volodya vanished to school and was actively preparing himself for final examinations.

The winter was a gay sunny one; the frosts were hard but invigorating. Outside in the yard, on the roofs and on the church steeple, the brilliant snow lay in drifts like feather cushions; and the sparrows chirped over the dung-heaps. Sometimes an old rag-and-bone merchant would go by with a small bundle under his arm, chanting in a bass voice his 'Rags to buy and sell', and then vanish without much profit. The young *dvornik* was clearing the snow off the pavement with a scraper.

At his writing desk, Father watched this habitual scene. Sometimes he would go up to the tiled stove in order to warm himself; he would look at the thermometer screwed on outside the window; he would tap the barometer: the weather showed no change! 'Just the time to go shooting hares,' he would think. 'The eye can see but the tooth will not bite.'

He could no longer afford these pleasures. It was economy now in everything. For dinner there was mushroom soup, a piece of boiled meat, and pancakes. No delicatessen or *zakuski*. 'We have lived.' And that was that!

Tatyana was laying the table, 'swishing her tail about', and looking at Father with concern.

'You should take a walk before dinner, *barin*, for the sake of motional digestion. They say they're putting booths on Sukharev Square—there's no end of people there,' Tatyana chirruped. 'But you sit there like Koschey the Deathless, turning all sorts of black thoughts in your head.'

'Yes, it's true,' said Father, undecidedly, 'why shouldn't I take a walk?'

Tatyana would bring in Father's fur coat and lambskin hat, hand him his walking stick with an ivory knob, and run to open the outside door. In the hall Father would take a long time to put on his heavy galoshes. Then he thumped down the steps; it was cold in the passage as Tatyana stood by the open door in a cotton bodice, but she did not feel it. 'I've got hot blood,' she smiled, 'the frost does not take me. There was a time I would run barefooted over the snow. What's that to us peasants, we've got thick hides.'

It was fine out in the open air. One could breathe it in freely and deeply. The frost was invigorating, it made you step out. There were few people in the street. The snow-covered road enticed with its virgin whiteness as if inviting a sledge to drive the first track along it. The forgotten words of a song came back:

> I'd shout, girls, sit down,
> Let's go, dearies, for a drive.
> Only mind, this counsel hold,
> Don't lose yourself all five.

Father could not remember when and how he had heard this song. He only remembered the snowy road, the laughing sun, *troikas*, and the women's charming faces. Verse after verse mechanically ran through his head:

> And I shan't forget this life
> How in freedom wandered I.
> How, the wicked troika harnessed,
> Faster than a falcon we did fly.

And suddenly the long-forgotten picture rose up before him in all its details.

It was winter: they were driving on a *troika* towards the Korennaya Monastery. He had just been married. With him were his Olya, Vanya Puzanov in a high beaver hat, and several pleasant young ladies. The band of them were squealing, shouting, and laughing. They arrived at an inn. It was packed—they just got one room. And so they slept all together: Olya on one side, himself in the middle, and Masha, Olya's bosom friend, on the other, all in one bed. And there was nothing to worry about, it was all in good faith. Ah, what was there not in one's youth!

Masha was a beauty then in looks and figure; but now she was like an overfed pig—two arms' length would not encircle her. When he met her afterwards, she would laugh: 'Do you remember how we slept the night together at Korennaya?' And her double chin would shake like a jelly on a plate. Yes. It all happened. But it is past.

Near Sukharev Tower, by the market, there was a mass of people, a buzz of voices, and it was not easy to push one's way through. Father turned to the left, to the guest-house of the Prince G., and walked past the iron railings. Somewhere in his head, there was a purring refrain:

> *Late at night from out the forest*
> *I was driving the geese a-home. . . .*

Father smiled and asked himself why he was so 'tuneful' that day. He had always loved that romantic legend about 'the young prince and the beautiful peasant girl'. Meeting her, the prince was struck by her beauty and married her without debating overmuch. The marriage turned out a happy one: the young princess made up a song for herself about their meeting, and the song spread among the people, together with the memory of the kind-hearted peasant-princess. All her life she had taken pity on the common folk. The guest-house and the song lingered in history, and survived to our day. Father did not know whether the story was a true one, but he loved the song and always remembered the beautiful princess—how she was minding the geese and met the prince:

> *I see, I hear, the* barin's *driving from the field*
> *Two dogs in front, two lackeys up behind*
> *And when he level drew with me*
> *His eyes did glance at me.*
> *"Hail thee, darling beauty mine!*
> *Whence are you? What village from?"*
> *"A peasant of Your Highness, sir,"*
> *I answered him.*
> *I answered him, my lord and master!*

When anyone told Father that this was not an authenticated fact, he grew angry: 'There, you're always like that. It's so good, that even if it had not happened, *it should have—if only for the sake of beauty!*'

The clock of the Sukharev Tower, an old clock of the days of Peter the Great, struck its twelve hoarse beats.

Father turned and went home. It was warm inside and the soup tureen was steaming. The logs crackled in the stove. There was an agreeable feeling in his heart, and he had an appetite too. He carved himself some meat and added horse-radish, which he liked, put the morsel in his mouth and then stopped. An expression of fear appeared in his face. Vera watched him with surprise: 'What is it, what's happened, papa?'

'I can't swallow it, I can't,' he said in a hardly audible voice. 'What a thing—I don't understand it!' Father got up agitatedly and went into his bedroom. Vera sat on, as if nailed to her chair, oppressed by a presentiment. Father walked across the bedroom and looked at himself in the mirror. A pale, astonished face looked back at him, with frightened eyes. 'It can't be?' he asked himself. 'It can't be? Well, my turn has come! It began like that with my father—he could not eat anything and died a hungry death. He was ruined like me too—an apple will not roll far from the apple-tree!'

Father sat down and looked at his troubled face in the mirror again, then with a shake of his head he pulled himself together and returned to the dining-room as if nothing had happened. Next day the same thing happened at dinner. Vera secretly telegraphed for Victor, who arrived and tried to persuade Father, diplomatically, to have a medical examination and to consult a specialist. He also prescribed a liquid diet: milk and a quiet life. But Father categorically refused the milk: he could not stand it from childhood; he did not need a specialist either—he knew what was the matter with him. It was nothing serious, just spasms in his throat. It would pass.

Troubled, Victor went back to his local patients. In a few days' time, the suspicious symptoms stopped: everybody at home breathed a sigh of relief; but Victor continued to worry, and studied the latest cancer researches about the contraction of the gullet, wrote letters to specialists, and prepared for the worst.

Father appeared outwardly calm, but in the depths of his heart he admitted that it was the 'beginning of the end': in two or three years it would all be over. 'So it was and so will be,' he said to himself, dropping his head.

Life went on. Volodya, the youngest son, finished his schooling successfully, contrary to all the prophecies of his elder brother. 'Look at this,' Father would say triumphantly showing the diploma to Victor, 'and you said that nothing would come of Volodya, that he was a lazybones and all the rest of it. But he will knock you all into a cocked hat!'

Vera was fitting Volodya out for his journey to Petersburg: she sewed the linen and wondered why he was going so far. 'Why not live with us here as before? Victor's gone. Nadya too. And now Papa will be left all alone and will have no one to talk to.' But Volodya was determined to seek his fortune elsewhere and make a new life for himself.

Nadya wrote occasionally from the provinces: there was nothing left of her brilliant butterfly life. Now she was married again, and, strangely enough, her new husband was that old friend of the family, Nicolai 'Cachalot'. They were living by a railway station, in an official house with a garden. From their dining room they could hear the signal bells and the puffing of the locomotives. Their one and only dream was to move to Moscow. Their slogan was Chekhov's 'To Moscow, to Moscow!'

Nadya was as beautiful and elegant as ever, but something had changed in her soul. Her enthusiasms were dimmed: the operettas, the balls, the handsome cavalry officers were no more. At first, they had retired only into the background; and then they had vanished like smoke; and now it seemed as if nothing like that had ever existed.

Cachalot and Nadya paid us occasional visits to spend a few days with Father. Cachalot would laughingly express indignation about someone and seek Father's support. In his passport he was still described as a 'merchant brother' in spite of his calling as mechanical engineer. 'But', he boasted, 'I have managed to be best man at my own wife's wedding! A rare thing indeed!'

Father laughed, with all, as if he had nothing on his mind. But in reality, anxiety had doubled and had taken two different turnings, both leading to annihilation, to non-being and death. For the day was approaching when the means of subsistence would end. At times, the oppression lifted and a hope sprang up out of the recesses of the soul. The days seemed brighter and one felt better. The summer had come. One wished to get out somewhere to a cottage, to lie down on the grass and fish for trout. But he had to stay in Moscow. Now every kopek had to be counted.

In the daytime it was hot in the apartment. The sun warmed the room like a hothouse. Even the furniture began to crack. But in the evenings it was cool and pleasant on the balcony.

Below, in the small garden, were seen the tops of young trees, reaching the level of the balcony and the roofs of neighbouring houses; the trees were still warm from the daytime sun; and above was the evening sky. Warded off by houses, the noise of the town barely penetrated to the balcony; but on Saturdays, when the church bells rang for the evening service, one could guess in which church and which street they were ringing. It was as if a map of sound were swimming in the air, and the fantasy rolled to and fro along the echoing streets.

Vera would bring in the candles under frosted globes and sit down to do her sewing, near Father. He would read over again the morning papers, smoke cigarettes, sometimes sighing heavily as if in answer to his gloomy thoughts. Gnats and moths of all kinds fluttered round the candle-flame; and it seemed strange and incomprehensible to Father how they managed to appear in the city in the midst of houses and roofs. And in this silence the quiet sultry evenings were spent: father and daughter knew each other so well that conversation seemed superfluous. Besides, there was nothing but sadness in their hearts. It was as if they were both concealing their thoughts from each other.

Vera sewed methodically and thought of Father. Victor was writing her alarming letters: he had no doubts about the seriousness of Father's illness. And there was Stepanich and his love; but how could she leave Father? Soon Mother would be back from the hospital, also requiring her support and attention for much of the time. The two of them together were like small helpless children!

Vera had not yet told anyone of Stepanich's proposal and of her resolve to marry him. Personal happiness appeared untimely and out of place now. Let us wait and see what happens: thus she consoled herself, glancing at Father. He was reading his *feuilleton* and smiling at the witticisms of the *Moscow Leaf* and seemed to be in the best of spirits; but his state of anxiety did not escape Vera's penetrating eyes.

It was now clear to Father that he was facing his last period: the period of greatest importance! 'The third bell!' It was time to start on the long journey. The oppression of the unknown had passed: the imminent reality was now fully revealed to him; it did not frighten him with its terrors but it induced a feeling of sadness, as if he were assisting at the requiem of his best friend. Self-pity and complaints about fate had yielded to a sense of the significance of the end of human existence. The petty annoying anxieties had disappeared, like a swarm of gnats blown away by the wind.

And so another day had passed! How insignificant man's individual existence seemed! The world would have been had I not existed: and once I am no more, nothing will have changed. And so they sat on, father and daughter, solitary, and dear to one another, each thinking his own thoughts until the candles guttered, and it turned cool, and the neighbouring roofs were swallowed up in the darkness. Sometimes the bell rang and Stepanich paid a visit. His presence temporarily changed their mood, but in the end he, too, fell into the general atmosphere, plunged into thought, and lowering his curly head, stared at an unfinished glass of tea.

'Well, Stepanich, tell us something! Why are you so silent?' He would start as if waking out of a long solitude and begin to relate some incident of regimental life.

That winter the symptoms appeared again. Now they no longer frightened him. He grew more calm of mind and his good nature increased, as it were, despite the course of events. It was as if he had come to a final and unalterable decision, and now he was able to look at everything cheerfully, and with kindly and all-forgiving eyes.

There was no resentment in him any longer, no nostalgia for the life that was slipping away. His thoughts had become reconciled with fate. His only worry was not to offend anyone. It was too late now for reproaches and scenes. He had lived his span and must give way to others.

In the meantime, affairs were going from bad to worse: the last day of dispatch, the end of the business he had started, had already been decided. Traders of a new type were now on the scene—Father could not hope to catch up with them. The commercial ship was sailing on, and he now found himself overboard.

Once he had built up a big business out of nothing; had fed himself and his family, and others, for some thirty years; and he had also amassed a capital for Petchke, his old partner. And now Petchke was writing to him to say that 'in spite of your services, etcetera, etcetera, while on the one hand we have to admit . . . on the other hand we have to recognize . . . and so on and so on . . . in view of the lack of increment, and the already considerable debts, of the recovery of which all hope has now been exhausted, we are now stopping the delivery of goods to Moscow and closing all the accounts. . . .' Well, let them close them,' thought Father, calmly looking at the calendar. 'We shall close them on the first of January and after-wards God will provide!'

He had some savings left, and there was the old house in the 'Blessed City'; if that were sold, with some care, there would be enough for two or three years. Father knew that two or three years was all that he could expect of life. He would try and live those years as best he could, without complaints, anguish, or reproaches.

They spent Christmas quietly and peacefully without going anywhere and without guests. In the spring Volodya and Step-anich went off to Petersburg. From there Stepanich wrote that he did not like the Military Academy of Law, and had decided to resign from the army and practise at the bar. Volodya lived modestly on his pittance and enjoyed the carefree student life.

It seemed to Father now that he was unwanted. None of his old friends or companions ever showed up. Father looked through his account books, starting from the beginning, over a period of thirty long years, and he checked the balances of the current year and began to await the final dispatch.

It turned out a cloudy and fitful day. The sun would peep out for a minute, then it would be almost as dark as night. Large flakes of snow were falling. Sharp continuous blasts of wind howled every now and then blowing the snow off the roofs and piling up snow-drifts in the corners of the courtyard. Father looked out of the window. Ravens were stalking about the yard monotonously, flapping their damp wings. Then Peter the carrier appeared, wrapped up to his ears in a coloured scarf, driving into the yard on a creaking sledge. Father put on his short overcoat, snow-shoes, and fur hat, and went down to the cellar.

'Hello, Peter. How's business? Have you brought it?'

Peter coughed from behind the scarf, produced a chit, and trying not to look at Father, handed him the greasy paper. They descended into the cellar down frosted steps. It occurred to Father that the steps should be scraped—otherwise one might slip and break one's neck. Then he remembered that he would not be using the cellar again, and he smiled sadly. They carried out the two last cases, put them in the sledge, and stopped. Peter looked gloomily round the yard, trying not to show his face. Father was looking down at his galoshes.

'Well, Peter. Goodbye!' There was a trembling note in Father's voice as he said it. 'Goodbye, and don't think badly of me.'

Peter shook himself like a bird, glanced at Father with his black eyes and twisted his lips in a smile, as tears appeared on his old pock-marked face.

'*Barin!* Yakov Akimich! I shall never forget your kindness! On my death-bed I shan't forget it! But Boris, that snake, I'll break his neck! That swine was the cause of our downfall! Ah, the scoundrel!' And Peter spat his rage into the snow.

'Don't worry, Peter! Let him be! You and I, we have lived. I've no grudge against him! But I'm grateful to you, my friend, from my heart I thank you—for everything, the long service, everything!'

And the old 'companions in arms', the master and the worker, stood embracing each other in the middle of the yard. There was a gust of wind. The ravens croaked hauntingly and flew away. Father felt for the lump of sugar in his pocket and treated the old mare to it for the last time. Peter got on the sledge, pulled on his mittens and, wiping away the last tears, jerked the reins: 'Gee, there—God bless you, *barin*—I shan't forget you in a century!'

Standing by the open cellar door, Father looked sadly in the wake of the departing Peter. For thirty years, he thought, for thirty years, this ailing consumptive man had come daily with the goods. For thirty years he had worked honestly and regularly. In all that time, he had been guilty of no negligence, uttered no word of dissatisfaction nor even looked discontented.

'My God, my God—' Now Father was in tears, but in his heart there was peace and joy. Yes. There were still true men on Russian soil. Father locked the cellar door, gazed at the key, and slowly went upstairs. He felt as if a long stretch of life had just come to an end.

That night a telegram arrived. His brother Paul had suddenly died. Poor, poor Pasha!

XXXIII

IN Pushkino, a summer resort not far from Moscow, on the estate of the barrister Lavrov, there stood a tiny cottage hidden behind the trees of a small park. It had but one room with a minute hall, and reminded one of a doll's house, or the fabled dwelling of Baba Yaga—'the hut on chicken legs'. A small garden, with common flowers, surrounded by a palisade, led up to the porch. On the door one might observe Father's card: *Yakov Akimovich Polunin*. In the hut there were only two little windows, which hardly gave any light owing to the tall overshadowing pine-trees outside. In the entrance hall stood a narrow bunk, a hand basin, an oil lamp and a stool. In the only room, which served as a bedroom, dining-room and drawing-room, there was a wide bed, two armchairs, and a cupboard with shelves. There was hardly room for two people in these miniature premises.

When all the accounts had been balanced, it emerged that Father had so little money left, that Victor and Nicholas had to come to his aid. They met, talked it over, and resolved to support Father and Mother as best they could. It was still not clear if they would succeed in selling the old house in the 'Blessed City', or just how much it would fetch; and in the meantime the old folk would have to live! The Baba Yaga hut cost a mere trifle, and it was warm and cosy in the summer.

It was decided to give up the Moscow apartment. The furniture was scattered: Nadya took some; part was stored—Vera might need it—and the greater part went to Nicholas' quarters.

After being surrounded for thirty years by his family, Father now found himself for the first time alone. True, Mother was with him, once more recovered, but she was indifferent to almost everything. She might not have been there! The silent, kindly, spineless creature took no part in life. She would sit for hours in one place plunged in her thoughts, or she would lie in bed smoking one cigarette after another. When Father asked her anything, she would start up as if returning from another world; she would answer in monosyllables and then withdraw into herself again. It seemed that no force could drag her out of her lethargy. Whatever might happen in and around the house, she would accept everything apathetically and as a matter of course.

What did she think about, all these long days? It was a mystery. It had a depressing effect on Father. He understood that the period of her illness had exhausted all her vital energy, all her emotions, leaving only the pale shadow of a former person, like a squeezed-out lemon. Father could not reconcile himself at all to this depressing silence and the loss of all initiative, this sad meekness and painful dejection.

'Olya,' he would say irritably, 'why are you always lying down? Why not take a walk in the garden? The sun is shining, the birds are singing—and you're smoking all the time, smoking and lying about in bed.'

'In a moment, Yasha, in a moment,' she would reply, making attempts to get up and then losing herself again in her thoughts.

'And what are you thinking and thinking about all the time? In any case, you won't get anywhere,' Father would say soothingly. 'Well, and what are you thinking about?'

'I am always thinking how you will live without me,' she would murmur finally, looking up at Father with guilty, faded eyes.

Sadly Father would go into the garden, while Mother remained lying down with her endless thoughts. Banging the gate, Father walked slowly along into the park. At Lavrov's next door there was animation. The lady of the house was giving orders in the hothouse while the daughters were digging among the flower-beds. Father politely raised his tussore cap by its peak, smoothed the folds of his Russian blue-belted shirt—he dressed 'simply', in Russian fashion when at the cottage—and exchanged a few words about the weather with the young ladies.

They were weedy-looking and not very beautiful—flat-chested city girls. Nothing went right with them. Their mama was a small square-built woman with short hair, and she talked in a low contralto voice, wore pince-nez, and had an aggressive nature. Her deep voice could be heard from afar. She is a rest-less woman, thought Father making haste to get away; once she begins talking, there's no end to it. And she's got a voice like a sergeant-major. They say she's clever—a 'skirted professor', but she's borne such daughters, it's better not to look at them.

The bright sun tremblingly filtered through the alley of silver-birch trees and lit up the path in spots. The bench by the wicket felt hot as if it had just been washed in boiling water. There were alleys running to the right and left. The sun was playing on the trellised fence. A young *dvornik*, looking like a dandy in a raspberry-coloured shirt, was sweeping the path. The serving-maids were crazy about him, when in the evenings, after a hot and busy day, they felt the need for relaxation. Behind the fence of a large cottage, an idiot boy was bellowing like a beast —a pretty servant girl was trying to quiet him, at the same time exchanging glances with the *dvornik*.

The idiot had the wrinkled face of a monkey: his huge head was set on a slender neck and looked as if it might break off at any minute. 'Bou, bou. . . .Mou. . . .Mou. . . .Cur. . . .' bellowed the unfortunate boy, thrusting his small hands into a pillow. This painful, senseless roar made shivers go down Father's spine—he shrugged his shoulders nervously as he walked down the alley towards the station. On balconies holiday-makers were to be seen in loose dressing-gowns. Some-one was practising on a piano, stopping every other minute and starting up again the very same passage. There were few men about: they had all gone up to town to work; only a band of adolescent gymnasium boys, with cigarettes between their teeth, in white shirts and wide belts, were crowding in the direction of the river like a herd of young colts: they were

z

obviously going for a swim. Further on Father passed an officer, a young lady with an open book, and some dogs chasing after a cyclist.

By the station the sun was blazing mercilessly. It seemed that all movement had died. In the station-master's room the tapping of the telegraph machine could be heard; there was not a soul on the platform; a porter was dozing on a bench, his face protected by his cap from the sun.

There was a whole hour to go before the arrival of the Moscow train. Father called in at the post-office to ask if any letters had arrived *poste-restante;* he got the newspapers, then went in to buy some cigarettes and walked towards the river. Here there was animation, here the youthful band of gymnasium boys were bathing. Pink and healthy bodies shone in the sunlight. Some did the side-stroke, cutting the water as with an axe; others floated luxuriously on their backs. There was young laughter there, and strong muscles. Father sat on the bank and observed the scene. Youth, youth! How easy and interesting everything was in youth! The boys were laughing loudly at something; they were splashing one another with water; they were ducking somebody—and he would come up again blowing. A company of girls appeared: they went aside some two hundred paces and also began to undress.

It was like a scene of the old patriarchal days! Once upon a time whole families would go to the baths and steam themselves, men and women together. That had seemed usual and normal. Morality had not suffered in the least thereby. In the villages that is the practice to this day.

In the distance the women's white bodies seemed more attractive than they were in reality. There was squealing and a great splashing of water: with the help of bladders the girls swam across the river, splashed about like ducks near the banks and then ran to dress themselves in the bushes. None of them paid any attention to the naked boys, who also seemed preoccupied with their own business. Now they were lying on the grass and sunbathing. The distant noise of an approaching train made itself heard, there was a puff of playful smoke, and the locomotive whistled. Father went to meet the Moscow train.

He had no one to meet, but it was a distraction to see new faces, the bustle of porters, the station-master, the gendarme in his blue uniform, and to receive a fresh Moscow paper. By the platform the locomotive was panting heavily, as if resting after a quick sprint. Passengers were gazing indifferently out of the windows. The chief guard, with silver braid on his uniform —he was tall and handsome—swept proudly up and down the platform, like a peacock. In the old days, when the railways were first built, the position of chief guard was accounted an honourable one. Many a merchant's son thought it an honour to wear the long uniform with silver trimmings, to raise a whistle to his lips and to leap smartly aboard the end of a departing train. It was fashionable in those days: young Dmitry Okorokov, the tallest of the whole Okorokov band, had passed two years train-riding in the Orlov district before his enthusiasm had spent itself and the fashion had died out.

Now the chief guards were recruited from ex-sergeants and ex-policemen of stately appearance: they accepted bribes on the quiet, allowed 'stowaways', delivered parcels, all this contrary to the strict rules and regulations, and in spite of frequent inspection. How petty they had grown! The uniform with the silver braid had lost its meaning, its attraction and status! The same had happened with the magistrates. Once they had held their banner high: now they were made up almost exclusively from ex-army officers or unsuccessful sons of the small nobility. Among them were no longer to be found men of the best families or titled notables. The fashion had changed; and the 'justices of the peace', now transformed into county officers, had turned into a reactionary caste, the bulwark of the monarchy, contrary to the reforming principles of Alexander the Second.

Father went home by another road, behind the cottages, leading over a wide meadow set with silver-birch trees. It was pleasant to walk on the fresh green grass, like treading on a soft drawing-room carpet. There was not a soul in sight; the quiet was absolute. Only the grasshoppers drummed their barely perceptible tattoo.

In the midst of leafy gardens there was a glimmer of decayed, long-forsaken buildings, with gaping windows—the remains of great Catherine's reign. Once the village of Pushkino had belonged to Count Alexei Orlov and in his day the palaces, villas, and mansions had been built. The Count was the first noble who had ordered that gipsy choirs be collected and he had assigned them to the village of Pushkino. Many of the most noted lords had been his guests and had enjoyed the gipsy singing in the gardens of Pushkino.

His Serene Highness Prince Potemkin, Zubov, and Zorich, all of them Catherine's favourites, had all been in raptures over the gipsy choir, under the direction of the famous Ivan Trofimov. Alexei Orlov, the owner of the choir, would have hysteria and weep bitter tears, remembering his exuberant youth so full of greatness and crimes. To the sound of the gipsy songs old scenes were resurrected. Now he would see Catherine, in guards uniform, mounted on a white charger at the head of her regiments, and he was by her side—her inspiration and esquire! Unforgettable times!

Then he would see the tragic night that Peter III was buried. It was twenty degrees of frost and there was the procession of mourning carriages, the torches and the black cloaks with crepe on them. The gloom of night, the grave silence of the thousandfold throng, the ominous flicker of the coffin torches, the pale corpselike faces, and there he was, Count Orlov himself, bearing the Emperor's crown on a velvet cushion. It was the crown of him with whom he had shared the last meal at Ropscha.

Only in the wild songs of the gipsies did Orlov forget himself and relax from these nightmares. Later, he 'freed' the whole of the choir, and when the Patriotic War of 1812 began, all the male gipsies volunteered into the ranks of a hussar regiment.

This choir had produced Stesha, who had captivated the poet Yazikov. Pushkin himself became almost hysterical when listening to Stesha, and 'Catalani', the great Italian prima donna, was in raptures at her singing, and publicly took off a priceless shawl and presented it to her.

Once Franz Liszt, absorbed by this gipsy singing, forgot completely about his recital, and, when he finally arrived late, he sat down at the piano and absent-mindedly started playing gipsy melodies: 'You will not believe, how dear you are. . . .'

Yes, many memories were evoked when gazing at the peeling cornices of the Orlov mansions, the overgrown gardens, the broken railings, and the ruined statues.

He opened the gate and sat down on his favourite bench. Here behind the trees, in the warmth of the sunshine, it was restful and one was unobserved. And ahead, there lay the view —an enchanting corridor of a green kingdom. A woodpecker hammering somewhere high up on a pine-tree produced distant intermittent sounds. Knock, knock, knock. . . . He would stop as if reflecting and then knock, knock, knock again.

Thoughts turned again to the past. The merchant world— it had also improved! Formerly the slogan had been: 'If you don't deceive, you won't sell'. Or the merchants used to say: 'It's not a question of a rouble as long as we can make a kopek at a time!' Another old proverb ran: 'Out of honest business you will not build stone mansions'. And so they took risks, and out of their profits built themselves stone houses, leaving honesty to poor old men and religious maniacs. To salve their conscience, these were given their 'farthings' and mites, and were treated to onions and *kvas* in the kitchen. The Russian merchant of old was God-fearing, but he was afraid of the earthly powers even more, and paid great respect to them, kow-towing before each petty policeman and always apprehensive of something, in case anything went wrong. He would bow low, distribute presents and deftly slip a wad of notes—to oil the machine and make it 'revolve more easily'. 'One thief can spot another.' The administration accepted the bribes and at regular intervals started another investigation. Each merchant had his own technique with his clients. The chief thing was to get the buyer into the shop and, to achieve this, loud-voiced fellows at the doors did their own deft soliciting: what did they not promise, what yarns did they not spin!

Provincial visitors especially were taken in and stripped to the bone. The merchant would start off eloquently, showering proverbs and adages, and patting a customer on the back. 'You are not in doubt, are you, countryman? We shan't charge you dearly, not you!' The shop-assistants would pile up mounds of goods on the counter: the countryman's eyes would swim; he would purchase a lot of unnecessary things, and when he got home, he would find it was all rotten stuff, not at all what he had bought; but it was too late to return the goods. And so it all went on the rubbish heap.

The merchant would treat another customer coldly and severely, putting up the price and not budging an inch. This had an effect on some, and they bought out of vanity. Sometimes the merchant would reduce the price considerably, 'out of respect'. This also was effective. They amassed capital through cunning, subterfuge, and deceit, and at home they held their families in a 'mailed fist', lived like pigs and trembled for every penny. When 'himself' died, the son would shave off his beard, put on a town suit and start building himself houses. Champagne would flow in a river, carousals would follow, and by the third generation nothing, except the memory of former riches, would remain.

Where have we got old merchant firms in Russia? Two or three generations and then 'stop': not as it is abroad, where some firms have existed five hundred years! Now, Father thought, things had improved: there was free competition. If you traded bad quality, you would soon be rubbed off the face of the earth. All the proverbs and adages would not help!

Father sat quietly on the bench, warmed by the sun and thinking his thoughts of the past. Deceived by the quiet, a squirrel ran across the path. Perceiving Father, it stopped dead, pressed its paws to its chest and leapt aside like a wound-up spring. In an instant it was already sitting on the top of a high pine-tree, preoccupied with its affairs. Father rose and went back to the hut.

'There lived an old man with his old woman by the shore of the blue sea'—he recalled the fairy tale of Pushkin. He wished the dinner might be served quicker—his palate was tickling. But Mother was still lying in bed in the same attitude as before.

'Olya! Do get up for God's sake! The dinner will be here any minute and you're still in bed.'

'Yes, I will, I will, Yashenka! Honestly, I'll get up at once.'

It would have been easier for Napoleon to command his whole army to move, than for Mother to get up at midday. Finally, after incredible efforts, she was to be found sitting in the garden, in ten minutes' time, staring indifferently at a flower-bed. Father was walking up and down the garden exclaiming indignantly: 'Why don't they bring the food? I'm famished! Olya, do go and see, they shouldn't keep a sick person waiting so long!'

'They'll bring it any minute now, any minute, Yashenka! You can't have it all so quickly, it's got to be cooked and collected.'

'Cooked? It doesn't take long to prepare two boiled eggs. It's as easy as anything!'

'All right, all right.'

There was a sound of approaching steps, and the *dvornik* appeared, smiling, with a tray of food.

'How often have I told you, Nicanor, to bring it on time, but you're always late.'

'But it's not my fault, *barin*. The cook got involved with the barrister's wife, and you could get no sense out of her. I cooked them myself, today,' Nicanor answered guiltily, placing the tray on the small table.

'Well, all right, but don't forget the coffee.'

Father ate an egg and tried the '*kasha* of manna'. 'I might be a child,' he thought, 'to be fed with semolina,' and he pushed the plate aside. The appetite had gone. 'Strange,' he thought, 'I felt terribly hungry, but as soon as you begin the appetite vanishes.'

'I simply don't understand it,' he said, turning to Olya.

'But you must try,' Mother said persuasively, 'eat the cheese at least.'

Having cut himself small slices of bread, Father smeared them over with his favourite 'Brie' and, swallowing the tiny portions with difficulty, frowned and again pushed the plate aside. Perspiration showed on his brow; and an expression of obstinate resignation appeared on his face: 'So it was and so it will be,' his eyes seemed to say.

Mother, who had no teeth now, masticated her semolina slowly and with enjoyment, and then as slowly finished her apple pie. 'A full man does not understand a hungry one!' After dinner, Mother went to rest, while Father stretched himself in a canvas chair and, picking up a paper, plunged into his favourite *feuilleton*. In half an hour he was already asleep, his face covered with the newspaper to ward off the flies.

The gnats disturbed the air; cockchafers droned, crashing in their flight, running into trees and falling heavily to the ground. Rising again, they unfurled their stiff wings and flew into the blue distance. The sun, dropping lower, was pouring its scarlet beams through the spaces between the tree-trunks. The paths were crossed with reddish shadows and the shades grew thicker. It was peaceful and quiet in the village of Pushkino. A cockchafer flew straight into the newspaper and crept droning over Father's hair. Father awoke, carefully picked off the cockchafer and let him go; putting on his glasses he looked round and called Mother.

'Olya, are you asleep? I've had a good doze. I've been having silly dreams, too—as if you and I were riding into Korennaya on camels—we arrived at the fair, but it turned out to be Yar's restaurant and Vanya Puzanov was beating a Turkish drum— and gipsies dancing, like real—and suddenly Pospolitáki appeared (do you remember him?) and said: "If I wish, I'll give; if I

don't, you'll die of hunger!'' And Vanya Puzanov tore himself
away from his drum and said to his face: "You haven't the
right!'' And there the cockchafer woke me. Are you sleeping?'

'No, I'm not. I'm just lying and thinking—'

'You might boil the kettle at least! I'm thirsty. It's getting
on to six.'

'I will, Yashenka, I will.'

Father stretched himself and yawned. He thought it strange
to feel so drowsy. He had only to settle himself comfortably
and his eyes closed. He must have slept two or three hours.
That never used to happen before. To sleep in the daytime—
that was unheard of: nothing would tempt him! It was his
weakness! His illness was undermining him! It had been the
same with Grandfather—his legs had begun to give way. Father
pulled up his trousers and looked at his thin boyish legs and
shook his head. 'Chicken legs!' He laughed. But how he used
to weave quadrilles with those legs in the old days:

> *On the floor in eight pairs*
> *The flies were dancing.*
> *Then they saw a spider*
> *And fell fainting.*

And Olya used to swim like a white swan. And now she lay
there like a block.

'Olya, are you sleeping?'

'No, Yashenka. I'm getting the tea ready. The water will
boil in a moment.'

'Do you remember how we danced, you and I, at the Nobles'
Assembly? And the dress you had? "Moldavon", was it? Or
was it "tarlatan"? I don't remember what it was called. But
the Governor enquired about you: " Who is she?" he said.
Don't you remember? And that same evening Vanya Puzanov
skidded on his behind the whole length of the ballroom. Do
you remember?'

'No, Yashenka, I don't remember. What wasn't there in our
young days—all kinds of foolery. Come, the tea is ready now.'

It was low and dark in the hut. Father's head almost supported the ceiling. The tiny room was lit by a small and feeble tin lamp. Crooked shadows ran about the walls and ceiling.

'What a fabulous and mysterious atmosphere,' Father joked, adding a little cognac to his hot tea and lemon. ' We're living like "Baba Yaga" in her hut on "chickens' legs".'

'Don't frighten me for the night,' Mother said fearfully. 'That's no joke. And you know cognac's harmful for you. You've forgotten what the doctor said.'

'I know what he said,' Father replied, 'But what's the harm? Judge for yourself! Cognac is distilled from the best grapes— and everyone knows that grapes are most nourishing. Why, they prescribe grapes for the dying—Yes! I'm telling you, and you keep arguing!'

Father laughed bravely. A warm breeze was blowing through the tiny windows; the lamp flickered; shadows scurried across the ceiling. Nearby, just outside the hut, a nightingale began to sing, as if it were afraid of no one and were alone in the whole universe. The old people fell silent. 'In the long past,' thought Father, 'in the Okorokovs' old park, the nightingales used to trill like that.' He used to climb over the wall stealthily and wander about with Olya along the dark garden paths, avoiding the light, so as not to be noticed from the house. How pretty Olya had been! What a figure, what eyes she had! What joys there were, what emotions, what hopes!

Now he could not recall these things without a wry smile. Now Olya was a strange, half-alive person. When she was ill, she remembered everything down to the smallest detail. She remembered such details that one was surprised that human memory could contain so much. Then she lived each minute in the past, talked with long-departed people, felt their joys and sorrows. In such periods Yasha was for her a living person, dear and beloved.

But as soon as she got better, a film seemed to cover everything: the past and the present, the dear and the near; she became indifferent to everything. Everything was the same!

It was a terrible existence: exactly as if another person had been substituted in her place. An irresponsible person had taken the place of a normal one, and vice versa.

He kept thinking 'how it would be without her?' Twenty years had passed during which the only thought had been how to look after her and control her illness. Her soul was asleep; living was drowsed; life was like a garden of weeds.

Father closed the windows to shut out the evening chill. He poured a little more cognac, and his thoughts again stretched back to the past. Why was it that at night thoughts crowded to the head, like night birds flocking to their nests? Why was one more at ease at night? Why could all injuries be more easily forgiven and all the uneven paths of life be smoothed?

There were the two families, that of the Okorokovs and our own. Of the Okorokovs there was almost no one left: only Olya and the miserly Platon. All the others had died without leaving any remembrance of themselves. Vassily alone, perhaps, survived in Olya's memory and that of his colleagues, the engineers. Of the twelve brothers, he alone had the strong will, talent, and bearing of the old man Okorokov.

'Of our family,' thought Father, sighing, 'Pasha died an anchorite. His solitary worship of Bacchus probably helped his end. Only I remain! And what am I?' Father paused. 'Archimedes said: "Give me a fulcrum and I will dislodge the world." But I would say: "Give me but one truth and I will do the same." But what is truth? Even Christ himself did not answer that question. Yes! "Start philosophizing and the mind will turn giddy!" '

Father poured out what remained of the quarter bottle of cognac, glanced at Mother, who was sleeping with her mouth wide open, yawned, and stretched his back. It was sultry as if a storm were brewing. A feeling of nervousness fluttered in his breast, like a bird in a cage. Father went out into the open air. There was dead silence in the garden. Dark clouds gathered low on the horizon, weighing down the stilled earth. It was hard to breathe. The flower-beds of petunias and tobacco plant gave off a suffocating spicy odour. At last, the silence became such that Father involuntarily stopped dead in the middle of the path, as if fearing to move. Then suddenly a dazzling flash of lightning divided the sky. The vast invisible skyline was illumined for a second with phosphorescent light, and a rolling deafening peal of thunder crashed down right over Father's head. His heart stopped and his knees bent of their own accord. Insignificant life was completely lost in the mysterious spaces of awesome nature. 'Glory, glory be to God Almighty,' his lips involuntarily framed the prayer of terror, learned in childhood.

And from on high, from the stormy clouds lit up for an instant, rolled the unceasing peals of thunder. It was as if an invisible orchestra of Turkish drums were savagely beating a mad tattoo.

How small, how insignificant was man! And how defenceless! A peal of thunder and the fortress would fall in ruins—upon it he had proudly built his life. Tongue-tied, all his philosophy gone, man will stand 'naked and good'.

The storm was noticeably moving away: the lightning was less frequent. The heavenly drums were beating a softer, more baritone note. A breeze sprang up and the leaves quivered on the trees. It became easier to breathe and the nerves were soothed. Life slowly returned and re-established its importunate rights. A few large drops of rain fell and suddenly, without any warning, a torrent of rain descended. Father ran up the steps and the noise of rain followed him inside. The rain beat on the windows, drummed on the roof, as if a hundred roofers were laying out iron roofs and were hammering in the nails. In a minute the paths had turned into mountain streams and the water ran noisily and gurglingly down the slope. Here, in the little house, it was fine and cosy 'as on Christ's bosom'.

It was already late and time for bed: but the storm-charged atmosphere and lulling sound of the rain reconciled one so to life that one felt like staying up and thinking about something nice, cheering and bright.

'Well, my personal life has been a failure,' Father argued. 'Poor Olya had her lion's share of suffering, but the children will remain! And what children! They're all "picked"— handsome, clever and decent. They have their own life. They're all different; each has his own qualities, and they also have something in common, something "good". They are one family—all "birds of one nest". If one could but live a little longer and watch how they go through life. But will I?'

Father wound his watch and pressed a spring: on the dial a minute train ran over a miniature bridge and disappeared. It was two o'clock. 'Heavens! It's late.' Father began to undress. 'Yes. What does tomorrow bode for us?' Sleep is easy and peaceful on a May night with the rain falling softly.

XXXIV

TIME passed. Father dragged through the Moscow winter. His illness did its ruinous work. It was no secret that his days were numbered. At every opportunity, more and more frequently, the children gathered around him and tried to hide their apprehensions. Father seemed to read their thoughts, but he was not agitated: he became more and more reconciled with fate, found everything as it should be, and laughed good-naturedly at them.

'Well, why do you hang your heads? With your tongues on your shoulders?' He teased at the dejected attitudes of his daughters. 'A frightened crow's afraid of a bush! Matthew, Matthew, live more merrily!' he joked, bursting into jerky laughter.

In the small room, with its familiar furniture, at the round table laid with *zakuski*, which no one touched, Father alone was cheerful and animated. His children were unable to shake off their oppressive thoughts, while Mother was silent and indifferent, as if among strange people. Only Father was not dejected.

'Stepanich, why don't you taste something and have a glass of vodka. Why not try the caviare and the pickled mushrooms? I prepared them myself. And you all sit there, as if soaking in water. I myself can't—it won't go down,' he confessed guiltily, pointing to the *zakuski*. ' "God does not give horns to a butting cow." We'll have to do with what we've got. What sort of young people are you? Victor does not drink! Kolya doesn't either! Stepanich refuses—you might at least have a bite of something!' And with a smile he poured out a glass of *zubrovka* and handed it to Cachalot.

'We'll not refuse a drop, Papasha,' Cachalot smiled, opening his great mouth, into which the liquid instantly disappeared.

'And a little caviare would do you no harm,' said Father.

'Splendid, splendid,' said Cachalot, swallowing three large sandwiches.

'To think of all the fish that have been destroyed—millions of them.' Father reverted to a favourite theme. 'To think that each grain would have produced a fish, and here you're nipping them in the bud! Ah, Cachalot, Cachalot! Have another drink so that they can swim! Fish love the liquid element!'

Now Stepanich joined in and Father took pleasure, as if he were one of them, in watching the bottles and the gurgling liquids, and he envied the healthy jaws and the youthful appetites.

A general conversation started up. Stepanich related how he had failed the exam at the Petersburg Military Academy: how he had gone to Kronstadt, to look over the battleships. Cachalot became engrossed in railway anecdotes. Victor suffered boredom in a corner and bit his nails. Nicholas and Vera were quietly consulting in another corner. Mother and Nadya were sitting silently on a divan.

'Well, we are all gathered here, the whole family,' Father spoke joyfully, 'only the youngest is missing! I wonder how he is doing there, in Petersburg?'

But when they were all preparing to depart, and were saying their long good-byes, Father felt as if his head were going round, his knees giving way, as if he had just run a dozen miles. Yes, I've grown weak, he thought, bowing his head. His energy, which had been wound up by those young voices, was failing now. He looked thinner and his lips twisted themselves in a crooked smile. Through the large window one could see the wet roofs, and the thawing snow splashed about in layers on the pavement. Spring had brought thaw, dirty melting snow, sharp winds, and strong showers. Would that summer were quicker in coming, thought Father sadly.

Vera was sobbing loudly by the staircase, while Victor was

explaining gruffly that nothing could be done to help Father. And it was no use thinking about an operation!

'What use would it be?' he was saying sternly, as if giving a lecture. 'A few months of life, a year, let us say, no more, and then one and the same end.'

'But it's so terrible, terrible, to die a hungry death.' Vera sobbed. 'What would I not give—to spare him that!'

'My children, tears will not help, and I have to get to the station. Patients cannot be kept waiting,' said Victor buttoning his fur coat. 'I'll be back next week. Well, all the best!'

The inclement weather continued for a long time. Spring was slow in assuming its rights. Rains alternated with fresh falls of snow: it was impossible to walk or drive in the streets. At last, Easter was over and the sun had appeared. It dried and caressed the earth, drove the torrents into the rivers, and brought the green grass to the surface.

By the middle of May the weather had become settled, sunny, and warm. Like Robinson Crusoe, father once more became 'king of his domain on the island' of Pushkino. His fishing gear, his Monte Cristo rifle, his game-pouch, all that was handy. Only strength was wanting. And so all this gear remained lying in a corner of the entrance hall. He even had to give up his walks to the station. A postman delivered the papers; and the cigarettes, the Brie cheese, and the medicines all came by parcel post, or by hand from Moscow. Father now rarely left the garden, except occasionally to sit on the bench by the meadow beyond the cottages. There was no one there to look at him pityingly, as on a doomed man. The eternally smiling Nicanor still came with his tray, bringing dinner or tea and, when late, blamed the cook for everything.

There was a whole month of cloudless sky. At night it was stuffy in the room, and Father would open the doors and windows. But Mother was afraid of thieves and ill-intentioned people:

'But you can't do that, Yashenka,' she complained. 'What if someone should enter suddenly at night? The doors are open, and there are all kinds of people about.'

'Nonsense! What is there to steal?' Father replied jokingly. 'Perhaps they might take your hairpins. Who'd bother about us?'

'But it's also damp at night. You might catch cold.' Mother tried to persuade him.

'What sort of dampness? It's like a steam bath. One can't sleep for the heat and you talk of catching cold!'

In the mornings they drank their tea in the garden beneath the pine-trees. Father wore his Russian shirt and top boots. His tussore cap with its straight peak was invaluable in the sunshine. After tea, Father would take his Monte Cristo and shoot at a target for a while, to pass the time. Lying on the bed, Mother started at each shot.

'I wish there were a pigeon handy,' thought Father, looking up at the trees, 'but it would not be easy to get with rifle shot, and besides it would be a pity—let it live! It's God's creature too, it surely wants to live.' The gate creaked—it was the boy from the station bringing the paper.

Taking off his dark glasses, Father plunged into the paper. He read slowly column by column, beginning with the leading article and ending with an advertisement about the 'hire of a shed'. In France there was a change of Cabinet. In the South of Russia famine was expected. All that was somewhere far off, far away—it did not really penetrate here. Here there was another reality: morning, evening, night—'eat, drink, and the day's gone'.

Dinner was still far off. Time passed slowly and heavily. If only a visitor were to come! But there was no one who could come. Who had need of the old folk? Who was interested in them? Everyone had their own affairs, their hands full. Victor had his patients, Nicholas his soldiers, Volodya was attending lectures in Petersburg. They had all gone their ways—they had scattered like birds in the sky.

Father would take up his fishing rods and tackle and spend a long time arranging them, measuring and screwing them up, so as to have something to do, to pass the time. It was too far for him to go to the river now, where there were still small fish to be found, mostly sticklebacks. And in the neighbouring pond there were only frogs and newts. Nevertheless, it was pleasant to adjust the hooks, to examine the variegated floats, to fold and unfold the rods. All these constituted riches, which had given him so much joy once upon a time!

He remembered the bright mornings on the shining river, the peaceful evenings among the reeds. He could hear the sound of the oars, the splash of the fish. He had forgotten where and when all that had been: only the joyful sensation remained in the memory. Men had gone, times had changed, important events had faded from the mind, but the warm feeling for nature persisted and warmed the stilled soul again. Weak is man and infirm is his body!

'I'll go for a stroll, Olya,' he would say.

'Yes, my dove, certainly, go for a walk. But don't go too far, or you'll exhaust yourself, like the other day. It will be dinner-time soon, don't be late,' Mother would reply, stretched out on the bed.

Holding his walking-stick, Father walked slowly along the clean-swept paths and wondered at his feebleness. His legs were as if not his own; there was a pain in his side; and there was a dryness in his mouth.

By his favourite bench sparrows were twittering; and white ducks were waddling across the glade, unhurryingly and importantly, one after the other, like a file of soldiers. Surrounded by willows, the pond showed up in a green sheet of duckweed. High above, a hawk circled in search of prey. Father dropped down heavily on the bench, pulled out his amber cigarette holder and inserted a cigarette. A wisp of blue smoke spiralled up transparently into the air; the sparrows rose and then settled themselves again on a hazel-bush.

'Well,' said Father to himself, 'what was I thinking about? Yes, it's strange, one forgets the most important thing: when it happened, who was there, what we talked about and did. But one remembers the sort of weather it was, the odour of the flowers, the trimming of a dress. For the life of me, I cannot remember when Victor was born; but I recall the flakes of snow, the slippery road, the flickering lantern at the midwife's porch—I can see it now as clearly as in a picture! Or take the hunting. With whom I hunted I don't remember, but I can see a section of the field in detail, with the hare running across it: the colour of its fur, its ears pressed back, and the somersault it turned as it fell lifeless! Whole pictures of childhood come back, each in great detail, but I cannot remember what happened yesterday. Positively I can't.'

The ducks were returning from the pond, cleaning their feathers on the way and arguing busily among themselves. A woodpecker, the anxious 'eternal worker', began his labours overhead. Tremble, innumerable beetles—bark-borers all—the woodpecker has come! There was a whistle of a train: the dinner would soon be ready. But what a dinner! Father smiled. Shadow without substance—semolina and baked apple! 'Bread and water, a soldier's feast'—that was the whole menu.

The mournful strains of an accordion drifted across from one of the cottages. A cock with his ladies was proudly strutting across a flower-bed at the Lavrovs'. There was a noise of shouting through their open kitchen door: the cook was evidently up in arms again; her temperament did not agree with that of the advocate's wife. Father turned along the path leading home. Near the gate the same thought always occurred to him—how long?

Sometimes one of the children would arrive by train from Moscow. Or, what joy, it might be his old friend Vanya Puzanov, come, as he said, to visit the 'old-world landowners'. Father would order a real dinner from Nicanor, telling him who had arrived, his profession and standing; growing excited, he exaggerated everything, making a mountain out of a molehill. Nicanor would put on a clean white jacket for the occasion, grease his hair, and, when the time came, bring in the tray like a real waiter, wearing neat white gloves, and do his best to keep up his reputation.

Mother put on a newer dress and took time over her hair. There were no bounds to Father's hospitality. He would offer prizes for a shooting match, elaborate on all the sights of Push-kino, as if, young and energetic, there were no question of any illness. The guest was not allowed to depart until the very last train, and he left warmed by their cordiality and kindness. Such visits gave food for pleasant reminiscences for a long time after: they were often discussed and served as a theme for con-versation. He had come, they would say, and had not forgotten them!

Whenever Vera came, there was no end to conversations and so in unison were their hearts, their farewells were long and lingering. She could not tear herself away from Father's blue childlike eyes, and as she walked away along the sunlit paths she was ready to turn back at any minute. How would she find him next time? Would she find him again? How weak he had grown, how thin. But his spirit was the same, that of a dear meek child. There were the same jokes, the same carefree laughter. 'He will be like that on his death-bed,' thought Vera, as the train bore her away in tears.

In the middle of the summer, the youngest son arrived from Petersburg. Father's emaciated appearance, his weakness, his aged looks, surprised him and made his heart sink. He wished he could do something to enliven the last days of this dear man. Father and son went for short walks, caught frogs in the pond, played draughts. The days passed monotonously, but the presence of his son had a noticeably stimulating effect on Father. He loved to sit in the evenings on his favourite bench and talk of old times.

'Yes, when one remembers how things were, how much savagery, rudeness and cruelty one saw, one is surprised how people could put up with it! where they got the patience! I remember when a policeman used to make his round of the fish market, everyone hid! Even the solid merchants, even your grandfather, crept under the counters! And you should have seen the policeman—what a 'mug', and drunk as a lord! And he'd swipe a shop assistant on the face, without any cause, just for fun, and the language he'd use: "Sons of bitches, I'll have you all locked up. You can feed the lice there. I want to see your master, quick. Why hasn't the Governor's order been obeyed? Ah? Look at the icy pavements, sheets of ice, that's what they are, and you haven't strewn any sand. What? That's obstruction of authority." And so he would shout and swear, as if he were a commander-in-chief, but the explanation was a simple one: the guardian of the law had come for a bribe. Slip him a twenty-five rouble note and he'd gradually see reason. In the meantime the merchant was shivering under the counters afraid to show his nose.'

Father had seen enough of that sort of thing in his day: it made him blush to remember it. 'And as for the law courts, the Lord preserve us from getting entangled with them—they'd swallow you up alive! Law cases might drag on twenty years and you'd die before the conclusion of the case. The bribers might spend a whole fortune on the *chinovniks*. In the administration everyone accepted bribes! And how could they help it? Their salary was infinitesimal, hardly enough to purchase a tie, but they led a spacious life—sturgeon, caviare, champagne, christenings, name-days, weddings. All that costs money, and so they went on taking bribes. And if a young man appeared, who refused bribes, and did not drink or smoke, they'd peck him to death, christen him a "dangerous character". They'd make his life a misery and squeeze him out. He's this and that, they would say, a "secret mason", spreading "Carbonari" ideas, with no faith in God, and so on. People would begin to avoid him, denounce him secretly, plot against him, and he would finally be driven away.

'Yes, and it was the same among the merchants. He, they would say, does not touch vodka, he does not crawl on his belly under an ikon, he does not rest after dinner. He does not keep the paternal behests—he's not our kind. Let's keep away from him.

'And what happened in the police stations would make your blood run cold! It was an iron cage, Czar Nicholas' age, and they were iron people! Say there was a recruiting drive. In the villages the women would be howling, the lads would be on the run, half of them hiding in the forests. They'd organize a beat. The police and the military would wreak their rage and start a "slaughter". They'd catch a lad, manacle him, whip him, and then "shave him" for a twenty-five year stretch: "Go and fight for your Czar and country, and for the Orthodox faith!" Many perished; but those that survived were tempered like steel—you just could not demolish them! In the ranks their soul would be thrashed out of them, leaving only an elastic body! At the end of their service, they would return to their native village and find their hut in ruins and their relatives dead; but they themselves would be as straight as a ramrod and not much caring whether they had been left alone or not: they could adapt themselves to anything.

'The gaols were worse than the cesspools of Constantinople. The dirt, the stink, and the filth of them! In the mornings the prisoners would be driven to work in chains! "A picture worthy of the brush of a great painter!" In rags, dirty, emaciated, they walked six abreast, asking charity on the way, like figures from the Inferno, Dantesque and horrid, their chains clanking, clanking, clanking the prison tune! They'd be driven to a brick factory to act as navvies. It was like Nekrasov's description:

> *He groans in gaols and prisons,*
> *In the mines, fettered in chains. . . .*

And in the evening there would be the clank, clank, clank of chains again, as if a band were playing them back. Believe me or not, I can still hear that unbearable music! It's as if someone were sawing on one's nerves.

'If a prisoner escaped, the alarm would be given through the town. Everyone would take fright, bolt their doors. And next day, in the market, there would be talk only of the escape.

"Have they caught him yet?" "Ours won't get him now." "They say he's hiding in the Eletsky district."

'Later on, I remember, the nihilists appeared: shaggy-headed folk they were . They went among the people, preaching "land and freedom". You'd listen to one of them—"he sings well, the dog, quite convincingly"—fussing all the time about justice. "Why," he would say, "does merchant Fatbelly shovel in the gold, while pleasant Eremka cannot keep his trousers up?" And he would answer himself pat: because this, because that, and it would all sound logical as if he were reading a text! Then there were uprisings in the villages and the "red cock" appeared—arson—in other words, all kinds of insubordination. Then the gendarmes got to work, searched houses, put up gallows, and the firing squads got busy. Then there was more: suddenly, bang! a bomb exploded—the Czar Alexander II was assassinated! Executions again, and the blue uniforms everywhere! Various revolutionary songs such as the "Dubinushka", "Show Me a Lodging Like That", became popular. Writers and scientists were driven by dozens in chains to Siberia. Hundreds of them got lost there! "In the mines fettered and in chains!" There was such a repression that people were afraid to speak aloud: they feared denunciation. And it became as quiet as in a graveyard. They were afraid to open their mouths!

'And then came the speculative era: they started building railways, roads, huge elevators; they started up joint-stock companies; profiteers came to the surface like bugs out of the corners: there you'd see a bridge collapsed and hundreds dead; here a bank bust and thousands ruined. And everywhere only talk of how to line their pockets quickly. You might be wheeling a barrow today, but you'd be a millionaire tomorrow. There were such "artists", especially in the matter of government contracts. They'd fleece the workers, load them, and feed them on rotten fish, but themselves make a pile out of it. All these Polyakovs and other rich people, the famous Gubonin, they used to run about trouserless; and now they're eminent citizens, honoured and bedecked with medals, like "cheese in butter rolling".

' "Who barks loudest, commands!"

'It happened that civil engineers might be building a railway to a town, but they'd stop some four miles out and say to the town authorities: so and so, "If you give us so much, we'll depart from the original plan and continue the railway to the centre of the town; if you don't, you can go on using horses!" Thus towns would remain without railway stations. Later on, they had to build their own connexions. They were cut off from the main line, and to this day they have to put up with delays, change of trains, and like inconveniences. The woes of the time were expressed in many a verse. And a lot of people lost their lives. Yes!

'There were epidemics, too, cholera, typhus, and the rest: people died by the hundred, like flies. Whole streets disappeared. It was like the plague! Doctors would be pursued and killed off when caught: they were accused of spreading cholera and poisoning wells! The savagery, rudeness and barbarism was indescribable. And then there would be investigations, man-hunts, again executions. The gaols were chock full, and there would be the eternal clank of chains on the road to Siberia—the "Vladimirovsky Track".'

Father paused, lit a fresh cigarette and smiled at something. 'I remember a curious incident. The mental patients revolted in a county hospital. They caught the chief doctor, a pleasant fellow—he was a fat German, Hektor Ivanich, I think—and they decided to boil the "Hun" in the hospital soup cauldron. Well, they caught hold of him and dragged him along to the kitchen and told him of their unbreakable resolve. The German was no coward, he had a head on him. "Gentlemen," he said, "I have nothing against this, and I am ready to do anything for such fine patients as you, but you must judge for yourselves if I am fit for your excellent scheme. Look at me: I am all dusty and dirty. Yes, and my clothes have suffered. You see, my trousers are torn! Let me change my suit and wash myself, and then I shall be at your service!'' The patients heeded the wise words of the obliging doctor and let him out of their deadly embrace. The doctor, of course, profited by his freedom and warned the warders. And so he was saved! He was an intelligent German and knew his patients' psychology.

'I recall a negro they exhibited at the Fair. He used to eat a live chicken, feathers and all. It was hard to believe it! As they say, ''Fresh the legend, but difficult to believe''. But it was a fact, and the police allowed it, and the public came. Crowds and crowds!

'In the schools they would have their ''Saturday floggings''. It was a system they had, ''pedagogics''. Fault or no fault, down you were laid. It would help you to grow, for future reference. Yes, ''my friend Horatio'', it was a wild time. It was, and is gone, and is grown over with moss,' Father concluded, smiling and rising from the bench.

In August the rains started. They were obliged, the three of them, to sit in the tiny room. The son slept in student fashion on a low folding bed in the hall. It was hot and stifling, and he had to sleep with the door open. In the mornings, after the rain, he could see the bubbles forming on the submerged paths, and it seemed that at any minute this watery mass might flood the room and flow over the bed. The rain and the mud made it impossible to go out. As if cut off from the world, they floated in their decrepit little house on the waves of an unknown sea.

Father grew quieter, more haggard and much weaker. There was a feeling of melancholy, discomfort, and loneliness. One wished to escape to town, to be among people, in spacious rooms and dry premises. But it would have been madness for a sick person to move in this weather. One had to wait and watch how with each day Father's strength diminished, and he grew more emaciated, and his energy slowly ebbed. Now Father's chief preoccupation was to preserve his last strength. He was not sure he could reach town. Two or three steps about the room were enough to exhaust him. He would collapse into an armchair. Large beads of perspiration would gather on his forehead, his legs would shake, and his head would go round. 'O Lord! How weak I am,' his blue lips would whisper.

A letter arrived from Nicholas saying that the rooms of his apartment were large and high, light and airy. 'You can breathe here,' he said. 'Come and stay with me.' But how were they to get there? 'Volodya! Can we get there?' Father asked.

'Don't worry, Papasha, we'll get there. Why shouldn't we? You're a determined man.'

'You're joking all the time. Get there, get there! But how can we do it, God forgive me, if I'm crumbling,' he complained. 'How shall I drag myself up to the second floor? Eh?'

XXXV

AFTER a whole month of unceasing rains, the weather settled at last. The turbulent torrents disappeared and the earth became dry: with each day the trees noticeably changed their hue. The green foliage was spattered with bright yellow tones; the purple and red leaves of the maple-tree burned like glowing copper; while the fine leaves of the silver-birch tree quivered like beads on a young girl's breast.

The sky was blue, transparent and immobile. The horizon was spread out for miles around. It was an Indian summer ('woman's summer' in Russian), the parting gift of a bright sun! A few days only remained before the departure.

In the garden among the autumn leaves, Father lay back in an armchair, a rug over his feet, and gazed at all this splendour as if bidding farewell to nature. He was firmly convinced that this was his last summer on earth. 'Farewell, festival of beauty!' In the city, the last stage would come, the end, when there would be no more illnesses or anxieties.

Yes, it was an end to toil, it was time, whispered those lifeless lips. And his hands dropped helplessly from his knees— and he had not the strength to lift them or arrange them more comfortably.

The eve of departure was particularly magnificent. Leaning heavily on his stick and hardly able to move his feet, with the help of his son Father slowly made his way towards his favourite bench, so that he might sit there for the last time and take his leave.

The meadow was an emerald green, the trees a golden hue; the frogs in the pond were croaking softly and quaveringly.

The sun stood low, very low, and the hot earth was giving forth its last moisture.

Somewhere in the distance a crow was cawing dully. 'Crow, crow, why do you crow?' Father asked himself, remembering a Ukrainian song. It was peaceful and quiet and fine in the meadow. A heavenly paradise! Father was moved and tears involuntarily started to his eyes and trickled down his sunken face as he thought: 'My God, my God, what blessedness is here.'

For a long while father and son spoke no word. Silence. It was as if the angel of peace and forgiveness had flown by and touched them with its wings. The sun was turning purple and was setting on the horizon. The fields were streaked with rose tints and the shadows thickened. A flight of birds winged its way on high.

'They're returning to their nest for the night,' Father remarked. 'I remember walking once through a forest glade—it was towards evening—and I sat down on a tree stump and lost myself in thought. Then suddenly I came to. There was an infernal noise of some sort. I looked up and saw the sky was black—black with birds. They were circling and circling over the glade, coming lower and lower, right over my head. It made me feel queer. In my life I had never seen so many crows. "They'll peck and tear me to bits," I thought. Well, would you believe it, I panicked and took to my heels. I ran, feeling ashamed. When I got some two hundred yards away, I stopped to see what was happening. The crows were circling lower and lower, they were almost touching the tree-tops. They went on circling and circling. They finally alighted and suddenly stopped cawing. And it was as silent as in a graveyard. Believe me or not, it was so terrifying that I instinctively crossed myself and began to say a prayer. . . . And I was shaking and my teeth were chattering—I couldn't tell you to this day why I felt like that! Unaccountable fear is a strange thing!

'In the old days many fears stalked the earth; folk were superstitious—"as a frightened crow is afraid of a bush". I called one day on a landowner I knew. A fine house it was with columns, a park with alleys, a poultry yard, a stud, and all sorts of comforts. I stayed the night and found myself lolling like a lord on a magnificent bed, under a silk canopy. A blessed state! The room was spacious and high: outside it was dark and silent, and the moon peeped through the window. So I fell asleep peacefully. Suddenly, in the middle of the night I felt as if I had been punched in the ribs. I started up. "What's that?" I asked myself. I looked round, but there was no one there: it was perfectly still and the moon shone hauntingly. I listened hard: there wasn't a sound. But I had a feeling that there was somebody in the room. Brrr. . . .

'And then all sorts of strange things happened: I was hot one moment and cold the next! I had shivers down my back and couldn't breathe for fear. I lit a candle—my hands trembled as I did it—but there was nobody. And yet I felt the presence of an unknown power. I began to recall prayers; recite them aloud; I even sang out the creed. I did indeed! I felt there, there, the unknown power would crush me. The perspiration was running from me and my hair was standing on end. My whole body was in the grip of such fear that I thought my end had come.' And here Father took out his handkerchief and mopped his perspiring brow.

'I was in this agony for a long time. Suddenly I heard a feeble, very feeble sound. It was the cocks crowing in the poultry yard! I felt easier at once. I looked at my watch—it was three. Then I fell asleep again like a log.

'I got up in the morning as if nothing had happened. "What nonsense," I thought to myself. And when we went hunting, I completely forgot about everything. We returned. My landowner persuaded me to stay another couple of nights. "Why not?" I thought. "The hunting is good and there's plenty of trout in the stream." I agreed. In the evening we settled down to cards.

'After supper I began to feel troubled again, and when I got to the bedroom I did not feel like myself. I examined all the corners by candlelight. The walls were hung with old portraits: young dignitaries in red *kaftans,* an old woman in a frontlet and with outspread fingers like bananas. Her eyes were black and terrifying: they just bored into one's soul. Strange thing—very strange—she had six fingers on her hand. There was a pile of oddments in a corner: Chinese nodding figures, Spanish ivory work, porcelain dogs. There was also a huge chest of drawers, a writing table, and a dressing-table: none terrifying. I was reassured.

'I undressed, and fell asleep like a newborn infant. I was sleeping when suddenly, in the middle of the night, I felt as if someone had hit me in the ribs. And then the history repeated itself: cold sweat, perspiration—I recited prayers, sang the liturgy, called upon all the saints. And then, as before, at three o'clock exactly, it all stopped: the cocks crowed and the unclean spirits were appeased. I could have kissed my cock-a-doodle-doos for their service! I fell asleep again till morning.

'The following night the story was repeated "according to programme". In the morning my landowner tried to persuade me to stay longer, tempting me with the hounds. "But no," I thought, "I have had enough pleasure: I might have a heart-attack or spleen from such exercises." And so the matter ended. I thanked him and departed. Several years passed and I met him again; I told him then about my adventures. His eyes looked startled.

' "Why didn't you tell me?" he said, "I'd have put you in another bedroom!"

' "Why should you have?" I said, "I stuck it out of curiosity. I wished to test my courage and explore the mystery."

' "Well, and did you find out? Did you see?" He moved nearer to me. "Did you?" And there was fear in his eyes.

' "That's the trouble," I said. "I didn't see anything. If I had, it would not have been so terrifying."

' "Thank God, you were lucky," he said, "that you didn't see anything. You were in great danger."

'And here he told me the family secret in detail.'

Father took out a cigarette, and without haste cleaned his cigarette holder and slowly lighted a match. It went out and he struck another, lighted the cigarette, inhaled and continued:

'This is how it was. His great-grandmother was pregnant: something frightened her and she lost her reason. Her child was stillborn and was buried. But she kept calling for the child, thinking it was alive, and was in such a state of anguish, tears, and sorrow, that one's heart bled to see her. The Emperor's physician was called in: he came and had a look at her. "It's a bad business," he said. "She'll die of grief if a child is not returned to her." But who would give up his child to this crazy woman? Even the serfs refused. So they had a waxen doll sent from the capital, so skilfully made that it looked exactly like a live baby. They gave it to her and she quieted down. And in a month's time she had completely recovered! The doll was then put away in a drawer of the dressing-table, and the whole incident was forgotten.

'One morning early the maid was suddenly discovered in a faint: she was lying senseless by the staircase. They gave her smelling salts and she came to, but as soon as she opened her eyes she began screaming in a hysterical voice: "The child, the child! It's walking about as if alive!" When she had recovered, she told them all about it. She was coming away from her lady's bedroom after midnight, with a poultice. The moon was shining through the windows; it was quite light: all the stairs could be seen, and suddenly she looked and saw a tiny child descending the stairs and making a soft noise with its little feet: tap, tap, tap. "I was so fear-stricken, I went limp—"

'The rumour spread through the house that the doll-child walked about at night! The domestics took fright and gave various excuses for taking other jobs and the house was emptied. My friend's grandfather then locked the chest of drawers to prevent the doll walking about. But in a few months' time it went for a stroll again, and the old nanny had heart-failure. There were many other incidents, but one can't remember them all.

' "But why didn't you do away with it, or break it?" I asked the landowner.

' "No, we couldn't do that," he said. "A belief had grown up in the family that if the doll were broken, our family would come to an end. None of us sleep in that room, nor even anywhere near it, and so half of the house remains unused."

'Just try and reason it out,' said Father. 'I knew nothing at all about it. Nobody had said a word, but I have a sensation of fear to this day when I recall those three nights.'

It was late already. There were single stars dangling in the greenish straw-coloured sky. 'The young moon shone above the water.' Father was loath to go away. When talking, his illness was forgotten; his weakness disappeared. Reminiscences followed one another, one story engendered another.

'I have been talking about country houses and terrors,' he began again, 'but here is another incident, taken from another "opera", which is characteristic:

'I happened to be visiting the Orlov province: I was driving through the local villages. Everywhere there were "nests of gentlefolk", as in Turgenev: squires' estates, with all sorts of contrivances—there is nothing left of them now: they've all been taken over by the "kulaks". Arriving at one estate—I forget what it was called—I was driving through the village and I was surprised: the people seemed very special and altogether different. It was as if they had all been picked, each one handsomer than the other! The girls were like Greek goddesses and the lads were like your Apollo Belvedere. I drove on. In the next village, the same thing! "Miracles in a sieve!"—that's what it was!

'I got talking with the estate manager about this and that, and enquired casually, "Where have all your handsome folk come from? One might say they had been selected." He replied with a smile, "You've hit the nail on the head. That's the way it was!" "How so?" I asked. And here's the story.

'In the days of Paul I there lived Count—' Father paused,

trying to remember his name. 'Well, it doesn't matter,' he continued. 'Anyhow, the Count was very handsome, and aide-de-camp to the Czar, rich and an eccentric such as you don't often find. At a parade once Arakcheyev picked on him, took him to task, and abused him. One of the front row soldiers had dropped his ammunition belt. The Count was angry: he could not bear the upstart Arakcheyev's unjust reprimand. He resigned his commission and settled for good on his Orlov estates. He had plenty of money and still more leisure: so he gave rein to his fantasy. He began to lay out parks, to clip the trees. He founded a serf theatre and staged ballets. He was an aesthete: Beauty was his god. And there was a lack of it, of this beauty, in the hamlets and villages of Russia. You may call Akulka "Alina," but she still smacks of the village.

'So the "wonder Count" thought it would be a fine idea to beautify the human species and match the sexes: in fact, to start a human factory in the manner of a stud. So he opened a register, set up an office. He made the inspection himself, registered the serfs, and noted down all the tokens and qualities of the village beauties; their age, habits, and propensities. "Here, I'll show you the register," said the estate agent. "It's an interesting document." He brought it and began to read from it. "Here for example: 'a robust girl in the style of Minerva. Greek nose, languishing eyes, firm breasts—"saucer-like", and so on. Or take this: 'Stately youth, Herculean build, plebeian nose—button-shaped, strong loins, sinewy buttocks, and so on.' Then after long discussion for and against, the Count summed up and issued an order. Here is one for example: 'By Trinity Day, wed Nikitka Pischalkin with Fyekla Bezdolina', or 'Mikitka so-and-so with Tanka so-and-so'. Or again, 'owing to her bodily deformity squinting Matrena is not to be allowed in marriage', and so forth.

' "He made notes in the register, you see: 'Carried out in May of such and such a year, issue is expected, Hellenic race!' And look here: 'September such and such, doubtful but possible, Etruscan culture!' For almost seventy years the old man persisted, and fostered three generations, compulsorily improving the beauty of the human race. Tears there were and dramas, but he gained his end, and planted the 'Russian Athens' in his villages. It survived until our day!"

'What times those were! The things people did! The Count at least cared for beauty, but there were others who simply occupied themselves with beastliness. They opened harems and staged all kinds of orgies. They say one squire begot some three hundred children. It was not difficult: there were wives for the asking—a new one every night: live for your pleasure and multiply serfs for yourself! One didn't know whether to laugh or cry.'

Father smiled, listening to something. Beyond the forest an unseen chorus was singing a song. Evidently a gathering of holiday makers were enjoying themselves. Father listened: 'They sing well. In the open air everything comes off.'

'And so, brother,' he went on, 'when you consider life more seriously, you see that King Solomon was right. "All is vanity, vanity!" There's a story I always remember—I can't forget it! Whether somebody told me it, or whether I read it—for the life of me I can't remember! But I've got the story pat, in all its details. It begins thus:

'In the old days there lived a small landowner. He lived in the wilds, never saw anyone and went nowhere. Suddenly an event occurred: by the will of God, his uncle died—somewhere abroad, in Germany let's suppose. Well, the messenger, he comes to our landowner. "Please," he says, "you must go abroad without delay to receive an inheritance." Our Russian arrived at Hamburg by sea. He washed himself, changed at the guest house, and sallied forth to view the city. From his birth he had never seen such magnificence. Sumptuous palaces, three-storied houses, streets full of elegant shops. His eyes popped out. One large house especially took his fancy: in the courtly style, with latticed windows, and all kinds of ornaments and gazebos in the park. He enquired of a passer-by in Russian—he spoke nothing else:

' "Tell me, please," he asked. "To whom does that fine house belong?"

'The passer-by looked surprised and snapped:

' "Kan nicht ferstahn!"

'Our landowner thanked him and went on. He walked along thinking to himself, "Seems he's a rich man, this Kanichtferstan!" He came to the port—there were a good hundred ships there, not counting the schooners and other small vessels. Our Russian was astonished: the amount of merchandise there was, heaps of it. He enquired of a passing sailor to whom all those riches belonged. The latter spat out some chewing tobacco, looked at him round-eyed and growled:

' "Kan nicht ferstahn!" and walked on.

'The landowner was amazed: the name was again "Kanicht-ferstan"! What a lucky devil that man was! He must be as rich as anything! He walked on and saw a crowd of people gathered in a square; he joined them. Some sort of gentlemen were there on a platform, in tail coats, in the middle of the day, making speeches. The crowd was listening and approving. Then out came a small grey-haired man, covered in medals, said something, turned and pulled at the canvas. The covering came off and revealed a bronze statue. There it was in all its beauty, an idol of some sort pointing with his finger at a book, and on the pedestal some words were cut out. He could not make head or tail of them. The ceremony was finished and the crowd began to disperse. "Here's a to-do!" thought the landowner. "Why did they collect and unveil the idol?" he asked someone, and they answered him again: "Kan nicht ferstahn!" "What!" thought the Russian, "they are putting up a statue to him while he is still living! He's got all the luck in the world, this Kanicht-ferstan!"

'Wearied of his foreign impressions, the Russian turned back in the direction of his hotel. It was time for a rest. But not a bit of it! He had just reached the hotel when he saw another crowd. The people were walking in pairs, dressed in dark clothes and top hats, and all looking very sad, and then a hearse

followed them, swaying. It was a funeral. And the hearse was
followed by one carriage after another. The landowner took off
his cap, made the sign of the cross, and composed a prayer for
the soul of the rich unknown.

'Out of curiosity he asked an elderly mourner: "And whom
are they burying?" And the other answered him in passing:
"Kan nicht ferstahn!" "What!' " the landowner opened his
mouth. "It can't be! O Lord, O Lord! How brief is life! Poor,
poor Kanichtferstan! He had everything: palaces and riches,
even his statue had just been erected, and he went off and died.
That's how life is! You may work hard and try, but the end is
one! Six foot of earth and a coffin! Vanity, vanity—" He departed home, the landowner, to his bear's lair, and kept
remembering all the time and pitying "poor, poor Kanicht-
ferstan!"

'Yes, brother,' Father said sighing, 'all is vanity in this world!
It's better to have nothing than the riches of Kanichfterstan.
There is a divine truth in that story. That's why I always remember it. And you must not forget it either! That's how it is,
my dear! That's how it is, brother, and you argue— It's time
for bed,' Father concluded with a smile, rising up with difficulty
from the bench.

The following day, dressed in a grey town suit, soft round
hat, and carrying a cane, Father found himself in a train, con-
versing with passengers and seemingly feeling fine. But when he
was driving from the station in an *izvoshchik*, he suddenly felt
giddy. He had a black-out, and caught hold of his son for
support.

The cab drove into the barracks yard, rolled over the smooth
asphalt and stopped by the porch of a long wing. Father looked
out of the cab at the long row of windows, sighed and barely
audibly whispered:

'Well, I shall never get out of this!'

But a hefty soldier on duty appeared, lifted Father like a
child, and taking the stairs two at a time, had in an instant
carried him up to the second floor. A guilty smile froze on

Father's face as if he were saying to himself: 'See what I've
come to—to be carried like a baby in arms!'

'Well, Papasha, you've arrived. We're delighted to see you,'
Nicholas greeted him cheerfully. Father looked round the room,
smiled feebly and, hardly breathing, collapsed limply into an
armchair which had been got ready for him.

XXXVI

THE long buildings of the Spassky barracks, painted a dark red-ochre colour, occupied a large area. In the square training went on and gymnastic exercises, and orderlies ran about. The absurd and discordant sounds of clarinets and trombones resounded in the musical quarters. Sometimes the very same passage was being annoyingly practised for hours on end by some pupil of little talent. But whenever the bandmaster appeared, there was a minute's silence, followed by a bold and tuneful orchestral execution of a resounding march— 'The Double-Headed Eagle' or the rhythmically drawn-out 'Blue Danube'.

Marching was easier to the lively sounds of the band, and even the horses grew lively and pranced under the young adjutants. From early morning to twilight the busy atmosphere of military bustle reigned here. Orders rang out, roll-calls were made, and there was a clatter of arms. A thousand feet stamped in unison and then came to a sudden halt as the soldiers froze rigidly to attention, caps in hand, to hear the divine service.

The officers' wing, also a low and awkward building, of a later period, stood to the side. The noise and animation of the square hardly reached there. On the ground floor there were the chapel, the officer's mess, and a hospital, while above them were the officers' club and apartments. A long wide corridor with a stone floor stretched the whole length of the building. To the left and right, whenever the doors of the officers' apartments opened, one caught a glimpse of the orderlies preparing samovars and cleaning boots, and one could hear the rattle of plates and the twang of a guitar.

There was something homely and 'civilian' about all these sounds; although sometimes an adjutant's spurs might sound along the corridor or a smothered command might be heard, and then there would be silence once more. Here the military atmosphere made itself heard but little, and the place reminded one more of a spacious monastery hostel, with bare walls, corridors, and cells.

On the other hand, in the officers' mess, the conversation turned on military life and the past glory of the regiment, and it looked like a war museum: the large rooms, the battle trophies, the portraits of the czars and of former regimental commanders, all in medals, with heroic faces and impressive attitudes. There were also engravings of picturesque battles: Poltava, Borodino, Plevna. The furniture was solid, and there were silken coverings, and on the wall hung a posthumous mask of the founder of the regiment—Peter the Great himself. A bronze bust of Napoleon, with folded arms, thoughtfully watched the scene.

The ballroom was spacious and had columns, as was the rule in old country houses, a worn parquet floor, and balconies for the orchestra. There was a billiard-room, and a reading-room filled with military books and engravings of regimental commanders, which created a military atmosphere. In a glass bookcase lay a bound gilt-edged book for important visitors. In it were to be found the signatures of czars, regimental commanders, and the great Field-Marshal Suvorov himself.

The regiment was proud of its past, and jealously recorded each event in its history. Whenever the Czar happened to wear the uniform of the regiment at a parade, that was accounted a special favour, and was recorded in history for the benefit of posterity. There was particular animation during the dinner hour. The young officers with their large appetites sat down at a vast table while the staff officers stood at the buffet and ignored the conventions. Everyone respectfully got up when the regimental commander entered with his adjutant; the colonel bade good-day from afar, and asked everyone to be seated. From his place at the head of the table he saw everyone and, talking with the adjutant, he would note that Captain Pchelko was already in his cups, that Lieutenant Zhdan Pushkin was improperly dressed, and that in general the officers of today were not as they had been: they had not the same bearing or dash as in the old days.

While eating the fish, the adjutant talked business with the colonel, made notes on his order-sheet, and thought about his 'hard labour'—'He won't even let me eat in peace, the old codger! Always business and business!' After the sweet the colonel and the adjutant rose quickly and disappeared into the offices.

The younger officers guffawed and undid their tight tunics. Pchelko asked for another cognac in his coffee. Zhdan Pushkin could not hold himself for laughter.

'What is it now, child? You're as playful as a foal.' Pchelko questioned him. 'Do I not care for you or forbid you to eat oats?' he declaimed in a tipsy voice.

'Gentlemen, Pchelko has turned poet: he is spouting verse! Ha, ha, ha!'

'Poet or not, it's like this with me: when I've had a glass, out comes Alexander Sergeivich Pushkin on the table and off we go, from cover to cover, till the second cock crows. The power that's in him, the beauty! "In silence I gaze on the shawl so black. . . ." I feel like crying—the sadness of it—what are you laughing at? You're always "Ho, ho, ho!" and "Ha, ha, ha!" There was a time I had Pushkin with me in the trenches. The Turks would let off their grapeshot and made the sky look like a sheepskin, but I'd huddle down and declaim: "I have attained to highest power!" That carried me through! Pushkin, brother, was a great 'un. Well, what about another drink? One more for the soul of God's servant, noble Alexander Sergeivich Pushkin!'

'And what about Lermontov, Pchelko? Have you forgotten him? He was one of us, a soldier.'

Then they would drink to Lermontov. They would remember Polezhayev and drink to him. Then to Denis Davidov, a dashing partisan he was, and a rake into the bargain. And so on and so forth. In the end, they would have to lead Captain Pchelko, the admirer of Russian poets, along the corridor, cautiously, so that no one should notice, to his bachelor quarters, and there hand him over carefully to his orderly.

On the other side of the wall, in Nicholas' apartment, another sort of life was going on, other scenes. In a large room, subdivided into three by partitions that did not reach the ceiling, Father was reclining on a comfortable armchair: in his dressing-gown and without glasses he looked like a skeleton, and was very ill. On his lap lay a copy of last year's *Neva* magazine, and on a nearby table a glass of cold unfinished tea. The old familiar furniture, witness of better times, had been arranged along the walls. They were all here: the round barometer, 'The Dear Guest' in a tarnished gold frame, and the grand-father clock. One could hear the flies flopping against the window-panes, falling back, and then droning their autumn songs high under the ceiling.

On first arriving from Pushkino, Father had found pleasure in the spacious rooms, where he could move about. He had even painted the round stove himself with gold paint. But now he was so much weaker that it cost him a great effort to make the few steps from the bedroom partition to his armchair. He could 'hardly recover his breath afterwards'.

A few days ago he had glanced at himself in the mirror and had started back: 'They bury handsomer people,' he said. 'It's better not to look any more. Dr. Venevidsky comes every day and prescribes medicines, but what's the use? Now it's clear that nothing will help.'

Father was lonely in these official quarters. The thick walls of the old building deadened all street noises. He seemed cut off from the world. The 'Lightning' lamp under its green globe illuminated only that part of the room near the table where he sat. The rest of the room was plunged in darkness.

'As for Nicholas, he must be in the office still: astonishing for a young man! Never goes out, no theatres—he lives like a monk! I must embarrass him a lot—I've taken up his whole apartment, but he doesn't seem to mind. "Don't worry, Papasha," he says, "I'll sleep in the corridor. I'll put my bed there, I don't need much!" He's got a heart of gold! He never grumbles or complains. He always finds everything all right, and he doesn't blame anyone or say a hard word of anybody. And where does he get it from? Victor is quite different—he always "insists on his rights". "I'll not allow anyone to tread on my corns," he will say. And off he goes. And the youngest is obstinate: if you approach him affectionately, he will do anything for you, but if anything goes wrong, he will take the bit between his teeth and streak away. He'll ruffle his feathers like a game-cock! But look at him. He's neglected his lectures, his amusements, to watch over me like a real sick-nurse. The other day I said to the doctor: "Don't you think Volodya should become a hospital assistant? He'd never become a doctor, but he would make a good assistant." And the doctor laughed: "They've turned out to be good children, whatever you may say. A rare thing in our times." '

The door banged, in came Volodya, bringing with him a draught of fresh frosty air. In his eyes there was anxiety for Father, on his cheeks a flush from the cold air.

'Have you been for a walk? Is it nice out?'

'Yes, fine. The frost and the snow. I walked as far as the "Red Gates" and back.' And sitting down near Father, Volodya asked: 'And how are you feeling?'

'I? Quite well. I've been reading the *Neva*, drinking tea, and thinking about you! I haven't much to do these days. A little reading, a sip of tea and over on my side! I'm yawning already, it's time! It must be eight o'clock.'

The son carefully helped the patient to reach the bedroom, assisted him to undress, arranged the pillows and quilt, and said:

'God bless you! Sleep now. If you should need anything, call me. I shall be there behind the partition!'

In the night, lying behind the thin partition, the son listened to the silence, to Father's peaceful breathing. Sometimes he would be alarmed; he had doubts and would go and look to see that everything was all right.

'Is that you?' Father would ask. 'Why don't you sleep at night? Now it's Kolya, now it's you. Am I about to die or what?'

'I only came to see if you wanted anything,' the son replied.

'Me? No. I don't want anything. I lie and think what fine children I've got—you and Nicholas and Victor. What is Vera alone worth—she's an angelic person! Well, turn me over on my left side, and go to sleep.'

In the morning Volodya's first thought was: how is Father? 'Not too bad,' Father would reply. 'What's the weather like? I saw a strange dream. An austere face, "not of this world".' It was as if something important and inevitable had been communicated to Father.

With each day he had less and less strength left. The children now came together every day: they sat in the outer room for tea and then gathered round Father's bed. They would talk a few minutes with him and, in order not to tire him, return to the front room and sit in silence thinking the same thoughts.

A week passed and Father no longer got up. The doctor now came twice a day and once, after a long visit and exchanging jokes with the patient, declared that there was no hope left, that the end might come at any minute and that if—. But tears welled up in his eyes and did not allow him to finish his sentence. He waved his hand and went out.

The sons stood with their heads lowered and the daughters wept softly behind the partition. Mother alone appeared calm. Had she understood what the doctor had said? It seemed she did, for she kept repeating senselessly: 'How is that, Yashenka? How will he be without me?'

XXXVII

THE ikon lamp glowed softly before the image of the Saviour in the bedroom. Severe but forgiving eyes gazed down from the ikon—eyes that reminded one lately so much of Father's. Another small lamp covered by a green shade lighted the wide bed, the bemedalled certificates in their frames that were hung carefully on the walls, a table with medicines, and Father's shrunken body under the baize quilt.

Father was reading a letter and smiling: 'Vanya's coming!' he said joyfully. 'He'll be here tomorrow. Ah, I shall not be able to meet him. I should go to the station, but I'll have to default instead—the first time in thirty years. Ah, Vanya, Vanya! He's a man of great soul. There are few such left! It's no joke: we've lived these fifty years in harmony. No quarrels, not a shadow of misunderstanding—a pure delight it was! I'll get up tomorrow! I must get up, absolutely must! I must do him the honours! You think I'm done for? No, brother, you're jesting. I'll show you yet!'

'But in the meantime you must sleep, Father! Morning is wiser than the night,' said Volodya, arranging the pillows and leaving the bedroom.

Early next morning, the broad figure of Vanya Puzanov rolled noisily into the apartment.

'Devil knows where you've got to! I searched and searched. I made the round of all the squads; the sentinel nearly skewered me with his bayonet! I'd got to the wrong place! Well, show me the patient,' Vanya said cheerfully. But when he was led into the bedroom, Father's appearance shocked him so much that he stopped dead in the doorway.

'Vanya!'—'Yasha!' And the two comrades fraternally embraced each other.

'My dear, so you've done me a favour and have come. And I thought I would never see "my bright falcon" again, But no, by God's grace, we are met,' Father was saying excitedly.

Vanya could not hold back his tears but began to spin yarns for all he was worth. He had come, he said, on business and would remain in Moscow for quite a while. Then, speaking of Father, he assured him that he looked well. He looked fine. When he had recovered, they would go to the 'Blessed City' to fish for trout, to steal apples, and to hear the gipsies.

Father listened, smiled, and nodded approval. On the threshold of death even he could not help being influenced by the effervescent vitality of his friend.

'Yes, yes, yes! You're right, we shall go there,' he agreed, and laughed like a child. 'Well, and how are things at home?'

'Still the same. If there's anything new, it's that they've done away with the tower on the Dvoryansky. It was falling to pieces! Do you remember how the brother-merchants used to be put in the stocks there, to cure their disorders? Ha, ha, ha! But "the gay days of Aranjuez" are past now. Nowadays they take them in a dignified manner to the police station—European fashion. Ha, ha, ha! Maltzev is alive and well, and sends you his greetings. He's grown as stout as a boar! Poromanov is waxing rich. Alechin has turned Tolstoyan and has given away all his fortune. Indeed he has! He bade us farewell: "Forgive me, kind people," he said, "if I have done any of you wrong." And off he went. Well, who else is there? Yes, everything is as it was: we live in a forest and pray to tree-stumps! That's how things are, friend Andrashy! I speak and you argue,' Vanya smiled, and the friends burst into gay laughter.

'I've decided to have a try with Shakespeare,' Vanya went on. 'I'm rehearsing Othello—yes, brother. But it frightens me: what if they hiss me suddenly! It's not like playing Gogol's Mayor in *The Inspector General*. Here in Othello it's different.

Here we have an African person. Vesuvius in eruption! I'm
frightened! But still I'm dying to portray the Blackamoor. To
try him once! Well, if he doesn't come off, I'll give it up. I'll
throw up the stage altogether!'

'You won't do that, Vanya, you're only saying it. You've
attempted it often enough: "I'll give it up, I'll give it up, I'll
wander off into the forest—"' Father joked. 'Do you remember how you played Uriel Acosta? The whole theatre was
agog, people jumped up from their seats, and you had stage
fright in the beginning. "I'll flop," you said, "bring shame on
the stage!" but what a success you had. And now you talk again
of giving it up. Eh, brother!'

Father was noticeably tiring, but his interest in the conversation did not flag. And when, soon after, Vanya took his leave
so as not to exhaust Father, promising to come again soon,
Father gripped his hand firmly—it had not lost its strength yet
—and whispered, with prayer in his eyes.

'If anything should happen to me, Vanya, and "we are all
God's children", do not abandon my children, my dear, look
after them, and help them with your counsel! Oblige me!
Help them—they're young folk but good.'

'My dear, I'll do all I can, but don't you worry about it!
Don't provoke the Lord! Don't tempt fate!' Vanya concluded
severely. 'Lie there and rest, and as for the trout, we shall fish
them yet,' he added cheerfully, leaving the bedroom on tiptoe.

'O Lord, O Lord! How he has changed! A living skeleton!
But his spirit is strong still, he's ready to go after the trout,'
he said to Victor in a whisper. 'What a man we are losing—
there's no price to him. A man of superlative heart!'

The days went by slowly and anxiously. Sometimes visitors
called to enquire how Yakov Akimovich was. Peter, the *izvoschik*,
dropped in to ask after the 'master'. To begin with, he sat a
while in the kitchen telling the orderlies what manner of a man
Father was, and then cleaned his boots thoroughly so as not to
carry in the snow. He entered the bedroom with a 'lenten face'
as if he were going to a requiem.

'Ah, Peter, friend,' Father greeted him gaily, 'you are still alive, are you? And how is the work?'

'Yes, we're still carrying on in a small way, *barin!* This accursed cough takes it out of me. It's worst in the mornings, and knocks me out, it does. I wish there was an end to me soon,' Peter complained.

'Enough of this. Don't draw the wrath of God upon you. I've been hearing that tune these thirty years! But you're still alive. You'll live another thirty. And what's happening in town? What are they talking about?'

Peter then related the news of the town.

'The Givartovskys are again mountain-climbing. The Petchke firm have recovered; they were asking after you—they are full of sympathy for you. I met Boris some days ago: he's in a state, he is, tearful—"I'm damned," he says. "To have driven such an angel"—meaning you—"into the grave! There will be no forgiveness for me," he says! And I said to him: "It's late in the day you've thought better of it. You've done your dirty work and feel sorry now."'

'Don't worry, don't worry,' Father reassured him. 'Better late than never. "If you never sin, you'll never repent." I've no grudge against him. Tell him so! We're all men, and human. "A horse has four legs but it stumbles too." That's how it is, brother. Well, goodbye—thanks for remembering and calling. I feel very tired today.'

The whole family gathered in the outer room; they sat about and talked in low tones. The door of the bedroom was open. Father asked now and then who had come, or whom they were still expecting. What sort of weather was it outside? And then he relapsed again. When he felt stronger, they all gathered round his bed and kept up a general conversation.

'Why are you so gloomy, all of you? You're young people, but you all look old,' Father said. 'Why so depressed? Live gaily, shuffle your feet!'

The conversation flagged. Everyone was thinking his own thoughts, depressing thoughts, about the end that was near.

'Ah, nothing will stir you!' Father chided them reproachfully. 'It's as if you were about to die. I'd better have a nap,' he smiled, closing his eyes. In a minute he was already asleep. Trying not to make a noise they all tiptoed out of the bedroom. They sat in silence, listening, as if expecting a catastrophe any minute.

The real winter began towards the end of November. The wind had heaped up mountains of snow, and a dazzling sun glittered forth. People went about full of joy and animation, rubbing their red cheeks with their coat-sleeves.

Victor would come along in his fur coat, shaking off the snow from his fur hat, and he would sit down by the stove. Nadya and Vera would take off their half-length fur coats and undo their fashionable spotted veils, and warm their frozen hands at the round stove. Father felt somewhat better, and he was sitting in the outer room in his dressing-gown and wrapped in blankets—for the first time in weeks. Nicholas came, clinking his spurs and smiling his dear smile, and joined the company. Stepanich, Cachalot, and Volodya were undoing some parcels. Mother sat on the divan, thinking her thoughts.

'Well, here we are all together,' Father smiled. 'A gala evening "with Italians".'

At dinner they all joked and played the fool: it seemed as if a weight had been taken off their minds. The steaming samovar was brought in. Puffs of steam rose to the ceiling, there was a clatter of cups. It felt good to be alive in the winter, with one's family sitting round the tea-table. The dear, dear faces, the familiar gestures, the natural smiles. And that feeling of cosiness was always there for some reason when there was tea or food. 'I wonder why?' Father thought.

'I can neither eat nor drink—yet when I see a steaming samovar, my heart feels more cheerful,' he began. 'I remember we would arrive, with grandfather and grandmother, at a wayside inn in the winter: a samovar would be brought, *kalatches*, curd-cakes, all sorts of cheese-fritters, and one would forget the cold, the hunger, and the long journey. It was so sweet to rest in

Father at Pushkino, with himself, 1901.

Last photograph of Father at Pushkino.

the warmth, to sit by a blazing stove. But they say the Germans live without samovars. I don't understand it.'

'They manage to get fat without any tea,' joked Cachalot.

'I remember your grandmother used to relate how she was sent tea from China for the first time,' Father continued. 'They looked at it, this outlandish grass: it smelt good, but they did not know what to do with it. They boiled a whole pound of it in a kettle and ate it all as it was. They were almost sick. The letter with directions for making tea reached them later. Ha, ha, ha! Then the samovar was invented and the use of it spread quickly: samovars were made in Tula, enough of them for the whole of Russia. But the Kalmyks, or is it the Kirghiz, eat tea in their soup to this day. Bars of tea. They boil them in a cauldron with mutton; they say they lick their fingers afterwards.'

'What dummies!' roared Cachalot.

The logs of silver birch crackled merrily on the stove. Even Mother was more animated than usual, and related how she used to be served with tea in the young ladies' finishing school. 'The cups were tiny, tiny, like a thimble, and the tea was very strong and served without sugar, real China tea, strong, very strong, and aromatic. It had a bouquet as if the room were full of flowers.'

'But we prefer it with a dash of lemon or with cognac, isn't that so, Stepanich?' Cachalot said, tipping the bottle over his glass. 'In the Russian manner: "Drive on, Matvey, spare not the horses!" Ah, Papasha, Papasha, you're the kindest of men!'

Twilight was falling slowly. Through the windows everything seemed blue: blue houses and blue snow. Blue shadows fell across the parquet. The fire in the stove glimmered more brightly.

'Well, I'll go and rest a bit! But you stay here, don't go away.'

They all got up. They helped Father to rise, and, leaning heavily on his sons' shoulders, he made his way slowly to the bedroom. But in the entrance he stopped and jestingly pushed the children away as if saying: 'Do you think me a complete invalid?' And he suddenly played a prank. Raising the folds of his dressing gown, he bared his emaciated legs in their drawers, and bent his knees in a comic bow.

'Wait, my dears, wait. Don't hurry so much. I can dance still,' he said to the astonished children. 'It's not the end of me yet. There's still powder in the magazine!'

The children felt embarrassed for Father: it was hardly fitting for a man in his condition to dance. But the dance continued only for a second. He swayed and fell into the arms of his son.

'Ah, my dear children! What is death? It's nothing! But one thing I regret, that is parting with you! That time is near. I know it, I know it, here in my heart'—tears interrupted his words. 'Live in peace! You're fine fellows! One thing I have done in life, and that was to bring you up! A great thing that!'

They were all agitated as they laid him exhausted to rest. And as if oppressed by fate, they gathered in the corner of the sitting room.

Next day the weather changed for the worse. The wind howled in the chimney, grey tufts of cloud raced on the horizon. Vera finally made up her mind to speak to Father of religion:

'Papashka,' she said tenderly, bending over him. 'One God alone disposes of life as of death! You should not forget about religion. Why not have a talk with the priest? It may ease your mind and bring peace to you. Do not be angry with me for what I am saying, my darling, but it would be better to commune with God than to leave it like this.'

'Ah, silly, silly girl! To commune with God? But I have been communing with God since I was a child—every hour of the day and in all sorts of ways. For is not God everywhere—in the fields, in the forests, and here now with us? God looks down on us and laughs, saying to himself, "God's servant Jacob has a kind daughter." You advise me to call a priest. But what is a priest? He's an ordinary man like any of us. He may be a worse man than I am. And what shall I talk to him about? So and so, I've sinned, and the rest of it. Be so good and pardon my grievous sins! Ah, there's nothing in it.

' "God sees the truth, but will not speak it soon." Thus shall I think of my life: everything is clear! Well, to whom did I do evil? With my hand on my heart, I shall answer: "To no one." Did I wish evil to my enemies? "There were none! I am sinless!" As before God I say: "There is no sin in me!" I shall say that to God!

'I shall appear before Him: the Creator will ask me: "Tell me, God's servant Jacob, in what have you sinned?" "There is no sin in me, Lord," I shall say, "only one fault have I committed and that was to have brought up a silly daughter!'

'Papashka, Papashka, what are you saying? It's not seemly to blaspheme.'

'Well, don't be angry with me, don't be angry. Send for the priest if you wish. Only not now—later. I'll tell you when to call him. Now I feel tired.' And Father dropped back on his pillows in exhaustion. 'Will you call Volodya, I have business with him.'

The youngest son came and stood by the bed:

'Did you call me, Papasha?'

'Yes, you can do something for me, brother. Will you get the keys and then that casket from the chest of drawers, the black one, the polished one—you know? Bring it to me when everybody's gone, otherwise they might laugh.'

When there was nobody left in the sitting-room, Volodya got the box and, bringing it into the bedroom, put it down before Father.

'Here, open it with this key.' Father pointed to a small golden-headed key.

But the box would not open.

'Ah, give it to me, I'll try myself,' Father said regretfully. 'What do they teach you in the University? Can't you open a casket even? Do you see? "It was simple to open the little coffer!" ' And he looked triumphantly at Volodya.

'But jokes aside and laughter too! Listen, my dear, and remember what I say. What's the use of writing a will? It's a waste of time. It's better in words. I'm not going to die yet.

I'll live another year or two with you, but remember this all the same, and don't get it mixed up when the time comes. And will you pull up the pillows—they've rolled down. Listen —when the house is sold, Grandfather's house, each of you sons is to get an equal portion and your sisters the half of that! Have you got that? This watch with the gold chain and diamond is for Victor, the eldest. Have you got it? These are for Nicholas,' said Father thoughtfully. 'Do you see the Swiss landscape and the train crossing the bridge, the month of the sun's eclipse?' and he pressed a spring. 'A cunning thing this, cost a lot of money in its time. And here is the chain—your Grandfather used to wear it—it's old-fashioned but could be altered; it's of sovereign gold.

'And this you can take for yourself,' he said, fetching out his favourite gold open-dialled watch and admiring the dial. 'There's an enamel picture in it—of great value. Don't open it yet,' he said, smiling. 'There's only one other such watch in the whole world. One is in the palace and the other you shall have —you'll remember that all right! The silver cigarette case— the precious stone has dropped out of the monogram, it should be put back—is for Stepanich. Let him smoke his cigarettes, and remember me!

'This rattling chain,' Father pulled out a long chain from which dangled various trinkets, matchboxes, little knives, scissors, brushes—a whole arsenal of baubles, 'give to Vanya, to Vanya Puzanov! He liked it very much: "You have a whole arsenal there, Yasha," he used to say. Let him wear it, and rattle it to the dread of his enemies. Well, do you remember everything? The rings, the brooches and all the jewelled trifles, give to your sisters. So? What is there left? Well, as for the rest, divide it up among you as seems best. Oh, I've forgotten the fur coat. Take the beaver coat for yourself. It's a warm coat and light, and it doesn't weigh on the shoulders.' Father's voice was growing perceptibly weaker and his breathing was growing more difficult.

'How tired I am!' he said. 'But in the meantime, don't say a

word, not a word to anyone, about what we've been doing!
They'll laugh at us! Now off you go! I'll rest a little—here in
bed.'

Nicholas returned from the mess. 'How's Papasha?' he asked.
'As usual! He's sleeping peacefully now!'

Stepanich came. Then Victor. Soon they had all gathered
round the dinner table. Only Vera was absent. She had sent
a message to say that she was at a neighbour's and that she could
be sent for if needed. They dined in silence. Every now and again
Volodya peeped into the bedroom to see how Father was.
'How is Papasha?' all eyes seemed to question him anxiously.
'He's sleeping peacefully, like a child, and his face is clear and
calm.'

Having forced themselves to eat—no one had any appetite—
they sat round on the Viennese chairs and spoke in low tones, so
as not to wake the patient. Vera looked in and then went back
to her friend's. 'The captain's wife, they say, has received a
new dress from the modiste's. It's simply marvellous.'

The family sat round, speaking little, as if listening to something. The wind had dropped. Large, wet flakes of snow began
to fall.

'How well he's sleeping! His breathing's even, no sign of
hoarseness or coughing,' Volodya thought aloud, and tiptoed
again to the bedroom.

Father was lying with his eyes open, and he looked calmly at
Volodya as he entered. He was trying to say something to him,
but his voice could not be heard. His lips moved; a three-
syllable word trembled on his lips, trying to make itself arti-
culate. But he had no voice! There was an astonished look in
his fine blue eyes at this new oddity. It was as if they were
saying: 'How is it, brother, you don't understand the Russian
language?' And his lips were again moving insistently.

A three-syllable word? A three-syllable word? No! Perhaps
he wanted a drink? A glass of water? No, it was not that. His
lips turned away. Air? The oxygen was at hand. No, it was not
that either. O Lord, what a strange look! What was that? A

long lingering look of farewell, as if saying: 'It doesn't matter—I can be patient!' The head rolled over slowly towards the wall. His blue eyes turned up unnaturally, revealing the whites of the eyes.

An animal cry, an unnatural voice resounded in the bedroom. Everyone dashed from his place and gathered round the dying man. Vera ran in, dropped on her knees by the bed, weeping. The panting priest came and, glancing round the room, declared like an expert:

'There is still life in him! The artery is still functioning. He can hear everything!'

While the priest was opening his prayer book and beginning the prayer for the dead, Father's body was still quivering. But soon everything was stilled.

Thus ended the terrestrial life of Yasha, and his blue childlike eyes were closed forever to this world.

In two hours' time, making a lot of noise, and not noticing where he was going, Vanya Puzanov burst into the apartment.

'Alive? Where?' he asked with terrible wild eyes; and he marched straight into the bedroom in his fur coat and galoshes.

Vanya locked himself in with his friend for a long time. Until late in the night he wept over Father's corpse and talked to him as if he were alive. He recalled their childhood, their pranks, their joys and sorrows: all that he had experienced together with his never-to-be-forgotten friend Yasha, that man of great soul!

EPILOGUE

AT FIVE o'clock today I finished my reminiscences about Father and there are tears in my eyes.

This work, which I have completed to the best of my power, I dedicate to my dear children.

Let them read these lines. Perhaps they will understand then their grandfather's kindly soul, so full of love for humanity.

Let others also read this simple chronicle and learn how natural and human is the real Russian; it may contribute to better understanding in this troubled world.

London, 25th May, 1956.

IN MEMORIAM

Vladimir Polunin

1880—1957